W9-CTZ-320

GREAT DOG STORIES OF ALL TIME

BOOKS ABOUT DOGS *by Fairfax Downey*

"GREAT DOG STORIES OF ALL TIME"

Selected by *Fairfax Downey*

ILLUSTRATED BY ALBERT ORBAAN

DOUBLEDAY & COMPANY, INC.
GARDEN CITY, NEW YORK, 1962

Library of Congress Catalog Card Number 62–14689
Copyright © 1962 by Fairfax Downey

When the Man waked up he said, "What is Wild Dog doing here?" And the Woman said, "His name is not Wild Dog any more, but the First Friend, because he will be our friend for always and always and always."

KIPLING: Just So Stories

FOREWORD

How did the ancient companionship between man and dog begin? It may well have been established when a primitive hunter chanced to find a puppy and carried it back to his cave. Or perhaps an older wild dog, hunger overcoming fear, was drawn to a campfire by the smell of roasting meat. Tossed a bone, it seized it and fled but returned again and again, finally to stay. For food and shelter the dog served as guardian against all enemies and helped man at his hunting and other tasks. So was formed between them a bond of dependence and devotion.

Certainly it was many centuries ago that the dog became man's First Friend, and ever since, man has recorded their friendship. A drawing of hunting dogs, discovered on the wall of a cave of the Palaeolithic Era, has been estimated to be 50,000 years old. The second story in this anthology, "The Doomed Prince," dates back 3,600 years. There are some forty references to dogs in the Bible. Countless books, tales, and articles celebrate them. The Peter Chapin Collection of Books on Dogs, in the Library of the College of William and Mary, alone contains more than 2,000 titles. No wonder that man has written so much about the dog and made so many drawings of him, considering the long duration and enduring fidelity of their comradeship.

As Cecil G. Trew points out in *The Story of the Dog*, "The family of the dog is today the most widely distributed of any of the four-footed animals . . . Species of one sort or another are to be found in every continent and in every climate practically from pole to pole . . . In every part of the globe inhabited by man, there is a dog to be found with him; and everywhere is the dog privileged to share man's dwelling."

The omnipresence of the dog is rivaled by his infinite variety, not simply as to the various breeds—the American Kennel Club recognizes more than one hundred—but in each one's individuality. Anyone who owns a dog will insist that, be it pedigreed or mongrel, it has character. It differs from other dogs as one human being from another. Need there be any better basis for the multitude of dog stories in print or told by word of mouth?

Most of the selections in this anthology deal with the particular and peculiar traits of the dogs they chronicle. Thereby hangs the tale.

Here, as in *My Kingdom for a Horse*, I have tried to concentrate on the unusual, or at least less known, stories and articles. Only a few of the classic dog stories are included. Through these pages parade dogs of olden days—valiant war dogs—dogs faithful unto death—dogs that brought the saving grace of laughter along with their other gifts to man.

Dogs, in spirit or as living presences, lie beside every writer or reader of dog stories. So, as this book was made, close to me in memory or in life lay friends of our household: Pat, an Airedale; Jocky, a Scottish terrier; and Demi Tasse, a poodle; Britta, a Brittany spaniel; Schnapps, a dachshund; Domino, a Dalmatian; and Carillon Linda, a poodle.

FAIRFAX DOWNEY
West Springfield
New Hampshire

CONTENTS

Part Three — STORIES OF BREEDS

Part Four — FAMOUS DOGS OF FAMOUS PEOPLE

Part Five — DOG WAGS

GREAT DOG STORIES OF ALL TIME

Part One
DOGS OF OLD

The dog was the guard of His Majesty. Abuwityuw was his name. His Majesty ordered that he be buried ceremonially, that he be given a coffin from the royal treasury, fine linen in great quantity, and incense. His Majesty gave perfume ointment, and ordered that a tomb be built for him by gangs of masons. His Majesty did this in order that the dog might be honored before the great god Anubis.

Inscription on a stone slab near the pyramid of Cheops, c. 3000 B.C.

ORDEAL BY FIRE

The Dog of Pompeii

LOUIS UNTERMEYER

Pompeii was buried by lava from an eruption of
Mount Vesuvius in A.D. 79. Excavations of the city
revealed the facts on which this short story is based.
The dog, sometimes called Delta but here given another name, was such a guardian as was portrayed in
mosaic in the floor of entrances to Roman villas. Beneath was inscribed the legend, CAVE CANEM [BEWARE
OF THE DOG].

TITO and his dog Bimbo lived (if you could call it living) under the
wall where it joined the inner gate. They really didn't live there; they
just slept there. They lived anywhere. Pompeii was one of the gayest
of the old Latin towns, but although Tito was never an unhappy boy,
he was not exactly a merry one. The streets were always lively with shining chariots and bright-red trappings; the open-air theaters rocked with
laughing crowds; sham battles and athletic sports were free for the asking in the great stadium. Once a year the Caesar visited the pleasure
city and the fireworks lasted for days; the sacrifices in the Forum were
better than a show. But Tito saw none of these things. He was blind—
had been blind from birth. He was known to every one in the poorer
quarters. But no one could say how old he was, no one remembered his
parents, no one could tell where he came from. Bimbo was another
mystery. As long as people could remember seeing Tito—about twelve
or thirteen years—they had seen Bimbo. Bimbo had never left his side.
He was not only dog, but nurse, pillow, playmate, mother and father to
Tito.

Did I say Bimbo never left his master? (Perhaps I had better say
comrade, for if any one was the master, it was Bimbo.) I was wrong.
Bimbo did trust Tito alone exactly three times a day. It was a fixed
routine, a custom understood between boy and dog since the beginning
of their friendship, and the way it worked was this: Early in the morning, shortly after dawn, while Tito was still dreaming, Bimbo would dis-

appear. When Tito awoke, Bimbo would be sitting quietly at his side, his ears cocked, his stump of a tail tapping the ground, and a fresh-baked bread—more like a large, round roll—at his feet. Tito would stretch himself; Bimbo would yawn; then they would breakfast. At noon, no matter where they happened to be, Bimbo would put his paw on Tito's knee and the two of them would return to the inner gate. Tito would curl up in the corner (almost like a dog) and go to sleep, while Bimbo, looking quite important (almost like a boy) would disappear again. In half an hour he'd be back with their lunch. Sometimes it would be a piece of fruit or a scrap of meat, often it was nothing but a dry crust. But sometimes there would be one of those flat rich cakes, sprinkled with raisins and sugar, that Tito liked so much. At suppertime the same thing happened, although there was a little less of everything, for things were hard to snatch in the evening with the streets full of people. Be-

sides, Bimbo didn't approve of too much food before going to sleep. A heavy supper made boys too restless and dogs too stodgy—and it was the business of a dog to sleep lightly with one ear open and muscles ready for action.

But whether there was much or little, hot or cold, fresh or dry, food was always there. Tito never asked where it came from and Bimbo never told him. There was plenty of rain water in the hollows of soft stones; the old egg-woman at the corner sometimes gave him a cupful of strong goat's milk; in the grape season the fat wine maker let him have drippings of the mild juice. So there was no danger of going hungry or thirsty. There was plenty of everything in Pompeii—if you knew where to find it—and if you had a dog like Bimbo.

As I said before, Tito was not the merriest boy in Pompeii. He could not romp with the other youngsters and play Hare-and-Hounds and I-Spy and Follow-Your-Master and Ball-against-the-Building and Jack-stones and Kings-and-Robbers with them. But that did not make him sorry for himself. If he could not see the sights that delighted the lads of Pompeii he could hear and smell things they never noticed. He could really see more with his ears and nose than they could with their eyes. When he and Bimbo went out walking he knew just where they were going and exactly what was happening.

"Ah," he'd sniff and say, as they passed a handsome villa, "Glaucus Pansa is giving a grand dinner tonight. They're going to have three kinds of bread, and roast pigling, and stuffed goose, and a great stew—I think bear stew—and a fig pie." And Bimbo would note that this would be a good place to visit tomorrow.

Or, "H'm," Tito would murmur, half through his lips, half through his nostrils. "The wife of Marcus Lucretius is expecting her mother. She's shaking out every piece of goods in the house; she's going to use the best clothes—the ones she's been keeping in pine needles and camphor—and there's an extra girl in the kitchen. Come, Bimbo, let's get out of the dust!"

Or, as they passed a small but elegant dwelling opposite the public baths, "Too bad! The tragic poet is ill again. It must be a bad fever this time, for they're trying smoke fumes instead of medicine. Whew! I'm glad I'm not a tragic poet!"

Or, as they neared the Forum, "Mm-m! What good things they have in the Macellum today!" (It really was a sort of butcher-grocer market place, but Tito didn't know any better. He called it the Macellum.) "Dates from Africa, and salt oysters from sea caves, and cuttlefish, and new honey, and sweet onions, and—ugh!—water-buffalo steaks. Come, let's see what's what in the Forum." And Bimbo, just as curious as his comrade, hurried on. Being a dog, he trusted his ears and nose (like Tito) more than his eyes. And so the two of them entered the center of Pompeii.

The Forum was the part of the town to which everybody came at least once during each day. It was the Central Square and everything happened here. There were no private houses; all was public—the chief temples, the gold and red bazaars, the silk shops, the town hall, the booths belonging to the weavers and jewel merchants, the wealthy woolen market, the shrine of the household gods. Everything glittered here. The buildings looked as if they were new—which, in a sense, they were. The earthquake of twelve years ago had brought down all the old structures and, since the citizens of Pompeii were ambitious to rival Naples and even Rome, they had seized the opportunity to rebuild the whole town. And they had done it all within a dozen years. There was scarcely a building that was older than Tito.

Tito had heard a great deal about the earthquake though, being about a year old at the time, he could scarcely remember it. This particular quake had been a light one—as earthquakes go. The weaker houses had been shaken down, parts of the outworn wall had been wrecked; but there was little loss of life, and the brilliant new Pompeii had taken the place of the old. No one knew what caused these earthquakes. Records showed they had happened in the neighborhood since the beginning of time. Sailors said that it was to teach the lazy city folk a lesson and make them appreciate those who risked the dangers of the sea to bring them luxuries and protect their town from invaders. The priests said that the gods took this way of showing their anger to those who refused to worship properly and who failed to bring enough sacrifices to the altars and (though they didn't say it in so many words) presents to the priests. The tradesmen said that the foreign merchants had corrupted the ground and it was no longer safe to traffic in imported goods that came from strange places and carried a curse with them. Every one had a different explanation—and every one's explanation was louder and sillier than his neighbor's.

They were talking about it this afternoon as Tito and Bimbo came out of the side street into the public square. The Forum was the favorite promenade for rich and poor. What with the priests arguing with the politicians, servants doing the day's shopping, tradesmen crying their wares, women displaying the latest fashions from Greece and Egypt, children playing hide-and-seek among the marble columns, knots of soldiers, sailors, peasants from the provinces—to say nothing of those who merely came to lounge and look on—the square was crowded to its last inch. His ears even more than his nose guided Tito to the place where the talk was loudest. It was in front of the Shrine of the Household Gods that, naturally enough, the householders were arguing.

"I tell you," rumbled a voice which Tito recognized as bath-master Rufus's, "there won't be another earthquake in my lifetime or yours. There may be a tremble or two, but earthquakes, like lightnings, never strike twice in the same place."

"Do they not?" asked a thin voice Tito had never heard. It had a high, sharp ring to it and Tito knew it as the accent of a stranger. "How about the two towns of Sicily that have been ruined three times within fifteen years by the eruptions of Mount Etna? And were they not warned? And does that column of smoke above Vesuvius mean nothing?"

"That?" Tito could hear the grunt with which one question answered another. "That's always there. We use it for our weather-guide. When the smoke stands up straight we know we'll have fair weather; when it flattens out it's sure to be foggy; when it drifts to the east—"

"Yes, yes," cut in the edged voice. "I've heard about your mountain barometer. But the column of smoke seems hundreds of feet higher than usual and it's thickening and spreading like a shadowy tree. They say in Naples—"

"Oh, Naples!" Tito knew this voice by the little squeak that went with it. It was Attilio, the cameo cutter. "*They* talk while we suffer. Little help we got from them last time. Naples commits the crimes and Pompeii pays the price. It's become a proverb with us. Let them mind their own business."

"Yes," grumbled Rufus, "and others, too."

"Very well, my confident friends," responded the thin voice which now sounded curiously flat. "We also have a proverb—and it is this: Those who will not listen to men must be taught by the gods. I say no more. But I leave a last warning. Remember the holy ones. Look to your temples. And when the smoke tree above Vesuvius grows to the shape of an umbrella pine, look to your lives."

Tito could hear the air whistle as the speaker drew his toga about him and the quick shuffle of feet told him the stranger had gone.

"Now what," said the cameo cutter, "did he mean by that?"

"I wonder," grunted Rufus, "I wonder."

Tito wondered, too. And Bimbo, his head at a thoughtful angle, looked as if he had been doing a heavy piece of pondering. By nightfall the argument had been forgotten. If the smoke had increased no one saw it in the dark. Besides, it was Caesar's birthday and the town was in holiday mood. Tito and Bimbo were among the merrymakers, dodging the charioteers who shouted at them. A dozen times they almost upset baskets of sweets and jars of Vesuvian wine, said to be as fiery as the streams inside the volcano, and a dozen times they were cursed and cuffed. But Tito never missed his footing. He was thankful for his keen ears and quick instinct—most thankful of all for Bimbo.

They visited the uncovered theater, and though Tito could not see the faces of the actors, he could follow the play better than most of the audience, for their attention wandered—they were distracted by the scenery, the costumes, the byplay, even by themselves—while Tito's whole attention was centered in what he heard. Then to the city walls, where the people of Pompeii watched a mock naval battle in which the city was attacked by the sea and saved after thousands of flaming arrows had been exchanged and countless colored torches had been burned. Though the thrill of flaring ships and lighted skies was lost to Tito, the shouts and cheers excited him as much as any and he cried out with the loudest of them.

The next morning there were *two* of the beloved raisin and sugar cakes for his breakfast. Bimbo was unusually active and thumped his bit of a tail until Tito was afraid he would wear it out. The boy could not imagine whether Bimbo was urging him to some sort of game or was trying to tell something. After a while, he ceased to notice Bimbo. He felt drowsy. Last night's late hours had tired him. Besides, there was a heavy mist in the air—no, a thick fog rather than a mist—a fog that got into his throat and scraped it and made him cough. He walked as far as the marine gate to get a breath of the sea. But the blanket of haze had spread all over the bay and even the salt air seemed smoky.

He went to bed before dusk and slept. But he did not sleep well. He had too many dreams—dreams of ships lurching in the Forum, of losing his way in a screaming crowd, of armies marching across his chest, of being pulled over every rough pavement of Pompeii.

He woke early. Or, rather, he was pulled awake. Bimbo was doing the pulling. The dog had dragged Tito to his feet and was urging the boy along. Somewhere. Where, Tito did not know. His feet stumbled uncertainly; he was still half asleep. For a while he noticed nothing except the fact that it was hard to breathe. The air was hot. And heavy. So heavy that he could taste it. The air, it seemed, had turned to powder, a warm powder that stung his nostrils and burned his sightless eyes.

Then he began to hear sounds. Peculiar sounds. Like animals under the earth. Hissings and groanings and muffled cries that a dying creature might make dislodging the stones of his underground cave. There was no doubt of it now. The noises came from underneath. He not only heard them—he could feel them. The earth twitched; the twitching changed to an uneven shrugging of the soil. Then, as Bimbo half-pulled, half-coaxed him across, the ground jerked away from his feet and he was thrown against a stone fountain.

The water—hot water—splashing in his face revived him. He got to his feet, Bimbo steadying him, helping him on again. The noises grew louder; they came closer. The cries were even more animal-like than before, but now they came from human throats. A few people, quicker of foot and more hurried by fear, began to rush by. A family or two—then a section—then, it seemed, an army broken out of bounds. Tito, bewildered though he was, could recognize Rufus as he bellowed past him, like a water buffalo gone mad. Time was lost in a nightmare.

It was then the crashing began. First a sharp crackling, like a monstrous snapping of twigs; then a roar like the fall of a whole forest of trees; then an explosion that tore earth and sky. The heavens, though Tito could not see them, were shot through with continual flickerings of fire. Lightnings above were answered by thunders beneath. A house fell. Then another. By a miracle the two companions had escaped the dangerous side streets and were in a more open space. It was the Forum. They rested here a while—how long he did not know.

Tito had no idea of the time of day. He could *feel* it was black—an unnatural blackness. Something inside—perhaps the lack of breakfast and lunch—told him it was past noon. But it didn't matter. Nothing seemed to matter. He was getting drowsy, too drowsy to walk. But walk he must. He knew it. And Bimbo knew it; the sharp tugs told him so. Nor was it a moment too soon. The sacred ground of the Forum was safe no longer. It was beginning to rock, then to pitch, then to split. As they stumbled out of the square, the earth wriggled like a caught snake and all the columns of the temple of Jupiter came down. It was the end of the world—or so it seemed. To walk was not enough now. They must run. Tito was too frightened to know what to do or where to go. He had lost all sense of direction. He started to go back to the inner gate; but Bimbo, straining his back to the last inch, almost pulled his clothes from him. What did the creature want? Had the dog gone mad?

Then, suddenly, he understood. Bimbo was telling him the way out —urging him there. The sea gate of course. The sea gate—and then the sea. Far from falling buildings, heaving ground. He turned, Bimbo guiding him across open pits and dangerous pools of bubbling mud, away from buildings that had caught fire and were dropping their burning beams. Tito could no longer tell whether the noises were made by the shrieking sky or the agonized people. He and Bimbo ran on— the only silent beings in a howling world.

New dangers threatened. All Pompeii seemed to be thronging toward the marine gate and, squeezing among the crowds, there was the chance of being trampled to death. But the chance had to be taken. It was growing harder and harder to breathe. What air there was choked him. It was all dust now—dust and pebbles, pebbles as large as beans. They fell on his head, his hands—pumice stones from the black heart of Vesuvius. The mountain was turning itself inside out. Tito remembered a phrase that the stranger had said in the Forum two days ago: "Those who will not listen to men must be taught by the gods." The people of Pompeii had refused to heed the warnings; they were being taught now —if it was not too late.

Suddenly it seemed too late for Tito. The red-hot ashes blistered his skin, the stinging vapors tore his throat. He could not go on. He staggered toward a small tree at the side of the road and fell. In a moment Bimbo was beside him. He coaxed. But there was no answer. He licked Tito's hands, his feet, his face. The boy did not stir. Then Bimbo did the last thing he could—the last thing he wanted to do. He bit his comrade, bit him deep in the arm. With a cry of pain, Tito jumped to his feet, Bimbo after him. Tito was in despair, but Bimbo was determined. He drove the boy on, snapping at his heels, worrying his way through the crowd; barking, baring his teeth, heedless of kicks or falling stones.

Sick with hunger, half-dead with fear and sulphur fumes, Tito pounded on, pursued by Bimbo. How long he never knew. At last he staggered through the marine gate and felt soft sand under him. Then Tito fainted. . . .

Some one was dashing sea water over him. Some one was carrying him toward a boat.

"Bimbo," he called. And then louder, "Bimbo!" But Bimbo had disappeared.

Voices jarred against each other. "Hurry—hurry!" "To the boats!" "Can't you see the child's frightened and starving!" "He keeps calling for some one!" "Poor boy, he's out of his mind." "Here, child—take this!"

They tucked him in among them. The oarlocks creaked; the oars splashed; the boat rode over toppling waves. Tito was safe. But he wept continually.

"Bimbo!" he wailed. "Bimbo! Bimbo!"

He could not be comforted.

Eighteen hundred years passed. Scientists were restoring the ancient city; excavators were working their way through the stones and trash that had buried the entire town. Much had already been brought to light—statues, bronze instruments, bright mosaics, household articles; even delicate paintings had been preserved by the fall of ashes that had taken over two thousand lives. Columns were dug up and the Forum was beginning to emerge.

It was at a place where the ruins lay deepest that the director paused.

"Come here," he called to his assistant. "I think we've discovered the remains of a building in good shape. Here are four huge millstones that were most likely turned by slaves or mules—and here is a whole wall standing with shelves inside it. Why! It must have been a bakery. And here's a curious thing. What do you think I found under this heap where the ashes were thickest? The skeleton of a dog!"

"Amazing!" gasped his assistant. "You'd think a dog would have had sense enough to run away at the time. And what is that flat thing he's holding between his teeth? It can't be a stone."

"No. It must have come from this bakery. You know it looks to me like some sort of cake hardened with the years. And, bless me, if those little black pebbles aren't raisins. A raisin cake almost two thousand years old! I wonder what made him want it at such a moment?"

"I wonder," murmured the assistant.

A DOG AND FATE

The Doomed Prince

ANCIENT EGYPTIAN TALE

Surely one of the oldest of dog stories is this narrative, written on papyrus some 3600 years ago and found in a tomb. The translation, by the noted scholar Sir William Matthew Flinders Petrie, is included in his *Egyptian Tales* (1899).

THERE once was a king to whom no son was born; and his heart was grieved, and he prayed for himself unto the gods around him for a child. They decreed that one should be born to him. And his wife, after her time was fulfilled, brought forth a son. Then came the Hathors to decree for him a destiny; they said, "His death is to be by the crocodile, or by the serpent, or by the dog." Then the people who stood by heard this, and they went to tell it to his majesty. Then his majesty's heart sickened very greatly. And his majesty caused a house to be built upon the desert; it was furnished with people and with all good things of the royal house, that the child should not go abroad. And when the child was grown, he went up upon the roof, and he saw a dog; it was following a man who was walking on the road. He spoke to his page, who was with him, "What is this that walks behind the man who is coming along the road?" He answered him, "This is a dog." The child said to him, "Let there be brought to me one like it." The page went to repeat it to his majesty. And his majesty said, "Let there be brought to him a little pet dog, lest his heart be sad." And behold they brought to him the dog.

Then when the days increased after this, and when the child became grown in all his limbs, he sent a message to his father saying, "Come, wherefore am I kept here? Inasmuch as I am fated to three evil fates, let me follow my desire. Let God do what is in His heart." They agreed to all he said, and gave him all sorts of arms, and also his dog to follow him, and they took him to the east country, and said to him, "Behold, go thou whither thou wilt." His dog was with him, and he went northward, following his heart in the desert, while he lived on all the best of the game of the desert. He went to the chief of Naharaina.

From *Egyptian Tales*, translated by Sir Flinders Petrie. Reprinted by permission of Methuen & Co., Ltd.

And behold there had not been any born to the chief of Naharaina, except one daughter. Behold, there had been built for her a house; its seventy windows were seventy cubits from the ground. And the chief caused to be brought all the sons of the chiefs of the land of Khalu, and said to them, "He who reaches the window of my daughter, she shall be to him for a wife."

And many days after these things, as they were in their daily task, the youth rode by the place where they were. They took the youth to their house, they bathed him, they gave provender to his horses, they brought all kinds of things for the youth, they perfumed him, they anointed his feet, they gave him portions of their own food; and they spake to him,

"Whence comest thou, goodly youth?" He said to them, "I am son of an officer of the land of Egypt; my mother is dead, and my father has taken another wife. And when she bore children, she grew to hate me, and I have come as a fugitive from before her." And they embraced him, and kissed him.

And after many days were passed, he said to the youths, "What is it that ye do here?" And they said to him, "We spend our time in this: we climb up, and he who shall reach the window of the daughter of the chief of Naharaina, to him will be given her to wife." He said to them, "If it please you, let me behold the matter, that I may come to climb with you." They went to climb, as was their daily wont: and the youth stood afar off to behold; and the face of the daughter of the chief of Naharaina was turned to them. And another day the sons came to climb, and the youth came to climb with the sons of the chiefs. He climbed, and he reached the window of the daughter of the chief of Naharaina. She kissed him, she embraced him in all his limbs.

And one went to rejoice the heart of her father, and said to him, "One of the people has reached the window of thy daughter." And the prince inquired of the messenger, saying, "The son of which of the princes is it?" And he replied to him, "It is the son of an officer, who has come as a fugitive from the land of Egypt, fleeing from before his stepmother when she had children." Then the chief of Naharaina was exceeding angry; and he said, "Shall I indeed give my daughter to the Egyptian fugitive? Let him go back whence he came." And one came to tell the youth, "Go back to the place thou camest from." But the maiden seized his hand; she swore an oath by God, saying, "By the being of Ra Harakhti, if one takes him from me, I will not eat, I will not drink, I shall die in that same hour." The messenger went to tell unto her father all that she said. Then the prince sent men to slay the youth, while he was in his house. But the maiden said, "By the being of Ra, if one slay him I shall be dead ere the sun goeth down. I will not pass an hour of life if I am parted from him." And one went to tell her father. Then the prince made them bring the youth with the maiden. The youth was seized with fear when he came before the prince. But he embraced him, he kissed him all over, and said, "Oh! tell me who thou art; behold, thou art to me as a son." He said to him, "I am a son of an officer of the land of Egypt; my mother died, my father took to him a second wife; she came to hate me, and I fled a fugitive from before her." He then gave to him his daughter to wife; he gave also to him a house, and serfs, and fields, also cattle and all manner of good things.

But after the days of these things were passed, the youth said to his wife, "I am doomed to three fates—a crocodile, a serpent, and a dog." She said to him, "Let one kill the dog which belongs to thee." He replied to her, "I am not going to kill my dog, which I have brought up from when it was small." And she feared greatly for her husband, and would not let him go alone abroad.

And one went with the youth toward the land of Egypt, to travel in that country. Behold the crocodile of the river, he came out by the town in which the youth was. And in that town was a mighty man. And the mighty man would not suffer the crocodile to escape. And when the crocodile was bound, the mighty man went out and walked abroad. And when the sun rose the mighty man went back to the house; and he did so every day, during two months of days.

Now when the days passed after this, the youth sat making a good day in his house. And when the evening came he lay down on his bed, sleep seized upon his limbs; and his wife filled a bowl of milk, and placed it by his side. Then came out a serpent from his hole, to bite the youth; behold his wife was sitting by him, she lay not down. Thereupon the servants gave milk to the serpent, and he drank, and was drunk, and lay upside down. Then his wife made it to perish with the blows of her dagger. And they woke her husband, who was astonished; and she said unto him, "Behold thy God has given one of thy dooms into thy hand; He will also give thee the others." And he sacrificed to God, adoring Him, and praising His spirits from day to day.

And when the days were passed after these things, the youth went to walk in the fields of his domain. He went not alone, behold his dog was following him. And his dog ran aside after the wild game, and he followed the dog. He came to the river, and entered the river behind his dog. Then came out the crocodile, and took him to the place where the mighty man was. And the crocodile said to the youth, "I am thy doom, following after thee. . . ."

[Here the papyrus breaks off.]

How does the tale of the Doomed Prince end? That will never be

known, for the last part of the papyrus was destroyed by a powder explosion during the excavation in which it was discovered.

"The close of the tale would have explained much that is now lost to us," Petrie adds as a postscript. "The crocodile boasts of being the fate of the prince; but the dog is with him, and one can hardly doubt that the dog attacks the crocodile . . . Then the dog is left to bring about the contest. Or does the faithful wife rescue him from all the fates? Hardly so, as the predictions of the Hathors strictly come to pass."

Other scholars could not resist the temptation to complete the story happily. They have the princess slay the crocodile. Then, pursued by former rivals for her hand, the young couple and the dog take refuge in a cave. They are betrayed when the dog barks a warning when the suitors are about to pass by. While the prince fights against heavy odds, the princess sacrifices herself for him, stepping in front to take a javelin, hurled at him, in her breast. The dog dies, too, defending his master, and finally the prince falls. Doom having been fulfilled, the Hathors, satisfied, restore all three to life. Such devotion, they decree, deserves to live on.

CARE OF DOGS

Third Georgic

VIRGIL

Nor last should be thy care of dogs. Feed fat
On whey, the Spartan's sprightly whelps, nor slight
They keen Molossians. Ne'er with trusty guards
Like these thou'lt fear the nightly thief's approach
Unto thy stabled flocks, nor inroads dread
Of wolves, nor, from behind, the base attacks
Of Spaniards who regard not law nor peace.
Oft in the course the timid asses wild
Thou wilt disturb with dogs, and oft the hare,
And oft the does, and oft, through tangled woods,
The wild boars hunt harassed by barking loud,
And through high mountains drive the stag immense
With clamor, headlong, safe within thy nets.

J. A. Wilstach, trans.

DOG AVENGER

The World's Most Famous Dog Story

FREDERICK REITER

Legend or fact, a dog story of the Middle Ages is here
finely retold. When it was made into a play, *The Dog
of Montargis*, it became a smash hit with long runs in
several European countries. Clever, well-trained per-
formers were required for the title role. Among the
feats called for by stage directions were: jumping a
gate and ringing a bell; numerous cues for barks;
pouncing on and downing the villain; taking a bow
with the rest of the cast at the final curtain.

THEY were a striking threesome—the blond rider, his handsome horse,
and the big, gray dog that followed them, barking happily.

For a moment the rider stopped his horse to enjoy the sight of the
landscape bathed in sunshine. The dog leaped up, placing his forepaws on the saddle, and licked his master's hands. The latter gently
patted the beast's enormous gray head. "Yes, you're my friend—good
old Hercules," he said. "Come on—let's go hunting!" He spurred his
horse and off they went into the twilight of the big forest.

Whenever Aubry de Montdidier managed to take a day off and relax
from the duties at the King's court, he went hunting, accompanied by
his dog Hercules. Ever since his father had given him the woolly puppy
five years before, dog and master had been inseparable. Aubry's father
had died meanwhile; and Aubry, who was a fine swordsman and soldier,
well liked by everybody, had become one of the King's favorite companions. Hercules had grown into the biggest dog around the court, and
he was as gentle as he was powerful. He had saved his master's life
twice. Once he had dragged him out of the Seine, and another time he
drove away a pack of wolves when Aubry was hunting in the mountains.

Aubry loved his dog dearly, and sometimes it seemed to him as though
the faithful animal were the only real friend that he had. The atmosphere
around the court was loaded with intrigue, and there were many who
grudged Aubry the King's favor. He was well aware of all this envy and
jealousy, although such sentiments were alien to his own disposition.
A knight, he thought, must never bear a grudge.

Reprinted by permission of Jeanne Hale.

One of his enemies was the Cavalier Macaire. Since the day Aubry
had defeated him in a tournament, the man had stopped talking to him.

As Aubry rode on, the dog roamed happily around, sniffing here and
there, until he stopped suddenly, his head cocked to one side, listening
tensely. Aubry halted his horse. Now he too could hear the sound of
tramping hoofs coming rapidly nearer, and soon he saw the figure of an
armored man on horseback emerge from the twilight. The hair on the

dog's back was raised, and out of his mighty chest sounded hostile growling.

"Why Aubry—this is a surprise!" shouted the armored man. When Aubry recognized him, he was surprised indeed. The man who had greeted him so jovially was none other than the Cavalier Macaire. Out in God's nature, a man's petty grudges are soon forgotten, he thought. And when Hercules' growl grew more menacing, he called: "Stop it, Hercules! Don't you know Macaire?" Obediently the dog calmed down.

"If you don't mind, I'll join the hunting party," Macaire suggested. And as they rode on, side by side, the dog seemed satisfied and continued his hunting game.

This was the moment Macaire had hoped for since the day of his defeat in the tournament. For weeks he had spied on Aubry. This meeting in the forest was carefully planned. Aubry was unsuspecting. They were alone. Everything had worked out beautifully so far. Carefully he began to keep his horse a few steps behind Aubry's. As the path grew narrower, he got his spear ready. He stopped his horse for a moment, then lunged forward, piercing Aubry's back with his spear.

Aubry sank to the ground with a groan and then lay still. Hurriedly Macaire dragged the body behind the bushes and threw it into a ditch. He began to cover it with earth and leaves, but before he could finish the job, Hercules was there. With a terrible howl he threw himself upon his master's body, removed earth and leaves, and began feverishly to lick the dead man's face and hands. This gave Macaire time enough to reach his horse and get away. He praised his good luck—nobody had seen him; nobody would ever find out. Now, with Aubry removed, nobody would stand in his way.

For two days and two nights Hercules stayed with his dead master. Nobody was around to disturb his vigil or to hear his desperate howling. On the third morning hunger and thirst drove him away. He returned to Paris, to the King's palace.

There the servants fed him, and wondered why Monsieur Aubry's dog was almost starved.

Suddenly Hercules ran upstairs, to where the cavaliers were accustomed to assemble. "Look," someone remarked, "Aubry's dog. Aubry must be back."

"Right," said another. "And I wonder where Aubry's been hiding for the last three days."

The dog looked around the big hall. Suddenly he raised his powerful head. He sniffed a few times, then lunged forward and attacked one of the cavaliers—it was Macaire. He shouted for help, and almost instantly the dog was separated from him and disappeared. Nobody could understand why Hercules, whom they knew as Aubry's gentle companion, had suddenly become violent. They started looking for Aubry. When they did not find him after some days had passed, rumors began to spread.

Hercules had resumed his vigil in the forest. For three days he stayed there, howling for help, licking the cold hands of his master. Then hunger drove him back to the palace once more. Again he was fed in the kitchen, and then ran upstairs. He found Macaire in no time, and again attacked him with fury. When some of the noblemen intervened, one of them got hold of the dog, put a leash on him, mounted a horse and let the dog lead.

When he discovered the body, he knew what had happened. He gave his dead friend a Christian burial and took Hercules back to Paris.

The King had been very fond of Cavalier Aubry de Montdidier, and when he heard how the dog had reacted, he decided that Hercules and the Cavalier Macaire should meet again. He had all his cavaliers assembled, hundreds of them. Then Hercules was brought into the hall and let loose. The dog started instantly to search for someone until he had singled out Macaire. With a ferocious howl he went for him.

Now the King had seen it with his own eyes: Hercules had pointed to Macaire as the guilty man. The King questioned the suspect, but Macaire kept denying that he had anything to do with Aubry's death.

When the King called in his counselors, they all agreed that the dog's behavior constituted a formal accusation just as though one of Aubry's kinsmen had accused Macaire before the King. When Macaire disputed the accuser's deposition, the King ruled that a duel should take place between Hercules and Macaire. The outcome of the ordeal would show the truth; the finger of God would point to the vanquished as to the liar.

In a small amphitheater near Paris the duel took place in the presence of the King and the entire court. The arms at Macaire's disposal were a shield and a heavy club. For the dog, an empty barrel, open on both sides, was rolled into the arena, as a retreat in case he should need it.

As though Hercules knew that in a knightly duel the first attack belongs to the challenger, he flung himself furiously upon Macaire. His opponent, however, was a strong man, and with his heavy club he managed to keep the dog at a distance. No matter which way Hercules turned he always found himself facing the club. But feigning attacks to both sides, he took advantage of that split second between the movements of the club, and in perfect timing fastened himself at Macaire's throat, brought the man down, and began to drag him through the arena.

With pitiful cries, Macaire declared himself defeated and begged that someone free him of the dog. When the King's judges entered the arena, Macaire confessed that he had slain Aubry de Montdidier in the forest of Bondis. He was sentenced to death, and quartered. His remains were dragged through the streets of Paris. Hercules had avenged the murder of his master!

This is the story of "The Dog of Montargis," the world's most famous dog story for more than six centuries. During the last eighty years it has fallen into oblivion, a fate as inexplicable as undeserved.

We do not know who wrote the story or who told it first. The legend of the dog who remains faithful to his master beyond death is as old as friendship between man and dog. Plutarch, the Greek historian, tells about a dog whom King Pyrrhus found guarding the body of a slain man; how the King, moved by so much faithfulness, buried the dead man and took the dog to his camp; how the dog during a parade suddenly attacked and bit two soldiers until they confessed to having murdered the dog's master. Similar reports can be found in the writing of Plinius, the Latin historian. Throughout the early Middle Ages, historians repeat this tale, and even the Arabian poets used it many times.

But only in one epos sung in the twelfth century by the minnesingers all over Europe, do we find, for the first time, all the ingredients of our story, including the duel and the actual names. In the library of San Marco in Venice, an Italian version of the poem was found. It bore the title "Macaire and Blanchefleur," and started with the heartbreaking story of a beautiful young Queen who was sentenced to die for an adultery of which she was innocent. The bad man, Macaire, had accused her falsely, thus taking vengeance because she had refused to love him. In the dark forest, cowardly Macaire kills the Queen's guardsman, the knight Aubry. But Aubry's dog, the only witness of the crime, runs back to the King's court and accuses Macaire. In the following duel, the dog remains victorious, the traitor is properly executed and in the end the innocent young Queen is saved.

We may safely assume that this old poem is the source of our story. It was kept alive by the minnesingers, and after the invention of the printing press, dozens of books in as many languages made it known all over the European continent.

This must lead to the conclusion that the story of the "Dog of Montargis" is fiction. And yet the historians of the seventeenth and eighteenth centuries considered it a fact, and even named the year 1371 as the year in which the duel took place, and in the reign of King Charles V of France, according to an inscription on an old etching depicting the duel.

Strangely enough, an error of punctuation seems to be the reason for assigning the duel to 1371. King Charles V of France had his castle Montargis redecorated in 1371. He had a mural of the famous duel painted on the wall above a fireplace, and the inscription on it read:

The duel between a dog and a nobleman who had killed his master, made at Montargis under the reign of Charles V in 1371.

Obviously it was the painting that was done in 1371, and not the duel. But the error stuck, and therefore all the later historians tell the story under the title, "The Dog of Montargis." Even Montargis itself, a small town two hundred miles south of Paris, accepted the historical error, and in its public garden there stands a statue illustrating the famous tale.

It is easy to understand why this story was popular during the Middle Ages. Not only is it a fine dog story with a knightly background, but the ordeal, the "Gottesurteil," where a public trial is interpreted as the expression of God's will, is quite typical for that period. One should think that with the beginning of the nineteenth century the story would have lost some of its appeal to the public. But just the opposite is true. "The Dog of Montargis" became a sensational hit, this time on the stage.

On June 18, 1814, the melodrama, *The Dog of Montargis* had its opening night at the Theatre de la Gaîté in Paris. It was such a success that it remained on the repertory for the next twenty years. The author of the melodrama, an obscure Monsieur Pixerecourt, could smile condescendingly upon the authors of such Broadway hits as *Abie's Irish Rose* or *Life with Father*.

The canine stars who appeared in the title role were sadly underpaid —they received five francs for each performance. One of them was called Vendredi—which means Friday. Oddly enough, Hollywood had a dog star by the name of Friday, the splendid shepherd dog who was so successful as Edward Arnold's guide dog in the thriller of a few years ago, *Eyes in the Dark*.

How big a box office attraction the melodrama, *The Dog of Montargis*, must have been is illustrated by the fact that the Convent Theatre in London hurried to produce it only three months after its opening in Paris.

The play found its way to the German stage also, through an episode well known in literature because it interrupted Goethe's career as a theatrical producer and broke off the famous friendship between Goethe and his Maecenas, the Grand Duke Charles August of Weimar.

At that time in 1817, Goethe was the great director of Germany's leading stage, the Weimar Theater, where most of the immortal plays of Goethe and Schiller had their opening nights. The lovely actress Karoline Jagemann was the Grand Duke's mistress. She had heard about the moving melodrama of the dog, and urged her lover to have it staged in the Weimar Theater. The Grand Duke readily sacrificed his literary standards for the whim of his charming lady friend. He ordered the melodrama to be translated and staged.

Goethe objected vehemently—that cheap tearjerker from Paris on Germany's most literary stage! What a humiliation! He offered his resignation as a director. Obviously his reasoning made less of an impression upon the Grand Duke than the means Mme. Jagemann had at her disposal. Goethe's resignation was accepted; a hack comedian by the name of Karsten, who owned a performing dog, was hired and the melodrama was played.

Stage success again made the story popular throughout Europe. During the first half of the nineteenth century it appeared in numerous anthologies and collections of anecdotes in all languages. In 1860 the well-known English editor William Chambers published it in his *Miscellany of Useful and Entertaining Knowledge*, which was later printed in the United States.

But from then on the story rapidly faded into oblivion. None of the numerous anthologies of dog stories published during the last fifty years so much as mentions "The Dog of Montargis."

However, this does not mean that the world's most famous dog story will stay forgotten. It is too beautiful a story to deserve this fate. No other dog story reveals more clearly the three qualities which make the dog man's best friend: intelligence, courage, and faithfulness.

Part Two
WAR DOGS

Cry "Havoc!" and let slip the dogs of war.

Shakespeare: *Julius Caesar*

JOY OF BATTLE

The Story of the Dog

CECIL G. TREW

Dogs in armor—on the decks of fighting ships—as sentries, scouts, and messengers—as military transport. Since early times man's canine companion has served him in warfare. The World War referred to in the text is, of course, the First.

THE use of the dog as an auxiliary of war is as old as war itself. Primitive man was quick to make use of the dog as a guardian for his family, his belongings and himself, and, as such, we may be certain that, when men began to live together in communities, their four-footed protectors were not denied the joy of battle when rival tribes came to blows.

In the days of primitive weapons, and, in fact, down to the time of the invention of gunpowder, the dog was used not only for purposes of defence, but actually as a force of attack. From about 700 B.C. on we have numerous references to the use of the dog in battle in Western Asia, Europe, and Northern Africa. The wonderful reliefs from the Palace of Nineveh (*circa* 650 B.C.), now in the British Museum, show very clearly the war dogs of Assurbanipal—a large, mastiff type of beast. Herodotus (v. 1), in his account of the battle between the Perinthi and the Paeoni, says: "Man was matched against man, horse against horse, dog against dog." On the frieze from Pergamum (*circa* 280 B.C.) we see representations of the type of dog used by the Assyrians in war, a big, shaggy creature, with pricked ears and a short, broad muzzle.

Certain nations, notably the Gauls, clad their war dogs in armour, but unfortunately no complete suit of this ancient dog armour has survived, and our only knowledge of what it was like comes from contemporary pictures. The only two suits of armour I have been able to trace are neither of them war armour, but were intended for protection in hunting such dangerous game as the wild boar. One suit, now in the museum at Madrid, is composed of metal plates and chain, with an undercoat of velvet, and belonged to King Charles V. The other, the property of the Dukes of Saxe-Weimar, and now in the Wartburg Mu-

From the book *The Story of the Dog and His Uses to Mankind*, by Cecil G. Trew. Published by E. P. Dutton & Co., Inc. and reprinted with their permission and Methuen & Co., Ltd.

seum, is what is known as an eyelet coat. It is made of several thick-
nesses of canvas, perforated and stitched together with close-set button-
holing, the stitching giving additional stiffness to the coat and the holes
supplying ventilation.

The Garamantes, the ancient nomadic people of the Sahara, depended largely on dogs for the defence of their camps, as did also the
Great Attila, King of the Huns. The Romans employed cordons of dogs
•to guard the ramparts of their towns, but do not seem to have used
them very much in actual battle.

From Homer we get the first mention of dogs being used as despatch
bearers, carrying letters attached to their collars.

When dogs were used for fighting, in addition to their coats of mail,
they were frequently armed with heavy iron collars from which spikes
and curved knives protruded at all angles. Animals so armed wrought
much havoc among enemy cavalry and not infrequently reduced the
ranks to confusion.

Throughout Europe the English mastiff seems to have been popular
as a war dog from the time of the Roman Conquest onwards, but I can
find no very early mention of their being used as such in England itself.
Henry VIII sent some 400 of these dogs to Charles V of Spain who was
at that time engaged in war with France, and these animals fought
so splendidly and proved themselves such a valuable asset to the Spanish
army that Charles held them up as an example to his soldiers. When
parties were sent out for reconnaissance they were accompanied by
dogs, and the animals' sense of smell discovered many an ambuscade as
well as helping to track a fleeing foe.

After the French had entered Alexandria in 1798, Napoleon wrote to
one of his generals: "They ought to have at Alexandria a large number
of dogs, which you can easily make use of by fastening them a short
distance from your walls."

One dog in particular became famous in the Napoleonic Campaigns,
a creature of unrecorded breed called Moustache. He first acquired
merit by warning the French of a surprise attack by the Austrians. He
also disclosed the presence of an Austrian spy, who, carefully disguised,
had managed to get into the French camp. But his greatest feat was at
the Battle of Austerlitz, where it is said, when he saw his master, the
standard-bearer, fall dead, Moustache rushed at the Austrian soldier who
had grabbed the cherished flag, tore it from his hands and dragged it,
torn and muddy, back to his company. For this deed Moustache was
personally decorated by Marshal Lannes.

An interesting story is told showing how dogs employed in war absorb
the military spirit. After the Battle of Talavera, word was brought to
General Graham that there was a dog on the battlefield who, in spite of
all inducements, refused to leave the side of its dead master, a Spanish

officer. Eventually General Graham managed to capture the desolate creature, and he had it sent to a friend of his who lived just outside Edinburgh Castle. The dog is described as a large, brown poodle, and he had had an ear shot off in battle. In those days of war, victories and important events were announced from the castle by the firing of guns, and whenever this happened, Muchuch, as the dog was called, would go wild with excitement. His sympathetic master would open the door of the house where they lived, whereupon Muchuch would rush up to the castle, where he would take up his position with the battery. He became a well-known character among the garrison and when, owing to some slight indisposition, he was confined to the house for some days, there was a continual stream of soldiers ringing the bell to enquire after the old warrior.

Admiral Collingwood had a Newfoundland called Bounce who was with him on the *Royal Sovereign* at the Battle of Trafalgar. On Collingwood's promotion to the peerage, Bounce assumed that the honour was extended to him also, and the Admiral wrote to his wife:

> I am out of patience with Bounce; the consequential airs he gives himself since he became a right honourable dog are insufferable. He considers it beneath his dignity to play with commoners' dogs. This, I think, is carrying the insolence of rank to the extreme.

Another dog to achieve military fame was Thonton, who was attached to the Zouave Guards. He served through fourteen campaigns and was twice wounded. His name was included in the roll call of the regiment, and when it was read out he would bark his "Sir."

Throughout the ages dog has helped man to fight his battles, and a charming little story is told of impartial recognition of his services. During the Revolutionary War, General Washington was dining one night, when a large dog suddenly appeared at the door of his tent. It was a fine animal but obviously was very hungry, and on examination its collar was found to bear the name of General Howe. Washington ordered the dog to be well fed, and then returned to the enemy lines under a flag of truce, for which gracious action he received a very grateful letter from General Howe.

In the World War a wire-haired terrier, Spot, shared with his master, General Townshend, the hardships of the siege of Kut, and was taken prisoner with his master when the Turks took the city. He was spared to return to England where he took a place of honour in a parade of famous war dogs. Unfortunately, on this occasion, probably bored by overmuch admiration, he insisted on showing that he was a war dog by starting a battle royal with one of his fellow veterans.

A remarkable, and authentic story is told of an Irish terrier, Prince, the property of a soldier in the Staffordshire Regiment. When the regiment was ordered abroad in 1914, Prince was left behind in charge of the soldier's family in Hammersmith. One day, greatly to the consternation of the family, Prince disappeared. In some unexplained manner he managed to get across the Channel—probably as a stowaway on a troopship—and, once in France, his extraordinary instinct led him to the Staffordshires, who were in the front-line trenches at Armentières, and to his master. He was then allowed to "serve in France" until his owner returned to England where Prince died in 1921.

Modern methods of warfare are very different from those of old, and the dog can no longer take part in the actual fighting; nevertheless, his uses, both on the battlefield and behind the lines, are many and indispensable. During the World War the dog, as some one put it, "had a paw in every pie."

To begin with, when Germany invaded Belgium, all the thousands of dogs which are commonly employed in the latter country for pulling small carts and tradesman's vans were of inestimable assistance in evacuating women, children, and household goods from the war zone. Later on dogs were used extensively in the Belgian Army for pulling machine guns and carrying reserve ammunition.

Guard dogs were used by practically every nation which took part in the conflict. Manpower was precious, and became increasingly more so, and the use of dogs to guard munition dumps, prisoners, food supplies, etc., released many a man from sentry-go. Where dogs alone were not sufficient their presence, with their sharp sense of smell and hearing, added much to the men's morale. Many a prisoner who would be willing to risk a bullet from his human escort would hesitate to try and circumvent the vigilance—and teeth—of a dog.

Strange though it may appear, whether it is by smell or by recognizing different uniforms, dogs have a wonderful faculty of differentiating between friend and foe, and have frequently discovered the presence of spies. (See previous anecdote of Moustache.)

On sentry duty, both in the trenches and in No Man's Land, the dog's keen scent and acute eyesight and hearing were a tremendous help. Many are the stories of surprise attacks frustrated by the sharp senses of dogs accompanying men on patrol, and in the dark, particularly, when a man's eyes are practically useless to him, the dog's marvellous senses saved many a human life.

Sentry dogs are in regular use in India on the North-West Frontier. A type of Afghan hound is used and the following description is from Hutchinson's *Dog Encyclopaedia:*

Chaman, you must know, is one of our principal posts on the North-West Frontier. . . . Two mud forts guard the railway station, one on each side; each fort is manned by one company of Indian infantry, and one squadron of native mounted levies and by *dogs.*

What strikes the newcomer entering either of the forts at any
hour of the day is the large, extraordinary-looking creatures sprawl-
ing all over the place, fast asleep. In size and shape they somewhat
resemble a large Grey-hound, but such slight resemblance is dis-
pelled by the tufts with which all are adorned: some having tufted
ears, others tufted feet, and others, again, possessing tufted tails.

They are known as Baluchi Hounds, and they get their daily food
ration from the commissariat babu; he is the only permanent resi-
dent of the fort. They will have no truck with any stranger, white
or black.

When "Retreat" sounds, the pack awakes, yawns, pulls itself together, and solemnly marches out to take up positions close to the
newly arrived night guard. *They appear to be under no leadership,*
yet as the patrols are told off a couple of dogs attach themselves to
each patrol, and they remain with their respective patrols till "reveille" next morning. Between a deep ditch and wall of the fort is a
narrow path. Throughout the night, this path is patrolled by suc-
cessive couples of dogs. Immediately one couple has completed the
circuit of the walls and arrives back at the main gate, another couple starts out.

When it is remembered that these extraordinary hounds have
never had any training whatsoever, that their duties are absolutely
self-imposed—for no human being has the slightest control over
them—the perfection of their organization and the smoothness with
which they carry out their tasks make mere man gasp!

Another field in which the dog proved his worth was that of messenger. By day or night a dog can slip swiftly and silently over ground
pocked with shell holes which would mean death from a sniper's bullet,
or at least, in all likelihood, a broken limb to a human being. When telephone wires were broken and visual signalling impossible, either because
of smoke, darkness or bad weather, dogs were, at times, the only possible
means of communication between advance posts and headquarters.

A messenger dog is in the charge of a keeper who he recognizes as his
master. When the dog is to be used he is taken, on the lead, away from
his keeper to the outpost from which messages may be required to be
sent, or led with a scouting party who anticipate difficulties in com-
municating with their base. When the necessary message has been written and placed in the special container attached to the dog's collar, he
is released, and he follows his natural desire to return to his master.

A greater nicety of training is required for the "liaison" dog, for in this
work the dog has to learn not only to return to his master if told to do so,
but possibly to leave his master and return to the place from which he
was released.

Sometimes, in cases of broken communications, a dog was sent to lay
a fresh signal wire. The wire was wound round a disc attached to an apparatus on his back, and he was trained to go at such a pace, and over
such ground, as was best suited for the unwinding and laying of this

precious link between two posts. The average dog can carry about fifty yards of telephone wire.

On the Italian front sledge dogs, imported from the North, brought provisions and munitions to men in the high Alps. It is on record that, after one very heavy snowfall, 150 dogs moved, in the space of four days, over fifty tons of supplies from the valley up to the front line high up on the mountain. During the year 1918 the French had over 8,000 sledge dogs working with their army in the Vosges Mountains alone.

But perhaps the most valuable service rendered by dogs in modern warfare is that of First Aid. Many a man alive today owes his life to the keen senses of the dog who, after the battle, is sent out to search for the wounded.

A wounded man's first instinct is to crawl to some spot where he is less likely to sustain further injury. This may be a shell hole, an abandoned trench, or behind any cover within his reach. Here perhaps he may lose consciousness, or become too weak to call out should help come within earshot. After dark, even if he stays out in the open, he will probably be invisible to the human eye, and as likely as not might never be found were it not for the dogs. A dog's sense of smell is independent of sight or hearing, and these First Aid dogs are trained to search out the living from among the dead. Sometimes a wounded man is able to avail himself of the supplies carried by the dogs in their First Aid outfits—bandages, small dressings and stimulant—and thus to get himself into a fit state to crawl back to safety. But if he is unconscious, or too badly hit to help himself even to this extent, the dog will return to the lines where its excited manner will attract attention, and stretcher-bearers will be sent out to follow the dog back to the wounded man.

Colonel Richardson tells me that, in spite of the splendid work done by dogs during the World War, there has been, as yet, no official recognition of the need of them in England, although he has been kept busy supplying them as guard dogs for private individuals.

Dogs employed in the World War were not of any one particular breed, though Airedales, Alsatians, and Collies were probably in the majority. When the Armistice was signed there were about 10,000 dogs at the actual battle front.

During the war many dogs were mentioned in despatches; and many more went the way of all good dogs without complaint or whimper.

SWIFT COURIER

War Dog

JOHN W. THOMASON

The messenger dog gave good and gallant service, for
she had been well trained by her German masters.
One of the skills she had learned was distinguishing
the colors of uniforms as a mark of friend or foe.

GRETA was a war dog in the service of H. M. the Kaiser and King. They
bred her in the kennels of a Pomeranian Junker who was reported dead
at Contalmaison on the Somme, in 1916. With the bleak autumn of that
year, his widow found that she could not endure alone the rambling old
estate on the dark North German plain; so she closed it, and went down
to Berlin, where, in the bitter wartime, there was at least company for
loneliness and misery.

Greta, with other matters pertaining to the house of a landed German
gentleman, came up for sale. A purchasing officer of the signal service,
waiting for a train in Pommern, saw her and bought her for the army.
She was then five months old, but the signal officer had a good eye.

She went across Germany and into France, boxed up in a military train,
and came to Seventh Army Headquarters, behind Laon. On a winter
morning they let her out of her crate into a swept courtyard where there
were soldiers and dogs, and you heard the guns along the Chemin des
Dames sound sharp and angry from the southwest across the new snow;
then some one thrust a mess of horse-meat stew under her nose, and she
found no concern for the far-off thunder.

The gross *Wachtmeister* of the Seventh Army *Meldehund-Trupp*—
on detail from a Uhlan regiment because of his handiness with animals
—observed the lanky puppy while, all legs and appetite, she wolfed her
food. Writing down her points in his book as he noted them, he decided that she had a good head and good legs, and when it caught up
with her belly, her chest would be broad and deep enough.

The color, too, was right—grayish, like the good German uniform;
you did not want blacks and tans in this war, where the harder you were

to see the longer you lasted. And she was the seventh puppy in this draft, so her name must begin with G—Gertrude—Garda—Gretchen—Greta. Greta would do. Here, having polished her pan, she sat back to ease her stomach, and cocked an amiable ear at the big man in the tight cavalry tunic.

"Attention, you!" he rumbled at her. "Your name is Greta. To begin with, you will learn that name—Greta—" Thereafter, the "Prussian Regulations for the Care, Training, and Handling of War Dogs, 1913: Revised, With Notes on the Recent Fighting, 1915," ordered her life.

More than any other detail of modern battle, the war dog has been swamped in sentimental nonsense. The fact is that the German armies found them useful in a certain limited field and employed them from sound tactical considerations where they were effective; for there was never any sentimentality about the German service.

Of course you saw nondescript and various mascots among the regiments, since there is a natural affinity between soldiers and dogs the world over; and in the trench sectors where the war settled into routine, the men in the listening-posts in front of the wire used to take out small alert animals that raised a helpful row when people approached from the wrong direction. But the real war dogs, rationed and quartered and borne on the regimental strength, were the clever brutes of the German shepherd breed, selected and trained to carry messages from a regimental headquarters to its battalions on the line.

This German shepherd dog is a northern strain, as old as history, and until late years entirely utilitarian, the colleague of herders and the assistant of the Continental police. He is sturdy and faithful, he takes kindly to discipline, and he is capable of a high degree of training along open-air lines. Commonly he is called the police dog, and he has other names.

His remote ancestors crossed the Rhine with the flocks of the Cimbri and the Teutons, and mediæval manuscripts show him exactly in appearance as he is now. More remotely, he is kin to the wolves that roamed the North German plain, and to this day the wolfish look is written large upon him.

In battle, they found that he could replace to a certain extent the regimental runner, that unfortunate whose duty takes him most frequently across the blazing forward zone of combat, maintaining touch between one post and another. Therefore, it was common sense to use him, because you can grow a dog in two years where a man takes twenty, and a dog may get through where a man cannot.

The war dogs then in the German service were the affair of the army signal-officer, along with radio, telegraph, the field-telephone, carrier-pigeons, flags, and signal-lanterns, and all the diverse means whereby a field army talks between its elements. In battle, everything mechanical has a way of going out of commission: there is a heat at the point of contact which fuses things.

A colonel in action might be able to talk over his field-telephone to Berlin, and not be able to get through to his forward-battalion half a kilometre away. To be certain, therefore, he must fall back on the means of communication that Cæsar used; he must send somebody with his message. The messenger may be a dog.

Buried in the war archives in Potsdam there is the final opinion in the matter: After exhaustive tests it was found that five dogs would do the regimental messenger work of sixteen soldier runners. The arithmetic is plain—five men to look after five dogs, and eleven rifles more for the firing line. So they used dogs when they could.

The army *Meldehund-Trupp*—messenger-dog outfit—took Greta and molded her to pattern in half a year. There were two basic lessons: the first was obedience to orders, and the second concerned the gray-green uniform of the German soldier. A puppy idled in the courtyard of the billet with Drina and Blitz and Eric and a dozen or so others, playing gravely after the fashion of the breed and keeping a watchful eye on the soldiers in the light gray shoulder-straps of the communication troops.

When one called Greta, you went swiftly to receive instruction, paying no attention to any other name. You carried things from one soldier to another, things fastened to your collar. First it was just across the courtyard; then it would be around the corner, and, later, your man would deliberately hide, so that you had to trail and cast about to find him.

Presently the affair took you out into the fields and up and down ravines, and there must be no loitering on the way. They worked you from one place to another place, and they worked you at night. Simple things, done over and over, they came to be second nature. And through every exercise ran the other lesson—respect for the uniform.

"Because, *Liebchen*," the *Herr Wachtmeister*, with the heavy voice and remarkably gentle hands, would say, "it would be frightful if, when you get Out There, you should take up with the wrong fellows. Those Frenchmen in their dirty blue breeches, or the English *Schwein* in khaki— So!" There were practical lessons.

The *Feld-grau* fed and cherished you. It cleaned your quarters and dispensed work and play and food and caresses. With civilians a dog had no contacts—dubious, mean persons, passed aloofly on the street. And once, Greta, carrying a message to the young *Gemeiner* on the other end of her run, found him in the place he ought to have been, wearing strange blue clothes.

It was puzzling; but the hands and the face and the smell of this private were familiar, and she accepted his blandishments and made him free of the tin cylinder at her neck. She never forgot what happened to her after that, for the *Wachtmeister* had a way of impressing things.

Again, it was a fellow in an English uniform; and when, the next day, a sorry file of khaki prisoners passed on the street, Greta had to be restrained. The conclusion was inevitable: people in gray-green were all right; otherwise, they were to be avoided if possible and attacked if not. In any case, they meant trouble.

Later, they ran Greta about the firing ranges of the army small-arms schools, and loosed off rifles and machine guns near her, and exploded things around her. The French planes also helped her education along with the occasional bombing-raids that an Army Headquarters must expect behind an active front.

Steady nerves and discipline and custom dissipated any gun-shyness she might have had. At the field trials of the new blood, which the *Meldehund-Trupp* held in the early summer, she got a message over a kilometre of broken ground in less than four minutes, which is classed as good in the Prussian service, and she received the compliments of exalted personages, even officers of the General Staff, turned out to observe the event.

She was a grave, upstanding dog, approaching her full growth, with a fine head and clean hard legs, and a close, grayish-tawny coat, when, in the late summer of '17, they certified her fit for field duty and drafted her to the 40th Fusilier Regiment in the 28th Infantry Division, the old regular division that they called the Conquerors of Lorette.

The 28th Division had been fighting in Caurieres Wood before Verdun and needed replacements of every kind. They went down into Alsace and entered the line northwest of Altkirch, which was a quiet sector and a suitable place for a division to renew itself; and here Greta had her first combat experiences, sharp enough and not too crowded, as is best for recruits, both men and dogs.

The war flickered languidly across the great still valleys of the region. Greta became acquainted with shell-fire and learned to cock an ear and gauge them, proceeding with a contemptuous flirt of her tail when the thing howled high or wide, and squatting like a soldier when the whine of it increased to a shattering roar and crashed down near at hand.

Incautiously quartering over a ridge, between reserve and the forward position, she drew long-range machine-gun fire and she deduced from that the wisdom of avoiding the sky-line and keeping away from the open. She watched the war-wise soldiers and patterned her conduct on theirs.

She followed her occasions up and down black ravines in the night, and under the flares of the front line she learned what dead men are like.

When the division, much restored, went up into the Champagne around the Butte de Mesnil, Greta went competently with them and did good service with the 1st Battalion of the 40th Regiment, which was her particular assignment, in that wilderness of shell holes and wire and old trenches where the war was always bitter.

Her division was one of those which rushed north for the counter-battle at Cambrai, and Greta saw her first tanks—disconsolate monsters, out of gasoline beyond the Nord Canal—and her first fighting English-men, and took the rifle-fire of a platoon of them at bay in the wreck of a wood; and there began to be stories about her in the regiment. The 28th wintered in the Ardennes and had a post of honor in the great March drive that rolled down to the gates of Amiens, and thereafter drew out and practised the arts of open warfare in the country behind Laon, through April and early May of 1918.

Near the last of the month the Seventh Army pounded across the Chemin des Dames, and four days later, in a red sunset full of crackling shrapnel, Greta lapped water from the Marne and heard her dusty sol-diers, filling their canteens by the blue river, talk of a place called Paris. Then they went back a little way and rested.

Always keen to the moods of soldiers, Greta sensed the anger and disgust in the ranks when the division was alerted and moved up to the front barely a week afterward. It was not their turn, the gray-green files growled. What was the war coming to, when the 10th Division—which had always been fairly good as front-troops went—lost a town to these Yankee amateurs the beaten French were putting in to plug their holes! However, they added with sour pride, the 28th would show them—and this is the proper and healthy frame of mind for soldiers.

Greta's Fusilier Regiment took over a narrow front, with the 1st Bat-talion in the corner of a wood through which the right division pro-longed the line, and the 2nd facing down on a battered village where shells were always falling. Going in with Regimental Headquarters, you noted that things here were quite lively. The columns did not tramp confidently along the roads, but went in hurrying groups across the fields and kept to the woods where it was possible. There was shelling always and everywhere, and many dead men and horses.

Greta's particular signalman—the stubby little private who always looked after her—was killed, taking her over her route the first time. They went from the wood where Regimental lived in holes, down a gully to the road. Then a ditch covered the way, as far as a railroad embankment.

That had to be crossed; here the enemy got the signalman and came near getting Greta. Bullets flung dust into her nose and ripped into the ground around her, and she fled straight across a wheat field to the edge of the wood and found her own people, more concerned about her than about the poor *Gemeiner* who lay now in plain sight on the embankment with his knees drawn up.

She was fired at in the dusk, when she went back, and every time thereafter when she had to move in daylight. There were no trenches; and things happened as often and as sharply as they did in the Champagne.

About the third day matters became very bad. All afternoon and all night the shells crashed down the woods and along the roads. The telephones went out. Greta, catching cat-naps in her hole, as a war dog must, was awakened by the heavy boots of the reserve battalion, brought up to Regimental before dawn, from rest billets in the rear area.

They sent her out when the sky was getting gray, and a machine gun, very near, spat a stream of bullets around her ears when she scuttled across the railroad. She made the shelter of the wood with her tongue out, and was confused. The place had changed its very shape. Some of her best landmarks were gone, and many dead lay about in field-gray uniforms.

In the place where battalion command post should have been, there was nothing but a great shell hole and an untidy litter of corpses. One of these was the Signal *Feldwebel*, who always took her messages. He lay now partly under a fallen branch, with dew on his yellow mustache, and Greta licked his cold jowl and permitted herself to grieve softly in her throat.

She went on with bristling shoulders and cast about through the wood to find her people, as she had been trained. She came to a narrow clearing, where a body lay in a strange khaki uniform. Stepping around it with distaste, she halted at the edge of the open, some wolfish instinct sounding an alarm.

Private Hense Jordan, of the Fifth Marines, noted with satisfaction that the night was about finished. A sickly bluish light came sifting into the woods. Shredded tree tops and splintered branches grew sharp against a pale green sky. The flailed and broken timber and trampled underbrush around him took form in the shadows. The dawn chill bit into his bones, and he shifted himself in the shallow hole he had scooped the night before, and drew his salvaged German blanket closer around his shoulders.

An agonizing cramp in his thigh jerked him painfully on his feet, to ease the tortured muscle. That spasm passing, he propped his rifle in a convenient crotch and remained standing, hunched over, his hands thrust into his breeches for warmth. He yawned and shivered miserably, his teeth chattering and his bony knees knocking together. It was the time of day when battles start and raids may be expected and reveille turns you out, and the time of day a man always feels the lowest!

Of all the duty you got, these listening-posts, out in front in a place like this, were the meanest. And double watches, because the major said there weren't enough men left in the battalion to run regular reliefs . . . Where, by the way, was that dam' sergeant with his relief? He'd been out here since the Major General Commandant was a corporal.

Meantime, his trained hard eyes searched restlessly in the brush for any movement; Private Hense Jordan was an old soldier, and he had no intention of dying for his country—not through carelessness, anyway. It was quiet, right here. Over on the left, toward the Veuilly Woods and Hill 142, the guns of the French division were shelling something, and you heard chaut-chauts and Hotchkiss guns. On the eastern face of this wood, single rifles were going—snipers, most likely; Heinie had good snipers.

Some of our machine guns were bickering with the Maxims across the fields from Bouresches. A quiet morning. Well, after last night, Private Jordan considered, everybody ought to have his belly full—and here *Minenwerfer* shells began to break regularly in the right rear, where the ravine that bordered the southern edge of the wood led back to the town of Lucy.

"Steppin' 'em up an' down that there gully, where the chow detail has to go," considered Private Jordan sadly. "Heinie's on the job, an' Gawd help them poor greaseballs, if they's any of them in there—hope some of them gets through with grub—an' oh, Lawd, let there be coffee." He couldn't remember when he had eaten, and he felt too weak to stand. He reached back and shook his canteen, although he knew it was empty, and he spat cotton from a dry mouth, and small irritations graveled him.

It was, he decided, no life for a white man. Lying out, nights. And being shelled. And fighting blind in the woods, and never getting any rations. "Gettin' us all bumped off like this, they might at least feed us." He hadn't had his shoes off for eleven days. He wished he was back on a battle-ship, where they piped for chow three times a day an' mornin' coffee before turn-to; and he regretted all the evil things he had said in his time about the navy.

"Leastways, you wear marine uniform, 'board ship." He crooked a torn khaki sleeve and regarded it with disgust. "First thing the army done was take away our Lewis guns an' give us chaut-chauts—take away our greens an' give us khaki—" That last rankled. Every man in the Marine Brigade considered it a blow struck at their morale by the envious army, when they were informed that in France they would receive no more of the forester-green winter field uniforms of the Marine Corps, but would go garbed in olive-drab.

"Same as any odd lot of doughboys—yeh!" What if it was very like the German uniform? "Time a Boche gets near enough to tell the difference, he's in danger, I'll tell the cockeyed worl'!" Only a few officers in the brigade clung to the old greens of the corps. The major was one.

Private Jordan considered him briefly, the memory of his last court-martial sour on his mind. A hard son of a dog, but he was up here last night with his little stick, when they reorganized after the attack, looking things over. "Well, if I was a major, they wouldn't get me in no army O.D., neither. Wouldn't have a chance. Recruitin' Office, Kansas City, Miz-zour-i: that would be my billet."

There was, in the brush ahead, something that moved. Private Jordan's rifle was by his knee, and his hands were in his pockets, which was bad; but he was too old a stager to duck and grab. He froze motionless, every sense alert. The weakness flowed out of him, and his eyes narrowed to slits. Which way, and what—

It was a dog, a dust-gray, tall fellow with pointed ears, and, when it lifted its wolfish head, pale color on its throat. It materialized from around a bush a dozen yards away and stood, a forefoot lifted, considering the next move. Private Hense Jordan remembered the order, reiterated when they came up to this fight: Kill all dogs. We don't use them, and the French don't. The Germans use them for messengers. Kill them, wherever seen—and search the remains—they're usually carrying something.

Private Jordan also reflected that the Boche was very close to him, on ahead through the woods, and he did not want to shoot or otherwise demonstrate from his position, if he could help it. But he'd have to get that dog . . . Looked like the critter might come on out into the open, where a snap shot would have a better chance—easy does it. Strictly as an afterthought, he loved dogs. But orders were orders.

Greta settled it for him. The day before, she had been right through here. There should be a section of her infantrymen and two light machine guns just past the clearing. She trotted out, her head low, taking a confusion of scents from the trampled ground, and the marine saw that she would come within a yard of him. Try it with the bayonet—no noise— He caught up his rifle and lunged in one motion, sudden as a snake's, but she was a split-second quicker, and recoiled.

In her schooled brain, as she faced him, the cold face of her *Feldwebel* back there, and the little *Gemeiner* on the railroad, and the mad things that zipped and droned around her in the wheat, all connected at once with this lean, brown man. Here was the enemy. She flung herself at him, slashing for the thigh, as a wolf does. He shifted his bayonet and caught her on it; the point slid inside her fore leg and back, by the angle of her leap, across her shoulder-blade.

But her weight overbalanced the man, and they went down together in a tangle which the rifle dominated. Rolling clear of her ringing jaws, Private Jordan brought one hobnailed boot down on her head and considered that it was enough. He got up, wrenched the blade clear, shot a quick glance around, and bent over the long, crumpled body, which quivered briefly and relaxed.

At her neck, hooked to the leather collar, was a thin aluminum cylinder.

"Active Boche, all right—in the messenger business. . . . Dam' it, I had to do it! An' it's a bitch, too! Arh! But there wasn't no way out of it—guess that got her in the heart." Kneeling, much desolated, he investigated the battered head and felt along her chest.

A sergeant and a private of marines came noiselessly up behind him. They spoke in husky whispers. "Got one, Hense? Seen anything else? If the mutt's got anything on 'im, rush it on back to the skipper. An' report to your platoon—moved it to the right this mornin'—Corporal Kent's in charge—they got some slum up. Here's the layout, guy," and the sergeant turned to instruct the relief.

Meantime, Private Jordan had noted that the dog's chest still bled, and the flow was bright and not sluggish. "Say," he said, without looking up, "she ain't dead! I never killed her. She—"

"Well, kill it an' get back from here," snapped the sergeant, in disgust. "This any place to be sobbin' over our dumb friends, you—" And Private Jordan slung his rifle, picked her up, and dodged into the brush to the rear, where he set her down and clumsily applied his first-aid bandage to stop the flow of blood.

Her skull didn't seem to be smashed, and although she was still entirely limp, he thought her heart went a little. Then he walked swiftly down through the position, along a very thin line of men in holes, who regarded him without curiosity and gulped cold slum and lukewarm coffee.

"Battalion?—down that there trail, fella." For he wasn't going to the company commander, a man not sympathetic to dogs or to irregularities.

"If the skipper says how come I went over his head, I'll tell him I thought orders was to take Boche dope right to the major—major used to have a dog," he planned uneasily; and passed through two platoons of the 2nd Engineers, unkempt and competent and constituting the battalion reserve; and found Battalion Headquarters group disposed in the ravine.

The major sat on a rock and drank coffee from a canteen cup. He was unshaven, and his eyes were red-rimmed from loss of sleep, and the shine had departed from his field boots, but he wore his stained forester-green uniform with an air, and his helmet, the chin-strap looped up over the brim, was slanted at a cocky angle. He conversed casually with his adjutant, and did not look around when Private Jordan, strangely burdened, slid down the bank of the ravine and was halted by the important sergeant-major.

"Private Jordan wants permission to speak to the battalion commander —got a Boche dog here, carryin' messages."

The adjutant, a young man in a soldier's blouse and quartermaster breeches everywhere too large for him, turned to hear, with a cold, bad-tempered eye.

"Sir, I'm on listenin'-post on the left, back there, an' just now, this here dog—I think she's a Boche messenger-houn', sir, like it says in orders—she tries to get by me, an'—" Then Greta came alive. Her lax body, sagging in the man's arms, quickened. She slashed Private Jordan's wrist wickedly, threw herself down and away from him, rolled over on her wrecked shoulder, and came in frantic haste to her three good feet, every tooth showing and her back hair all on end.

The adjutant swore and plucked out his pistol, and the battalion gas non-com clubbed his rifle, and Private Jordan, clutching at his wrist, rocked on his feet and pleaded foolishly, "Aw, don' kill her—don' kill her. She's a bitch, too." The major walked toward her.

Sick and dizzy, with an unaccountable weakness dragging at her, and surrounded by khaki, Greta whirled on this new enemy, to do what she could. The fire went out of her eye. For the man had on a green uniform and had also the stiff, high look of her own officers. It was all very confusing, but with her people here, it would be all right. He held out his hand, and stooped to her, and spoke softly. Greta lunged painfully to him, tried to lick his hand, and collapsed against his boots.

The major detached the aluminum cylinder, and thrust it at his adjutant. "See if it's anything, Le Grand. And my compliments to the surgeon—want him here. Now, old lady, did they do you wrong? Damnation! Bayonet—and you've bashed her eye out, you—"

"Sir"—Private Jordan, much distressed, pulled away from the file who was working at his wrist—"I done my best not to kill her! Sir, I never hurt a dawg in my life—I—"

"Oh, all right! All right. Surgeon, give me a hand here—maybe we can patch her up—dam' fine animal, I think. Yes, what is it?"

The adjutant, with the aid of a navy hospital corpsman who had studied in Vienna, had a translation. "It's addressed in code and signed in code, sir, but I think it's from Regimental to battalion. Says, KTK Battalion will approach position under cover from the right, pass through you, and attack to recover lost position. Says, you will support attack after it has passed through. Says, half-hour SMW—must mean heavy *Minenwerfer*—preparation, starting at five-fifteen—A.M., sir. And the time sent is four-thirty-five—don't get that, for it's just after four now—and it says, acknowledge with two yellow smokes."

Said the major, his head on one side: "Their time's an hour ahead of ours. Sergeant-major, you inventoried those captured pyrotechnics, you said. Ought to be yellow smoke rockets among 'em. Go forward a little way and send up two. Pick a place in the clear, so they'll get above the trees." The sergeant-major saluted and set off at a trot. "Where's that engineer officer? Mr. Shank, have your platoons stand by to reinforce the left company, in half an hour. Go up there now and look it over; you'll put them in as the company commander directs. Tell him about it; they'll come that way. Work in through the woods and hit the left, I think. Le Grand, get Regimental. I want some artillery."

A runner said: "Hi! Ol' sergeant-major sure made knots—there go them yellow smokes!" And very soon afterward the *Minenwerfer* shells began to crash into the woods. In the 40th Fusilier Regiment they never understood why their counterattack failed so disastrously. The lieutenant-colonel had a very bad time explaining it.

And Greta lives now in Quantico, when she's at home. Her major has a regiment there. She carries her years well, although she is one-eyed and has a heavy limp. She is an aloof, unfriendly dog to every other person but her colonel; yet it is noted that in the fall and winter when the marines go in forester green her temper becomes more genial, and she allows familiarities on the part of the rank and file.

FOR BETTER OR FOR WORSE

Verdun Belle

ALEXANDER WOOLLCOTT

The stray dog and the young marine met close to the
front in France during the First World War and decided that they belonged to each other. How they
strove to keep that compact at all hazards is told by a
master story-teller.

I FIRST heard the saga of Verdun Belle's adventure as it was being told
one June afternoon under a drowsy apple tree in the troubled valley
of the Marne.

The story began in a chill, grimy Lorraine village, where, in hovels
and haymows, a disconsolate detachment of United States marines lay
waiting the order to go up into that maze of trenches of which the
crumbling traces still weave a haunted web around the citadel bearing
the immortal name of Verdun.

Into this village at dusk one day in the early spring of 1918 there
came out of space a shabby, lonesome dog—a squat setter of indiscreet,
complex, and unguessable ancestry.

One watching her as she trotted intently along the aromatic village
street would have sworn that she had an important engagement with
the mayor and was, regretfully, a little late.

At the end of the street she came to where a young buck private
lounged glumly on a doorstep. Halting in her tracks, she sat down to con-
template him. Then, satisfied seemingly by what she sensed and saw,
she came over and flopped down beside him in a most companionable
manner, settling herself comfortably as if she had come at last to her
long journey's end. His pleased hand reached over and played with
one silken chocolate-colored ear.

Somehow that gesture sealed a compact between those two. There
was thereafter no doubt in either's mind that they belonged to each
other for better or for worse, in sickness and in health, through weal
and woe, world without end.

From *The Portable Alexander Woollcott*, selected by Joseph Hen-
nessey. Copyright 1927 by Alexander Woollcott. Reprinted by permission of The Viking Press, Inc.

She ate when and what he ate. She slept beside him in the day, her muzzle resting on his leg so that he could not get up in the night and go forgetfully back to America without her noticing it.

To the uninitiated onlookers her enthusiasm may not have been immediately explicable. In the eyes of his top sergeant and his company clerk he may well have seemed an undistinguished warrior, freckle-faced and immensely indifferent to the business of making the world safe for democracy.

Verdun Belle thought him the most charming person in all the world. There was a loose popular notion that she had joined up with the com-

pany as mascot and belonged to them all. She affably let them think so, but she had her own ideas on the subject.

When they moved up into the line she went along and was so obviously trench-broken that they guessed she had already served a hitch with some French regiment in that once desperate region.

They even built up the not implausible theory that she had come to them lonely from the grave of some little soldier in faded horizon blue.

Certainly she knew trench ways, knew in the narrowest of passages how to keep out from underfoot and was so well aware of the dangers of the parapet that a plate of chicken bones up there would not have interested her. She even knew what gas was, and after a reminding whiff of it became more than reconciled to the regulation gas mask, which they patiently wrecked for all subsequent human use because an unimaginative War Department had not foreseen the peculiar anatomical specifications of Verdun Belle.

In May, when the outfit was engaged in the exhausting activities which the High Command was pleased to describe as "resting," Belle thought it a convenient time to present an interested but amply forewarned regiment with seven wriggling casuals, some black and white and mottled as a mackerel sky, some splotched with the same brown as her own.

These newcomers complicated the domestic economy of the leathernecks' haymow, but they did not become an acute problem until that memorable night late in the month when breathless word bade these troops be up and away.

The Second Division of the A.E.F. was always being thus picked up by the scruff of the neck and flung across France. This time the enemy had snapped up Soissons and Rheims and were pushing with dreadful ease and speed toward the remembering Marne.

Foch had called upon the Americans to help stem the tide. Ahead of the marines, as they scrambled across the monotonous plain of the Champagne, there lay amid the ripening wheat fields a mean and hilly patch of timber called Belleau Wood. Verdun Belle went along.

The leatherneck had solved the problem of the puppies by drowning four and placing the other three in a basket he had begged from a village woman.

His notion that he could carry the basket would have come as a shock to whatever functionary back in Washington designed the marine pack, which, with its neat assortment of food supplies, extra clothing, emergency restoratives, and gruesome implements for destruction, had been so painstakingly calculated to exhaust the capacity of the human back. But in his need the young marine somehow contrived to add an item not in the regulations—namely, one basket containing three unweaned and faintly resentful puppies.

By night and by day the troop movement was made, now in little wheezing trains, now in swarming lorries, now afoot.

Sometimes Belle's crony rode. Sometimes (under pressure of popular clamor against the room he was taking up) he would yield up his place to the basket and jog along with his hand on the tailboard, with Belle trotting behind him.

All the soldiers in Christendom seemed to be moving across France to some nameless crossroads over the hill. Obviously this was no mere shift from one quiet sector to another. They were going to war.

Everyone had assured the stubborn youngster that he would not be able to manage, and now misgivings settled on him like crows.

He guessed that Verdun Belle must be wondering too. He turned to assure her that everything would be all right. She was not there. Ahead of him, behind him, there was no sign of her. No one within call had seen her quit the line. He kept telling himself she would show up. But the day went and the night came without her.

He jettisoned the basket and pouched the pups in his forest-green shirt in the manner of kangaroos. In the morning one of the three was dead. And the problem of transporting the other two was now tangled by the circumstance that he had to feed them.

An immensely interested old woman in the village where they halted at sunup, vastly amused by this spectacle of a soldier trying to carry two nursing puppies to war, volunteered some milk for the cup of his mess kit, and with much jeering advice from all sides, and, by dint of the eye-dropper from his pack, he tried sheepishly to be a mother to the two waifs. The attempt was not shiningly successful.

He itched to pitch them over the fence. But if Verdun Belle had not been run over by some thundering camion, if she lived she would find him, and then what would he say when her eyes asked what he had done with the pups?

So, as the order was shouted to fall in, he hitched his pack to his back and stuffed his charges back into his shirt.

Now, in the morning light, the highway was choked. Down from the lines in agonized, grotesque rout came the stream of French life from the threatened countryside, jumbled fragments of fleeing French regiments. But America was coming up the road.

It was a week in which the world held its breath.

The battle was close at hand now. Field hospitals, jostling in the river of traffic, sought space to pitch their tents. The top sergeant of one such outfit was riding on the driver's seat of an ambulance. Marines in endless number were moving up fast.

It was one of these who, in a moment's halt, fell out of line, leaped to the step of the blockaded ambulance, and looked eagerly into the medico top sergeant's eyes.

"Say, buddy," whispered the youngster, "take care of these for me. I lost their mother in the jam."

The Top found his hands closing on two drowsy pups.

All that day the field-hospital personnel was harried by the task of providing nourishment for the two casuals who had been thus unexpectedly attached to them for rations. Once established in a farmhouse (from which they were promptly shelled out), the Top went over the possible provender and found that the pups were not yet equal to a diet of bread, corn syrup and corned willy. A stray cow, loosed from her moorings in the great flight, was browsing tentatively in the next field, and two orderlies who had carelessly reminisced of life on their farms back home were detailed to induce her cooperation.

But the bombardment had brought out a certain moody goatishness in this cow, and she would not let them come near her. After a hot and maddening chase that lasted two hours, the two milkmen reported a complete failure to their disgusted chief.

The problem was still unsolved at sundown, and the pups lay faint in their bed of absorbent cotton out in the garden, when, bringing up the rear of a detachment of marines that straggled past, there trotted a brown-and-white setter.

"It would be swell if she had milk in her," the top sergeant said reflectively, wondering how he could salvage the mascot of an outfit on the march.

But his larcenous thoughts were waste. At the gate she halted dead in her tracks, flung her head high to sniff the air, wheeled sharp to the left and became just a streak of brown and white against the ground. The entire staff came out and formed a jostling circle to watch the family reunion.

After that it was tacitly assumed that these casuals belonged. When the hospital was ordered to shift further back beyond the reach of the whining shells, Verdun Belle and the pups were intrusted to an ambulance driver and went along in style. They all moved—bag, baggage, and livestock—into the deserted little Château of the Guardian Angel, of which the front windows were curtained against the eyes and dust of the road, but of which the rear windows looked out across drooping fruit trees upon a sleepy, murmurous, multi-colored valley, fair as the Garden of the Lord.

The operating tables, with acetylene torches to light them, were set up in what had been a tool shed. Cots were strewn in the orchard alongside. Thereafter for a month there was never rest in that hospital.

The surgeons and orderlies spelled each other at times, snatching morsels of sleep and returning a few hours later to relieve the others. But Verdun Belle took no time off. Between cat naps in the corner, due attentions to her restive brood and an occasional snack for herself, she managed somehow to be on hand for every ambulance, cursorily examining each casualty as he was lifted to the ground.

Then, in the four o'clock dark of one morning, the orderly bending over a stretcher that had just been rested on the ground was hit by something that half bowled him over.

The projectile was Verdun Belle. Every quivering inch of her proclaimed to all concerned that here was a case she was personally in charge of. From nose to tail tip she was taut with excitement, and a kind of eager whimpering bubbled up out of her as if she ached to sit back on her haunches and roar to the star-spangled sky but was really too busy at the moment to indulge herself in any release so satisfying to her soul. For here was this mess of a leatherneck of hers to be washed up first. So like him to get all dirty the moment her back was turned! The first thing he knew as he came to was the feel of a rough pink tongue cleaning his ears.

I saw them all next day. An ambling passer-by, I came upon two cots shoved together under an apple tree. Belle and her ravenous pups occupied one of these. On the other the young marine—a gas case, I think, but maybe his stupor was shell shock and perhaps he had merely had a crack on the head—was deep in a dreamless sleep. Before drifting off he had taken the comforting precaution to reach out one hand and close it tight on a silken ear.

Later that day he told me all about his dog. I doubt if I ever knew his name, but some quirk of memory makes me think his home was in West Philadelphia and that he had joined up with the marines when he came out of school.

I went my way before dark and never saw them again, nor ever heard tell what became of the boy and his dog. I never knew when, if ever, he was shipped back into the fight, nor where, if ever, those two met again. It is, you see, a story without an end, though there must be those here and there in this country who witnessed and could set down for us the chapter that has never been written.

I hope there was something prophetic in the closing paragraph of the anonymous account of Verdun Belle which appeared the next week in the A.E.F. newspaper, *The Stars and Stripes*. That paragraph was a benison which ran in this wise:

Before long they would have to ship him on to the evacuation hospital, on from there to the base hospital, on and on and on. It was not very clear to anyone how another separation could be prevented. It was a perplexing question, but they knew in their hearts they could safely leave the answer to someone else. They could leave it to Verdun Belle.

FIGHTING HEART

Dogs at War

CLAYTON G. GOING

Chips, part Husky, collie, and German shepherd, was tough. Loyal guardian of the family to whom he belonged, he was the bane of postmen, garbage men, and bicyclists. When he chose to nap at street intersections, policemen prudently detoured traffic around him. In the Second World War his owners volunteered his martial talents to the K-9 Corps. None can doubt how valiantly Chips displayed them in battle.

CHIPS joined the K-9 Corps because he bit a garbage man! And within a year this German shepherd saw action in North Africa and Sicily, met President Franklin D. Roosevelt and Prime Minister Winston Churchill, was recommended for the Distinguished Service Cross, won the Silver Star, and bit General Dwight D. Eisenhower.

Chips never once paraded before the critical eyes of a dog judge. He never won a best-in-show, best-in-class, or even a third-place ribbon at a single dog show.

But during a few brief and brutal seconds on a Sicilian beach, this mutt proved himself the top thoroughbred of the K-9 Corps, a champion of champions.

The story of Chips begins just before Christmas 1940. He was one of a litter whose father was a Husky and mother was part collie and German shepherd. From each of them Chips inherited those qualities of stamina, intelligence, and aggressiveness that so plainly showed when machine-gun bullets began churning up little geysers of sand at the feet of American doughboys wading ashore on that island beach in the pre-dawn blackness of a historic day some two and one-half years later.

Chips' first taste of battle, however, was not in Sicily. It was in French Morocco. He was a member of the American force under "Old Blood and Guts"—Major General George S. Patton, Jr.—that landed under fire November 8, 1942, near Casablanca as part of the now-famous Yankee-British squeeze play which on May 13, 1943, completed the clean-up of North Africa when the remnants of Rommel's once-vaunted

Afrika Korps and the Italian fascist lackeys surrendered unconditionally on Cape Bon in Tunisia.

Chips barely finished training in time for the North African invasion. Late in September, 1942, he was assigned to his first handler, Private John R. Rowell of Arkansas. The two worked together at Front Royal for three weeks and then hurriedly joined Rowell's infantry company at Camp Pickett, Virginia, only a few days before it sailed from an eastern United States port.

During the voyage across the Atlantic, Chips was seasick, but received good care and, luckily, before landing regained his canine composure.

Chips saw quite a bit of action during the fighting before the armistice. At first he was very frightened by the whine and explosions of the shells. But he quieted down after two hours and became a battle-tested veteran as good as any of the men. Chips was under fire on several patrols and he even went on scout duty with Rowell behind enemy lines.

After hostilities in French Morocco ceased, Chips was assigned to a bivouac at Casablanca and it was here he first came in contact with world leaders.

Between January 14 and January 24, 1943, Chips was part of an elaborate network guarding the house where President Franklin D. Roosevelt and Prime Minister Winston Churchill held their historic Casablanca conference evolving the "unconditional surrender" formula for dealing with Axis military forces and also mapping the next Allied campaign in which Chips was to distinguish himself.

Each night the dog patrolled the area where the two leaders conferred with their military staffs into the early morning hours. Before the conference ended, President Roosevelt and Prime Minister Churchill met their four-footed protector. Chips was a thoroughly tired soldier when his tour of duty was over. He gulped down his biggest meal in days and then slept for nearly twelve hours without waking up.

About this time, Rowell was taken ill and sent to a hospital. Sergeant William Haulk of Macomb, Illinois, took over the handling of Chips.

"We had four war dogs in our battalion," Haulk relates, "and Chips was the best liked of them all.

"After our stay at Casablanca we moved all over North Africa and then into Tunisia. Chips missed the action in Tunisia, but after the battle for Africa was over we trained for the invasion of Sicily."

While training near Algiers Chips had a love affair. She was a "WAC" member of the dog unit. Her name was Mena and she had very soulful eyes. When Chips sailed for Sicily, he left behind his Mena and nine puppies. Haulk recalls that the new father was both "love sick and seasick on the trip across the Mediterranean, but got over both amazingly quick when the firing began."

The War Department isn't commenting, but Chips' amorous adventure may have been the cause of an order that later went out to the commanding officers of all war dog reception and training centers in the United States. The order said that it had been determined the spaying of bitches was a military necessity and to the best interests of the military service.

The Sicilian invasion, which historians may record as the beginning of the actual liberation of the European continent from Nazi and Fascist domination, began before dawn on July 10, 1943, with what was then the largest amphibious operation in the history of warfare. More than three thousand ships of every description transported men, machines, and dogs to the island after air-borne units had landed to divert the defenders.

Chips was one of three dogs with the Third Division Infantry Regiment of the American Seventh Army under Patton, now a lieutenant general. The Seventh formed the left flank of the attacking force, with Canadian troops in the center and the British Eighth Army on the right flank.

Chips' outfit landed just east of Licata at a spot on Sicily's southern coast known as Blue Beach. It was near this area where the crucial point of the entire operation developed when the German Hermann Goering and Fifteenth Armored divisions launched a tank-supported attack driving the Americans, at one point, back to the sea.

And it was here that Chips became the first American dog hero of the Second World War.

Chips was led ashore by Private Rowell, who had returned to duty after being discharged from the Casablanca hospital.

Rowell and Chips cautiously advanced in the early morning blackness and were at a point about three hundred yards inland from the water when red-hot lead suddenly and unexpectedly began pouring at them from the darkness ahead, spraying the beach area. The firing came from two machine guns in a pill-box, which had been camouflaged as a peasant's hut.

Yankee soldiers threw themselves flat, hugging the sand.

Here Chips demonstrated the reckless insubordination that sometimes makes wartime heroes. Without waiting for an order from his handler to attack, Chips broke loose and, with teeth bared, charged the machine-gun nest, completely disregarding the steady deadly stream of bullets.

Private Rowell describes what happened then as follows:

"There was an awful lot of noise and the firing stopped. Then I saw one Italian soldier come out the door with Chips at his throat. I called him off before he could kill the man." Three others followed holding their hands above their heads.

In a few brief and dangerous seconds, this American war dog single-handed and at great risk of his own life eliminated an enemy machine-gun position and saved the lives of many of his comrades. His bravery enabled the inland advance to continue.

But Chips paid a price. He suffered powder burns and a slight scalp wound when one of the Italian soldiers attempted to shoot him with a revolver during the scuffle inside the pill-box.

Chips was given immediate first-aid and his wounds were not serious enough to prevent his continuing in action. Shortly before daybreak Chips' keen sense of smell gave warning of ten Italian soldiers moving silently along a road toward the beachhead which the Americans had established. Private Rowell took all ten prisoners.

While this has not yet been confirmed officially by the War Department, Chips has been credited with their capture by the national head-quarters of Dogs for Defense.

Later, incredulous officers of the Third Division Infantry Regiment checked and verified the story of Chips' deed in tackling the machine gunners. On September 9, 1943, it was recommended "that Chips, U.S. Army dog, Company I, Thirtieth Infantry, be cited in orders and awarded the Distinguished Service Cross for extra heroism in action." The recommendation was signed by Captain Edward G. Paar.

"Chips' courageous action," Captain Paar stated, "singlehandedly eliminating a dangerous machine-gun nest and causing the surrender of its crew, reflects the highest credit on himself and the military service."

Major General Lucian K. Truscott, Jr., commander of the Third Division, impressed by the dog's gallantry and contribution to the success of the invasion, decided to waive War Department regulations which prohibit the actual bestowing of medals on animals. So on November 19, 1943, "somewhere in Italy," while a group of soldiers stood at attention and heavy guns pounded enemy mountain positions to the north, Chips was awarded the Silver Star medal for "bravery in action against the enemy." He was the first dog in United States history to receive this honor.

Press dispatches from Italy reported that at the same time Chips was given the Distinguished Service Cross and the Purple Heart. Dogs for Defense, after obtaining verification from the Quartermaster General's office, announced proudly that Chips had received the Distinguished Service Cross. The War Department later denied this, saying that it had no record that Chips was presented with the Distinguished Service Cross or the Purple Heart, although it admitted he did receive the Silver Star.

Anyway, Chips probably will be the last dog in this country to get an army medal. News stories of his decorations brought a protest from William Thomas, 1943 national commander of the Military Order of the Purple Heart.

Mr. Thomas, who is principal of the Lincoln School at New Rochelle, New York, wrote letters to President Roosevelt, Secretary of War Henry Stimson and Major General J. A. Ulio, Adjutant General of the U.S. Army, specifically objecting to the awarding of the Purple Heart to Chips.

Mr. Thomas, in his letter to the President, said that "the award of the Purple Heart, in any instances other than to persons, is an indirect insult to our first President, General George Washington, who instituted the badge of military merit," and that its presentation "to one Chips, a G.I. battle dog, decries the high and lofty purposes for which the medal was created."

The past commander added, however, that "lest there be the slightest misunderstanding regarding my appreciation for the contribution that our four-footed friends have made and are making to the successful prosecution of the war on the field of battle, it is humbly suggested that a distinct medal be created for the specific purpose of rendering tribute to man's most faithful friend."

General Ulio in reply, February 3, 1944, wrote that in order to prevent a recurrence the following instructions had been issued by the adjutant general's office:

"1. The award of War Department decorations to other than persons, that is, human beings, is prohibited.

"2. If it is desired to recognize the outstanding services of an animal or a fowl, appropriate citation may be published in unit general orders."

Chips stayed on duty with his battalion until the Sicilian fighting ended on August 17, 1943. Later he went with Lieutenant General Mark W. Clark's Fifth Army which landed on the Italian west coast at bloody Salerno a month later.

It was in Italy that Chips had his second meeting with the great—a meeting in which he was guilty of misconduct, insubordination, disrespect for a superior officer, violation of the Articles of War, and third-degree assault!

Any other private would have been hurried unceremoniously off to the guardhouse, there to await the stern efficiency of a court-martial. But not our mutt. He got away with it!

General Dwight D. Eisenhower, Allied Commander-in-Chief in the Mediterranean theater, had arrived in southern Italy from Allied headquarters in Algiers for one of his periodic inspections of the battle area.

It was natural that proud officers should introduce General Ike to the hero of the Sicilian landing. The general had heard of the valor of the canine soldier under his command and had been impressed.

He did the logical thing on meeting Chips—bent over to pet him.

But the private reacted in an entirely illogical way toward this attention from the commanding general.

Chips bit the four-starred hand!

It would have been bad enough if Private Chips grabbed a sergeant, or maybe even a second lieutenant, but, no, he picked on the top man, the head of all American, British, and French forces in the Mediterranean war zone—the man who later was to be named supreme commander of the Allied Expeditionary Forces for the invasion of western Europe.

Just what General Eisenhower said to Private Chips or to his embarrassed and red-faced junior officers is not known. But General Ike, a soldier's general and a man of infinite patience and good humor, surely must have thought that the Army had trained this trigger-tempered warrior well.

As a direct result of his intensive military teaching Chips developed a dislike for anyone in civilian clothes. On the day he met Chips, General Eisenhower, dressed for comfort on his fighting-zone tour, wore hi-cuts and no tie. Perhaps Chips thought the general was a civilian. But, mistaken identity or not, a private bit a general, and that's news in any army.

Sergeant Haulk wrote to the former owner on December 13, 1943, from "somewhere in Italy": "Chips has been with us through all our combat in Italy. In the last few weeks, however, Chips has grown kind of nervous of shell-fire, so we have had him transferred to our division headquarters where he is doing guard duty for our commanding general.

"Although we miss him very much in the company, we know that he deserves the break. We hope to get him back after the war is over and keep him until he is returned to you.

"I think I miss him most, as every day he would come to me and play, and we were constantly together."

Chips finally came home. Rating eight battle stars for his service in campaigns in Italy, France, and Germany, he was returned to his owners, the Wren family of Pleasantville, New York. Like other veterans he suffered from combat fatigue and was no longer his belligerent self. Loved and honored, he was cared for until 1947 when the old warrior's fighting heart ceased to beat.

PACIFIC ISLAND SCOUTS

Dogs for Defense

FAIRFAX DOWNEY

Many a soldier's life was saved by dogs in the Second
World War. Those trained as scouts often spotted the
carefully concealed Japanese ambushes in the jungle
before fire could be opened. This selection is a chapter from a book written for the fine organization that
recruited most of the American dogs for service as
sentinels, scouts, messengers, transport, and other purposes—Dogs for Defense.

I

THE scout dog—typical of many another in the Army or Marine war-
dog platoons—understood almost everything that was happening. You
could take the word of his proud handler for that and find it was easy
to believe, noting the alert intelligence in the dark eyes and his ready
response to commands. He seemed to be aware of it when, training
completed, he and his handler became members of a newly organized
platoon, for now they were a group of men and dogs set apart, standing
formations, and going on maneuvers as a unit. *Esprit de corps*, that
feeling of belonging to a team and determination not to let anybody
on that team down, began to animate the outfit. Perhaps the scout dog
sensed even that, since it was no more than a development of the bond
of service and loyalty between him and his master.

II

It was not in the shell-wracked chaos of amphibious assaults that the
K-9 Corps found its best opportunity to serve. On the beaches the dogs
chiefly proved that they could stand fire, although they were of value
in warning of Jap night counterattacks. When the beachhead was se-
cured, and the columns began to push inland, then our war dogs came
to their own.

Before the invaders lay the green menace of the tropical jungles, dark

From *Dogs for Defense*, by Fairfax Downey. Reprinted by permission.

and somber shadows beneath its thick canopy of foliage even at high noon. Trails, tunnels through the dense vegetation, were the only entrances unless new paths were slowly and laboriously hacked. Deep within the jungle, along those trails, were laid Japanese ambushes. For the first American patrols thrusting in, that inscription which Dante pictured over the gates of Hell might almost have rung true: "All hope abandon, ye who enter here." Nevertheless they drove in. Brave men died when ambushes were sprung, but the Japs were finally outflanked, and the patrols pushed on.

Yet when a scout dog and his handler were at the point of the patrol, then it was different. A keen canine nose caught the Jap scent anywhere from a score to several hundred yards away. The dog froze into rigidity, an almost inaudible rumble in his throat. The patrol halted while scouts wriggled through the jungle to the flanks and dealt with the enemy machine gun covering the trail, or the patrol leader sent for a mortar section, perhaps by messenger dog, to blast out the ambush. Sometimes a canine muzzle would point up a tree. The Jap sniper, hidden in its branches, had made himself almost invisible to human eyes by painting his body green. But canine eyes, which are color-blind, had not been deceived by the green paint, nor had keen ears failed to catch a slight rustling overhead. The dog continued to point. So Yank sub-machine guns sprayed the tree with lead, and the sniper's body hurtled to the ground or hung limp from the belt that had bound him to the trunk.

Now and again the dogs failed. But this sentence keeps recurring in reports on war dog platoons by the divisions to which they were attached:

"No patrols led by dogs were fired on first or suffered casualties."

III

There were eight war dogs in the first K-9 tactical unit to take part in operations in the Southwest Pacific, not enough for a platoon—only a detachment. Six were scouts, two messengers—all German and Belgian shepherds. Their names were "Sandy," "Lady," "Dick," "Duke," "Rocky," "Husky," "Teddy," and "Ranger." Not one of them returned. Five died on duty and three, just before they were to be sent home, were found to be infected with typhus and had to be destroyed.

Much depended upon the service of this detachment. Whether war dogs would be used further in the Pacific theater virtually rested on their performance. How the eight discharged their duty might furnish a theme for a K-9 Odyssey, worthy of chronicling by Homer who wrote so movingly of "Argus," the old hound of Ulysses. Even a bare account of the detachment's campaigns, first with the Australians on New Guinea and later with the Marines on New Britain, has an epic flavor.

Trained at Beltsville, Maryland, the unit was put under the command of Second Lieutenant Robert Johnson. Handlers were Technicians Fourth Class Herman H. Boude, William M. Jorgensen, Guy C. Sheldon, and Arthur N. Tyler. Landed at Port Moresby, New Guinea, and hardened again after the long sea voyage, the outfit was flown to the front in August, 1943, and attached to an Australian battalion of the force driving the Japs back through the Markham and Ramu valleys. For forty-eight out of fifty-three days the K-9's spearheaded the reconnaissance patrols pushing through the jungles. The scout dogs repeatedly spotted Japs or groups of natives not known to be in the vicinity; and the messenger dogs, plunging through streams or shouldering a path through six-foot Kunai grass, kept contact with troops following the advance.

" 'Duke' could scent a Jap three-quarters of a mile away in an open field when the wind was right," declared his handler, Sergeant Tyler. "In the jungle he would always warn us when the enemy was two or three hundred yards away. While we were with the Australian Army 'Duke' was responsible for tipping us off on something like fifty Japs."

A report on the drive reads as would others to follow: "Patrols led by the dogs were never ambushed and suffered no casualties." The dogs' service could have no greater tribute.

By the time the detachment was reassigned to the Marine Raider Regiment of the Sixth Army for the New Britain campaign, the dogs had made such a reputation that they were given air transportation in a plane with a group of staff officers. All went well until a rough landing jounced one dog into another's private niche—on top of its occupant. Ensued a dog fight of such far-ranging fury that the "brass" had to make a hasty exit from the plane by the escape hatch.

In the Cape Gloucester attack, the dogs went ashore with the first wave. While the Marines held on and consolidated the beachheads, the dogs stood guard at night, giving warning of Jap attempts to infiltrate. The canine detachment led the advance up the coast from the cape. The dog "Dick," constantly alerted to Japs in the path of the advance, ranging from spotting single stragglers to full platoons. Once as the patrol approached a group of five camouflaged huts, "Dick" insisted in pointing only one of them. Marines, trusting him, ignored the four huts and concentrated their fire on the fifth. Investigation gave the dog a perfect score. Four of the huts were empty. In the fifth four Japs had been waiting in ambush until Marine bullets riddled its walls.

"Duke" again distinguished himself. The two-year-old, sixty-pound German shepherd now won a reputation as a bring-em-back-alive expert. Although prisoners were especially desired by intelligence officers for questioning, the rank and file of the Marines kept forgetting whenever they met Japs until it was too late. So also did the K-9 handlers at first.

" 'Duke' led me up to a hut one day," Sergeant Tyler, his handler, related. "I found a Jap outside and stabbed him. 'Duke' stayed on the alert. I found a second Jap hiding inside and knifed him."

But after two days of killing Japs, the Americans remembered prisoners were needed. "Duke" led a patrol around a hill in an approach so stealthy that three Japs were captured at their noon meal with their mouths still full of rice. That same afternoon the dog took other prisoner-hunters undetected to within fifteen yards of a Jap captain and two men. The fugitives jumped into the sea but were fished out. Three more Nips were tallied for the dog before the day was over. "Duke's" total for the campaign was: fifty Japs flushed, with twenty-two of them captured and the rest killed.

Meanwhile the redoubtable "Duke" continued saving American lives. Working with a patrol on the mission of locating the point on the coast where the Japanese were evacuating their troops, the dog sniffed and alerted. The patrol, noting the spot, started to slip away. But the presence of the Americans had been discovered by the enemy. Jap counter-patrols began to close in, determined that news of the embarkation place would never get out. It was "Duke's" keen nose that guided the Marines out from between the pincers. On a dozen other occasions he prevented scouts from running into ambushes.

"Sandy" was one of the two messenger dogs with the detachment. He had iron nerves—shelling never seemed to bother him. All through the campaign, the black shepherd, a big fellow weighing a good sixty pounds, was to be found with one of his handlers bringing up the rear of patrols, led by one of the scout dogs. Swiftly and surely, he carried messages back and forth between his first master and his second, following with the main body. The damp of the jungle had forced the design of a new moisture-proof container which, fastened to "Sandy's" collar, held the dispatches he delivered.

Now as torrential tropical rains poured down, the walkie-talkie radio sets began to blank out—and just at a critical moment when communication was most needed. The Marines, advancing on a strategic Jap air strip, had run into strong defenses near Turzi Point. Direct infantry assault of the Jap pillboxes would cost many lives and might take more time than could be spared. Artillery fire was needed to blast the way clear.

Radio was modern and dogs primitive, but radio was out and it was up to "Sandy." Runners might have made it in time, but the going was tough, and there was a Jap barrage to get through. The officer commanding scribbled the co-ordinates of the pillboxes with an urgent request for artillery fire on them and handed the slip to Sergeant Brown. The handler put it in "Sandy's" pouch, gave him an affectionate pat on the rump and ordered, "Report!"

Mortar and tank shells burst around the dog as he sped off. For much of his run he was under heavy fire. He plowed through tall, thick, sharp-edged Kunai grass, plunged into and swam a river. For twenty-four hours he had not seen Sergeant Sheldon. Furthermore, his second handler had moved to an entirely different place from that where Brown and the dog had left him to go forward with the advance. Yet an unerring instinct was guiding the dog.

Back in the position occupied by the main Marine force, Sheldon was one of many men crouched in foxholes behind barbed wire entanglements. But "Sandy" was looking for him and him alone. The sergeant glanced up to see sixty pounds of black dog hurtle over the wire barrier and land right on top of him. "Sandy," panting and dripping but tail joyously wagging over the reunion and Sheldon's praise, had delivered his message.

They sent the strong dog straight back with an acknowledgment. Soon an artillery concentration came crashing down on the pillboxes, pounding them and their garrison to pieces. The advance surged forward over the rubble.

IV

Scout dogs saved lives in jungle warfare. That had been brilliantly demonstrated by the Army K-9 detachment, small as it was.

Meanwhile, the Marine Corps had been training its own war dogs and organizing them and the personnel handling them into platoons, to be regularly attached to battalions or regiments in combat.

To command the first Marine dog platoon the Corps picked Clyde Henderson, a young chemistry teacher, a fancier of Doberman Pinschers, and a specialist in obedience training. Commissioned a lieutenant in the Corps, he was ordered to Camp Lejeune. In the spring of 1943, his outfit was ready: twenty-four dogs, all Dobermans except for three German shepherds, and fifty-five men. A special train took them to the Pacific coast and they shipped in May.

Marine officers in the field were not easy to convince, but Henderson persuaded them to give his dogs a trial. Their performance in one week of maneuvers overcame skepticism. However, some time was spent in staging areas before orders into action arrived. The platoon was attached to the Second Marine Raider Battalion and on October 4, 1943, they sailed for Bougainville in the Solomon Islands. Aboard a landing craft under heavy shellfire, the platoon headed for the beach on D-Day, November 1, 1943.

There were several thousand Japs on the island toward which they were speeding and most of them seemed to be shooting at this particular landing craft with artillery and small arms. Lt. Henderson watched the dogs milling about nervously. He and the handlers were equally edgy—it was the first time any of them had been under hostile fire. The men had their arms around dogs, trying to quiet them yet reassuring themselves as much as the dogs.

A grinding, neck-jerking jolt. The barge had grounded on a sand bar about ten yards offshore. Henderson and his men jumped overboard—started wading for the shore, water up to the waist, the dogs swimming after them. Dripping, they emerged on the bullet-spattered beach. Across that strip of sand they dashed at top speed for the shelter of the jungle. The lieutenant shouted orders to take cover until he could find the regimental command post.

Two dogs detailed to M Company happened to draw the most crucial task that day. Their names were "Andy" and "Caesar."

"Andy" was a Doberman whose proud stride had won him the nickname of "Gentleman Jim." He was an affectionate dog with his friends, but the Marines had trained him "to be a mean hombre with strangers." He and his handler were sent straight out to the point of one of M Company's patrols boring into the jungle.

"Andy," differing from the average scout dog, liked to work off leash. When the order came to advance, he trotted casually up the trail about ten yards ahead of his handler. To the racket of battle off to the flanks he paid no attention whatever. Here was his job. About four hundred yards up the trail he halted. His handler watched him for a moment, then passed the word back through the column that it probably was only a wild boar in the brush. But about one hundred and fifty yards further the dog froze in his tracks. His pointed ears pricked up even more sharply and his hackles rose. A soft growl rumbled in his throat and his head pointed slightly to the right. His handler, Pfc. Robert Lansley, whispered back, "Well, this is it. There's a Jap sniper back in there, probably about seventy-five yards."

The scout leader was skeptical, never having worked with dogs before, but a couple of automatic riflemen were sent ahead to investigate—just in case. A few minutes later there was a rattle of fire. A rifleman came back and said with a grin, "We figured the Jap must be hiding in a mangrove tree just off the trail, so I gave it a good spraying. Sure enough, a Jap tumbled out." Everybody looked at "Andy" with new respect and reliance. Twice more before they reached a trail junction and established a road block "Andy" alerted to the presence of snipers. That day, Company M advanced further than any other company and occupied the only major position captured by the Americans.

"Caesar" had his chance as the Jap resistance stiffened. Henderson knew him as a big, bashful, German shepherd, given through Dogs for Defense the day after his owners, three brothers, had all entered the service. As a messenger dog, he was in sudden demand when the walkie-talkie radios failed to carry through the dense jungle. He made runs back and forth between his two handlers with Jap snipers taking pot shots at him enroute. The light was bad and "Caesar" fast. He got through.

In his secondary role as a sentry dog "Caesar" showed both bravery and perfect obedience. Henderson tells the story. "It's a harrowing thing to try to relax and sleep in a foxhole when you are wondering if a Jap may creep in and knife you when you sleep. The Japs had been devils at infiltrating outposts at night. So we placed dogs to supplement the human sentries.

"We had our first casualty at dawn of the third day. It was Caesar, the German shepherd, who was already the darling of the raiders. The Japs had launched a dawn attack. Caesar, hearing the Japs coming, jumped out of the foxhole and ran toward them. Handler Mayo called Caesar back. Just as Caesar stopped grudgingly to turn back, a Jap pumped bullets into him.

"During the confusion of battle Caesar disappeared. Mayo was frantic. He called me to learn whether I had seen him. He was half shouting and half crying. I hadn't seen Caesar. Soon we found a trail of blood through the jungle. As I suspected the dog had returned to the battalion command post and had taken refuge in the bushes near Johnny Kleeman, his other handler. Kleeman hadn't heard him come in.

"There was Caesar on the ground, barely conscious. Mayo ran and lay down beside him and hugged him gently. Three raiders were busy improvising a special stretcher. They had chopped down two long poles and lashed them to two short cross poles. To this frame they fastened a blanket so that it made a deep hammock.

"When the trip started to the regimental first-aid station a dozen raiders volunteered to carry Caesar's stretcher for Mayo and Kleeman. The two handlers waited outside the hospital tent. After twenty minutes the regimental surgeon came out and announced that the bullet in Caesar's shoulder was too near the heart to operate, but that he might pull through.

"He did. While he was convalescing, the raiders insisted on getting daily bulletins on his condition and tried to pamper him by sneaking him food, choice morsels of 'C' ration! Caesar was able to return to active duty about three weeks later. He still carries a Jap slug in his shoulder."

Daily as the Marines drove deeper into the island, the war-dog platoon added to its record. "Jack," a Doberman, spotted a Jap sniper in a tree, pointing him like a bird dog. The sniper, shot out of his perch, proved to have had a light machine gun trained on the company command post. Another "Jack," a German shepherd, was shot in the back as he was carrying a vital message from a road block being attacked by the

Japs—the telephone line had been shot down. The dog gallantly ran on and delivered his dispatch which brought reinforcements and stretcher bearers for the dog's wounded handler, among others. The Doberman, "Otto," was at least one hundred yards distant when he alerted to an enemy machine gun; before it opened fire, the Marine patrol had time to take cover. The Doberman, "Rex," warned of a Jap surprise attack at dawn and it was blasted to bits.

Although six of the dogs, including the bitches, had to be washed out by Lt. Henderson for front-line duty, the rest of them carried through the campaign or fell in action like "Kuno." "Kuno," a Doberman, was severely wounded in the head and stomach by the explosion of a Japanese grenade and had to be put out of his pain by an injection. The platoon buried him with honor beneath a marker.

The dogs were going strong on the fourteenth day of the fight. It was then that "Andy" performed what Lt. Henderson considered the most extraordinary feat of the Bougainville operation. This is the story as he told it in an article in *The American Magazine*.

"An advance had been stalled for several hours by nasty machine-gun fire. No one could figure quite where it was coming from. Finally Andy's handlers, Pfc. Lansley and Pfc. John Mahoney, volunteered to locate the trouble. They pushed off into the jungle, with Andy ahead.

"When Andy froze, this time, he seemed a bit confused. First he turned sideways in the trail and began moving forward side-leggedly. That was Andy's own peculiar way of saying there was a whole mess of strangers up ahead. Then finally he pointed decisively to the left, then decisively to the right. Lansley crawled up beside Andy and peered through the foliage. All he could see of interest was a small trail with a banyan tree to the left of it and another to the right.

"Lansley studied the branches of both trees and could see nothing unusual. Then he noticed that bushes hiding part of the huge aerial roots of both trees didn't look quite right. He had it! The Japs had set up camouflaged machine-gun nests beneath the roots of these trees. That would give them a murderous cross fire of the trail. Telling Mahoney to cover him, Lansley sprayed both tree bases with machine-gun fire, then raced forward and hurled grenades into dugouts he found beneath both trees.

"All the Japs there were wiped out by Lansley or the men who followed him. The entire sector was able to move forward. That clinched it for the dogs. The next day, Colonel Shapley, who had been dubious originally, sent a long report to Washington citing six of the dogs specifically for outstanding performance (Andy, Caesar, Otto, the two Jacks, and Rex), and concluded with this statement: 'The Dog Platoon has proved itself an unqualified success.'"

The Commanding General of the First Marine Amphibious Corps officially reported that "the dogs have proven themselves as message carriers, scouts, and vital night security; and were constantly employed during the operation of securing and extending the beachhead. They were remarkable and more are needed." Lieutenant General Thomas Holcomb, the Marine Corps Commandant, wrote personal letters to the donors of the six cited dogs. Indeed, Bougainville lent tremendous impetus to the cause which Dogs for Defense had launched with such difficulty little more than a year before.

Tributes from the "brass" are of considerable account. But to Lieutenant—to be promoted Captain—Henderson and the personnel of the First Marine War Dog Platoon, certain actions of comrades-in-arms spoke more loudly than words. When handlers and their dogs joined a Marine outfit in action, foxholes would be voluntarily dug for them.

"If a man will dig a foxhole in the front line for another guy," ran a Leatherneck saying, "he wants that guy around."

FOR FREEDOM

That Greek Dog

MACKINLAY KANTOR

"The fight for freedom is never won permanently. It is a fight that every generation must make in its own behalf, for freedom is not something that may be taken safely for granted," declares an introduction to this story. In a little town in the Midwest, Duboko, the mongrel, helped his master, a veteran of the First World War, wage another battle against the forces of oppression.

IN those first years after the First World War, Bill Barbilis could still get into his uniform; he was ornate and handsome when he wore it. Bill's left sleeve, reading down from the shoulder, had patches and patterns of color to catch any eye. At the top there was an arc—bent stripes of scarlet, yellow, and purple; next came a single red chevron with the apex pointing up; and at the cuff were three gold chevrons pointing the other way.

On his right cuff was another gold chevron, only slightly corroded. And we must not forget those triple chevrons on an olive-drab field which grew halfway up the sleeve.

People militarily sophisticated, there in Mahaska Falls, could recognize immediately that Mr. Basilio Barbilis had been a sergeant, that he had served with the Forty-second Division, that he had been once wounded, that he had sojourned overseas for at least eighteen months, and that he had been discharged with honor.

His khaki blouse, however, was worn only on days of patriotic importance. The coat he donned at other times was white—white, that is, until cherry sirup and caramel speckled it. Mr. Barbilis was owner, manager, and staff of the Sugar Bowl.

He had a soda fountain with the most glittering spigots in town. He had a bank of candy cases, a machine for toasting sandwiches, ten small tables complete with steel-backed chairs, and a ceiling festooned with leaves of gilt and bronze paper.

Beginning in 1920, he had also a peculiar dog. Bill's living quarters

were in the rear of the Sugar Bowl, and the dog came bleating and shivering to the Barbilis door one March night. The dog was no larger than a quart of ice cream and, Bill said, just as cold.

My medical office and apartment were directly over the Sugar Bowl. I made the foundling's acquaintance the next day, when I stopped in for a cup of chocolate. Bill had the dog bedded in a candy carton be-hind the fountain; he was heating milk when I came in, and wouldn't fix my chocolate until his new pet was fed.

Bill swore that it was a puppy. I wasn't so certain. It looked something like a mud turtle wearing furs.

"I think he is hunting dog," said Bill, with pride. "He was cold last night, but not so cold now. Look, I make him nice warm bed. I got my old pajamas for him to lie on."

He waited upon the sniffling little beast with more tender consid-eration than ever he showed to any customer. Some people say that Greeks are mercenary. I don't know. That puppy wasn't paying board.

The dog grew up, burly and quizzical. Bill named him Duboko. It sounded like that; I don't know how to spell the name correctly, nor did anyone else in Mahaska Falls.

The word, Bill said, was slang. It meant "tough" or "hard-boiled." This animal had the face of a clown and the body of a hyena. Growing up, his downy coat changing to wire and bristles, Duboko resembled a fat Hamburg steak with onions which had been left too long on the griddle.

At an early age Duboko began to manifest a violent interest in com-munity assemblage of any kind or color. This trait may have been fos-tered by his master, who was proud to be a Moose, an Odd Fellow, a Woodman, and an upstanding member of the Mahaska Falls Commer-cial League.

When we needed the services of a bugler in our newly formed Amer-ican Legion post and no bona fide bugler would volunteer, Bill Barbilis agreed to purchase the best brass instrument available and to practice in the bleak and cindery space behind his store. Since my office was up-stairs, I found no great satisfaction in Bill's musical enterprise. It hap-pened that Duboko also lent his voice in support; a Greek chorus, so to speak, complete with strophe and antistrophe.

Nevertheless, I could register no complaint, since with other members of the Legion I had voted to retain Bill as our bugler. I could not even kick Duboko downstairs with my one good leg when I discovered him in my reception room lunching off my mail.

Indeed, most people found it hard to punish Duboko. He had the ingratiating, hopeful confidence of an immigrant just off the boat and assured that he had found the Promised Land. He boasted beady eyes, lubberly crooked paws, an immense mouth formed of black rubber, and pearly and enormous fangs which he was fond of exhibiting in a kind of senseless leer. He smelled, too. This characteristic I called sharply to the attention of his master, with the result that Duboko was laundered weekly in Bill's uncertain little bathtub, the process being marked by vocal lament which might have arisen from the gloomiest passage of the *Antigone*.

Mahaska Falls soon became aware of the creature, in a general municipal sense, and learned that it had him to reckon with. Duboko attended every gathering at which six or more people were in congregation. No fire, picnic, memorial service, Rotary conclave, or public chicken-pie supper went ungraced by his presence.

If, as sometimes happened on a crowded Saturday night, a pedestrian was brushed by a car, Duboko was on the scene with a speed to put the insurance-company representatives to shame. If there was a lodge meeting which he did not visit and from which he was not noisily ejected, I never heard of it. At Commercial League dinners he lay pensive with his head beneath the chair of Bill Barbilis. But, suffering fewer inhibitions than his master, he also visited funerals, and even the marriage of Miss Glaydys Stumpf.

Old Charles P. Stumpf owned the sieve factory. He was the richest man in town; the nuptials of his daughter exuded an especial aura of social magnificence. It is a matter of historical record that Duboko sampled the creamed chicken before any of the guests did; he was banished only after the striped and rented trousers of two ushers had undergone renting in quite another sense of the word. Grieved, Duboko forswore the Stumpfs after that; he refused to attend a reception for the bride and bridegroom when they returned from the Wisconsin Dells two weeks later.

There was one other place in town where Duboko was decidedly persona non grata. This was a business house, a rival establishment of the Sugar Bowl, owned and operated by Earl and John Klugge. The All-American Kandy Kitchen, they called it.

The Brothers Klugge held forth at a corner location a block distant from the Sugar Bowl. Here lounged and tittered ill-favored representatives of the town's citizenry; dice rattled on a soiled mat at the cigar counter; it was whispered that refreshment other than soda could be purchased by the chosen.

The business career of Earl and John Klugge did not flourish, no matter what inducement they offered their customers. Loudly they declared that their failure to enrich themselves was due solely to the presence in our community of a Greek—a black-haired, dark-skinned Mediterranean who thought nothing of resorting to the most unfair business practices, such as serving good fudge sundaes, for instance, to anyone who would buy them.

One fine afternoon people along the main street were troubled at observing Duboko limp rapidly westward, fairly wreathed in howls. Bill called me down to examine the dog. Duboko was only bruised, although at first I feared that his ribs were mashed on one side. Possibly someone had thrown a heavy chair at him. Bill journeyed to the Clive Street corner with fire in his eye. But no one could be found who would admit to seeing an attack on Duboko; no one would even say for a certainty that Duboko had issued from the doorway of the All-American Kandy Kitchen, although circumstantial evidence seemed to suggest it.

Friends dissuaded Bill Barbilis from invading the precinct of his enemies, and at length he was placated by pleasant fiction about a kicking horse in the market square.

We all observed, however, that Duboko did not call at the Kandy Kitchen again, not even on rare nights when the dice rattled loudly and when the whoops and catcalls of customers caused girls to pass by, like pretty Levites, on the other side.

There might have been a different tale to tell if this assault had come later, when Duboko was fully grown. His frame stretched and extended steadily for a year; it became almost as mighty as the earnest Americanism of his master. He was never vicious. He was never known to bite a child. But frequently his defensive attitude was that of a mother cat who fancies her kitten in danger; Duboko's hypothetical kitten was his right to be present when good fellows—or bad—got together.

Pool halls knew him; so did the Epworth League. At football games an extra linesman was appointed for the sole purpose of discouraging Duboko's athletic ardor. Through some occult sense, he could become aware of an approaching festivity before even the vanguard assembled. Musicians of our brass band never lugged their instruments to the old bandstand in Courthouse Park without finding Duboko there before them, lounging in an attitude of expectancy. It was Wednesday night, it was eight o'clock, it was July; the veriest dullard might know at what hour and place the band would begin its attack on "The Light Cavalry Overture."

Duboko's taste in music was extensive. He made a fortuitous appearance at a spring musicale, presented by the high-school orchestra and glee clubs, before an audience which sat in the righteous hush of people grimly determined to serve the arts, if only for a night.

The boys' glee club was rendering selections from Carmen—in English, of course—and dramatically they announced the appearance of the bull. The line goes, "Now the beast enters, wild and enraged," or something like that; Duboko chose this moment to lope grandly down the center aisle on castaneting toenails. He sprang to the platform. . . . Mahaska Falls wiped away more tears than did Mérimée's heroine.

In his adult stage, Duboko weighed forty pounds. His color suggested peanut brittle drenched with chocolate; I have heard people swear that his ears were four feet long, but that is an exaggeration. Often those ears hung like limp brown drawers dangling from a clothesline; again they were braced rigidly atop his skull.

Mastiff he was, and also German shepherd, with a noticeable influence of English bull, bloodhound, and great Dane. Far and wide he was known as "that Greek dog," and not alone because he operated out of the Sugar Bowl and under the aegis of Bill Barbilis. Duboko looked like a Greek.

He had Greek eyes, Greek eyebrows, and a grinning Greek mouth. Old Mayor Wingate proclaimed in his cups that, in fact, he had heard Duboko bark in Greek; he was willing to demonstrate, if anyone would only catch Duboko by sprinkling a little Attic salt on his tail.

That Greek dog seldom slept at night; he preferred to accompany the town's watchman on his rounds, or to sit in the window of the Sugar Bowl along with cardboard ladies who brandished aloft their cardboard sodas. Sometimes, when I had been called out in the middle of the night and came back from seeing a patient, I would stop and peer through the window and exchange a few signals with Duboko.

"Yes," he seemed to say, "I'm here. Bill forgot and locked me in. I don't mind, unless, of course, there's a fire. See you at Legion meeting tomorrow night, if not at the County Medical Association luncheon tomorrow noon."

At this time there was a new arrival in the Sugar Bowl household—Bill's own father, recruited all the way from Greece, now that Bill's mother was dead.

Spiros Barbilis was slight, silver-headed, round-shouldered, with drooping mustachios which always seemed oozing with black dye. Bill put up another cot in the back room and bought another chiffonier from the secondhand store. He and Duboko escorted the old man up and down Main Street throughout the better part of one forenoon.

"I want you to meet friend of mine," Bill said. "He is my father, but he don't speak no English. I want him to meet all my good friends here in Mahaska Falls, because he will live here always."

Old Mr. Barbilis grew deft at helping Bill with the Sugar Bowl. He carried trays and managed tables, grinning inveterately, wearing an apron stiff with starch. But he failed to learn much English except hello and good-by and a few cuss words; I think that he was lonely for the land he had left, which certainly Bill was not.

One night—it was two o'clock in the morning—I came back to climb my stairs, stepping carefully from my car to the icy sidewalk in front of the Sugar Bowl. I moved gingerly, because I had left one foot in the Toul sector when a dressing station was shelled; I did not like icy sidewalks.

This night I put my face close to the show window to greet Duboko, to meet those sly and mournful eyes, which, on a bitter night, would certainly be waiting there instead of shining in a drifted alley where the watchman prowled.

Two pairs of solemn eyes confronted me when I looked in. Old Mr. Barbilis sat there, too—in his night clothes, but blanketed with an over- coat—he and Duboko, wrapped together among the jars of colored candy and the tinted cardboard girls. They stared out, aloof and digni- fied in the darkness, musing on a thousand lives that slept near by. I enjoy imagining that they both loved the street, even in its midnight desertion, though doubtless Duboko loved it the more.

In 1923 we were treated to a mystifying phenomenon. There had never been a riot in Mahaska Falls, nor any conflict between racial and religious groups. Actually we had no racial or religious groups; we were all Americans, or thought we were. But, suddenly and amazingly, fiery crosses flared in the darkness of our pasture lands.

I was invited to attend the meeting and did so eagerly, wondering if I might explore this outlandish nonsense in a single evening. When my car stopped at a cornfield gate and ghostly figures came to admit me, I heard voice after voice whispering bashfully, "Hello, doc," "Evening, doc. Glad you came." I was shocked at recognizing the voices. I had known the fathers and grandfathers of these youths—hard-working farmers they were, who found a long-sought freedom on the American prairies, and never fumed about the presence of the hard-working Cath- olics, Jews, and Negroes who were also members of that pioneer com- munity.

There was one public meeting in the town itself. They never tried to hold another; there was too much objection; the voice of Bill Barbilis rang beneath the stars.

A speaker with a pimply face stood illuminated by the flare of gaso- line torches on a makeshift rostrum, and dramatically he spread a dollar bill between his hands. "Here," he cried, "is the flag of the Jews!"

Bill Barbilis spoke sharply from the crowd: "Be careful, mister. There is United States seal on that bill."

In discomfiture, the speaker put away his bank note. He ignored Bill as long as he could. He set his own private eagles to screaming, and he talked of battles won, and he wept for the mothers of American boys who lay in France. He said that patriotic 100-per-cent Americans must honor and protect those mothers.

Bill Barbilis climbed to the fender of a car. "Sure," he agreed clearly, "we got to take care of those mothers! Also, other mothers we got to take care of—Catholic mothers, Greek mothers, Jew mothers. We got the mothers of Company C, One Hundred Sixty-eighth Infantry. We got to take care of them. How about Jimmy Clancy? He was Catholic. He got killed in the Lorraine sector. Hyman Levinsky, he got killed the same day. Mr. Speaker, you don't know him because you do not come from Mahaska Falls. We had Buzz Griffin, colored boy used to shine shoes. He go to Chicago and enlist, and he is wounded in the Ninety-second Division!"

It was asking too much for any public speaker to contend against opposition of that sort; and the crowd thought so, too, and Duboko made a joyful noise. The out-of-town organizers withdrew. Fiery crosses blazed less frequently, and the flash of white robes frightened fewer cattle week by week.

Seeds had been sown, however, and now a kind of poison ivy grew within our midnight. Bill Barbilis and Duboko came up to my office one morning, the latter looking annoyed, the former holding a soiled sheet of paper in his hand. "Look what I got, doc."

The message was printed crudely in red ink:

"We don't want you here any more. This town is only for 100-percent law-abiding white Americans. Get out of town! Anti-Greek League."

It had been shoved under the front door of the Sugar Bowl sometime during the previous night.

"Bill," I told him, "don't worry about it. You know the source, probably; at least you can guess."

"Nobody is going to run me out of town," said Bill. "This is my town, and I am American citizen, and I am bugler in American Legion. I bring my old father here from Greece to be American, too, and now he has first papers." His voice trembled slightly.

"Here. Throw it in the wastepaper basket and forget about it."

There was sweat on his forehead. He wiped his face, and then he was able to laugh. "Doc, I guess you are right. Doc, I guess I am a fool."

He threw the paper away and squared his shoulders and went downstairs. I rescued a rubber glove from Duboko and threw Duboko into the hall, where he licked disinfectant from his jaws and leered at me through the screen.

A second threatening letter was shoved under Bill's door, but after that old Mr. Spiros Barbilis and Duboko did sentry duty, and pedestrians could see them entrenched behind the window. So the third warning came by mail; it told Bill that he was being given twenty-four hours to get out of town for good.

I was a little perturbed when I found Bill loading an Army .45 behind his soda fountain.

"They come around here," he said, "and I blow hell out of them."

He laughed when he said it, but I didn't like the brightness of his eyes, nor the steady, thrice-assured activity of his big clean fingers.

On Friday morning Bill came up to my office again; his face was distressed. But my fears, so far as the Anti-Greeks were concerned, were groundless.

"Do you die," he asked, "when you catch a crisis of pneumonia?"

It was one of his numerous cousins, in Sioux Falls. There had been

FOR FREEDOM 73

a long-distance telephone call; the cousin was very ill, and the family wanted Bill to come. Bill left promptly in his battered, rakish roadster.

Late that night I was awakened by a clatter of cream cans under my window. I glanced at the illuminated dial of my watch, and lay wondering why the milkman had appeared some two hours before his habit. I was about to drop off to sleep when sounds of a scuffle in the alley and a roar from Duboko in the Barbilis quarters took me to the window in one leap.

There were four white figures down there in the alley yard; they dragged a fifth man—nightshirted, gagged, struggling—along with them. I yelled, and pawed around for my glasses, spurred to action by the reverberating hysterics of Duboko. I got the glasses on just before those men dragged old Mr. Barbilis into their car. The car's license plates were plastered thick with mud; at once I knew what had happened.

It was customary for the milkman to clank his bottles and cans on approaching the rear door of the Sugar Bowl; Bill or his father would get out of bed and fetch the milk to the refrigerator, for there were numerous cream-hungry cats along that alley. It was a clinking summons of this sort which had lured the lonely Mr. Barbilis from his bed.

He had gone out sleepily, probably wondering, as I had wondered, why the milkman had come so early. The sound of milk bottles lulled Duboko for a moment.

Then the muffled agony of that struggle, when the visitors clapped a pillow over the old man's face, had been enough to set Duboko bellowing.

But he was shut in; all that he could do was to threaten and curse and hurl himself against the screen. I grabbed for my foot—not the one that God gave me, but the one bought by Uncle Sam—and of course I kicked it under the bed far out of reach.

My car was parked at the opposite end of the building, out in front. I paused only to tear the telephone receiver from its hook and cry to a surprised central that she must turn on the red light which summoned the night watchman; that someone was kidnapping old Mr. Barbilis.

The kidnappers' car roared eastward down the alley while I was bawling to the operator. And then another sound—the wrench of a heavy body sundering the metal screening. There was only empty silence as I stumbled down the stairway in my pajamas, bouncing on one foot and holding to the stair rails.

I fell into my car and turned on the headlights. The eastern block before me stretched deserted in the pale glow of single bulbs on each electric-light post. But as my car rushed into that deserted block, a small brown shape sped bullet-like across the next intersection. It was Duboko.

I swung right at the corner, and Duboko was not far ahead of me now. Down the dark, empty tunnel of Clive Street the red tail-light of another car diminished rapidly. It hitched away to the left; that would mean that Mr. Barbilis was being carried along the road that crossed the city dump.

Slowing down, I howled at Duboko when I came abreast of him. It seemed that he was a Barbilis, an Americanized Greek, like them, and that he must be outraged at this occurrence, and eager to effect a rescue.

But he only slobbered up at me, and labored along on his four driving legs, with spume flying behind. I stepped on the gas again and almost struck the dog, for he would not turn out of the road. I skidded through heavy dust on the dump lane, with filmier dust still billowing back from the kidnappers' car.

For their purpose, the selection of the dump had a strategic excuse as well as a symbolic one. At the nearest boundary of the area there was a big steel gate and barbed-wire fence; you had to get out and open that gate to go through. But if you wished to vanish into the region of river timber and country roads beyond, you could drive across the waste-land without opening the gate again. I suppose that the kidnappers guessed who their pursuer was; they knew of my physical incapacity. They had shut the gate carefully behind them, and I could not go through it without getting out of my car.

But I could see them in the glare of my headlights—four white figures, sheeted and hooded.

Already they had tied Spiros Barbilis to the middle of a fence panel. They had straps, and a whip, and everything else they needed. One man was tying the feet of old Spiros to restrain his kicks; two stood ready to proceed with the flogging; and the fourth blank, hideous, white-hooded creature moved toward the gate to restrain me from interfering. That was the situation when Duboko arrived.

I ponder now the various wickednesses Duboko committed through-out his notorious career. Then for comfort I turn to the words of a Greek—him who preached the most famous funeral oration chanted among the ancients—the words of a man who was Greek in his blood and his pride, and yet who might have honored Duboko eagerly when the dog came seeking, as it were, a kind of sentimental Attican natu-ralization.

"For even when life's previous record showed faults and failures," said Pericles, with the voice of Thucydides, to the citizens of the fifth cen-tury, "it is just to weigh the last brave hour of devotion against them all."

Though it was not an hour by any means. No more than ten minutes had elapsed since old Mr. Barbilis was dragged from his back yard. The militant action of Duboko, now beginning, did not occupy more than a few minutes more, at the most. It makes me wonder how long men fought at Marathon, since Pheidippides died before he could tell.

And not even a heavy screen might long contain Duboko; it is no wonder that a barbed-wire fence was as reeds before his charge.

He struck the first white figure somewhere above the knees. There was a snarl and a shriek, and then Duboko was springing toward the next man.

I didn't see what happened then. I was getting out of the car and hopping toward the gate. My bare foot came down on broken glass, and that halted me for a moment. The noise of the encounter, too, seemed to build an actual, visible barrier before my eyes.

Our little world was one turmoil of flapping, torn white robes—a whirling insanity of sheets and flesh and outcry, with Duboko revolving at the hub. One of the men dodged out of the melee, and stumbled back, brandishing a club which he had snatched from the rubble close at hand. I threw a bottle, and I like to think that that discouraged him; I remember how he pranced and swore.

Mr. Barbilis managed to get the swathing off his head and the gag out of his mouth. His frail voice sang minor encouragement, and he struggled to unfasten his strapped hands from the fence.

The conflict was moving now—moving toward the kidnappers' car. First one man staggered away, fleeing; then another who limped badly. It was an unequal struggle at best. No four members of the Anti-Greek League, however young and brawny, could justly be matched against a four-footed warrior who used his jaws as the original Lacedaemonians must have used their daggers, and who fought with the right on his side, which Lacedaemonians did not always do.

Four of the combatants were scrambling into their car; the fifth was still afoot and reluctant to abandon the contest. By that time I had been able to get through the gate, and both Mr. Barbilis and I pleaded with Duboko to give up a war he had won. But this he would not do; he challenged still, and tried to fight the car; and so, as they drove away, they ran him down.

It was ten A.M. before Bill Barbilis returned from Sioux Falls. I had ample opportunity to impound Bill's .45 automatic before he came.

His father broke the news to him. I found Bill sobbing with his head on the fountain. I tried to soothe him, in English, and so did Spiros Barbilis, in Greek; but the trouble was that Duboko could no longer speak his own brand of language from the little bier where he rested.

Then Bill went wild, hunting for his pistol and not being able to find it; all the time, his father eagerly and shrilly informed Bill of the identifications he had made when his assailants' gowns were ripped away. Of course, too, there was the evidence of bites and abrasions.

Earl Klugge was limping as he moved about his All-American Kandy Kitchen, and John Klugge smelled of arnica and iodine. A day or two passed before the identity of the other kidnappers leaked out. They were hangers-on at the All-American; they didn't hang on there any longer.

I should have enjoyed seeing what took place, down there at the Clive Street corner. I was only halfway down the block when Bill threw Earl and John Klugge through their own plate-glass window.

A little crowd of men gathered, with our Mayor Wingate among them. There was no talk of damages or of punitive measures to be meted out, to Bill Barbilis. I don't know just what train the Klugge brothers left on. But their restaurant was locked by noon, and the windows boarded up.

A military funeral and interment took place that afternoon behind the Sugar Bowl. There was no flag, though I think Bill would have liked to display one. But the crowd of mourners would have done credit to Athens in the age when her dead heroes were burned; all the time that Bill was blowing taps on his bugle, I had a queer feeling that the ghosts of Pericles and Thucydides were somewhere around.

MARINE MASCOT

The Odyssey of a Little Dog

JOHN W. THOMASON

Absent without leave, the pet of U.S. Marines met
hard adventures on the land and on the sea. Not until
he landed in Panama was the situation well in hand.

THE cruiser's yearly overhaul in New York Yard was finished, and she
cast off her lines. The deck trembled to the beat of the main engines and
a tug nosed alongside to take hold. Up forward, a bugle went, one strong
high note. The ensign at the stern came down and streaming colors ran
up to the main gaff. Pier 8 slid from her, and the cruiser was under way.

The port quarter, where the Marines muster, was cluttered with wet
Manila lines, and pools of water froze on the planking. Also, there was
miscellaneous gear, last-minute matters pertaining to the harassed pay-
master, boxes and bales and crates; and bluejackets scuttled to and fro
among them on various small jobs. Further, the saluting-battery crew
on the boat-deck just above was whipping the canvas covers from their
little guns; so the captain of Marines led his tall fellows across the
quarter-deck and formed the guard to starboard, facing the dock; they
stood at ease, a hundred men in long gray-green overcoats. On the pier,
there were no sweethearts or wives or such, for it's bad luck to watch
your man's ship sail, but a few yard workmen waved, as somebody always waves to men who go down to the sea.

The Marine captain said to his junior by the life-line: "Look—ain't
that our former gunnery-sergeant retirin' up the dock yonder? The
scoundrel shoved off without sayin' *bon voyage* or anything. See him?"

"Yes, sir; I was talking to him below. Said he had a week-end liberty
from Quantico; said he just stood by to see us off. I didn't see him go
over the side, though—oh, forward gangway, of course."

"Well, he was a good man. Wish him joy. Still, we'll get along with
this new bird they sent us. Seems to know his profession. You know, I
kinder thought old Murph would get off with Mike, havin' him up
with his folks to live since that last blizzard. Told me his mother was

crazy about him—Mike, I mean. But a couple of the young men went up an' got him last night. They knew Mike's routine—watched for him on his little run-around before taps an' shanghaied him in a taxi right under the nose of Murph's old man, who was convoyin' him. Reported him aboard just now, an' accounted for expense money that I advanced."

"Yes, sir. Murph did say, when he was transferred, that Mike would go with him—bet he was wild this morning! Murph always claimed Mike was his dog—but the guard wouldn't be the guard without Mike."

A bugle blew "Attention!" They rounded into the stream, and the saluting guns rendered the prescribed honors to the commandant's flag. Manhattan Bridge and Brooklyn Bridge loomed over the cruiser's housed topmasts. On the starboard hand the fabulous towers of New York, whitened a little by last night's snow, receded under a pale winter sun that had no heat or color in it. The guard, standing easy and shuffling their feet in the bitter wind, looked briefly on the Statue of Liberty that was silhouetted in the harbor haze, and turned their faces toward the bow and the sea in waiting outside the Narrows.

"Dam' foolishness, standin' top-side in this breeze," grumbled the captain of Marines.

"Old man's all for dog, regardless. Rest!" and the guard relaxed and talked among themselves.

"Fourteen thousand miles last cruise—wonder what we log, this."

"Well—be back next year."

"Yeh, an' it's time to shove off now—money's all spent; girls all kissed —an' there's better likker in Panama!"

"An' she says to me, she says, 'My beautiful blue-eyed bozo, you goin' off for a year on that fool ship, an' if you think this baby will wait that long on any guy, you're all wet—I'll say you are.'"

"Naw—it don't cost any more down there than it does up here, an' you know what you're gettin'."

"Tell you about this broad I fell in wit' last night? It was right by—"

"Belay! there's retreat."

The line stiffened.

"Guard—'tention! First sergeant—dismiss the guard."

Returning the salute, the captain ran a practical eye down the line. "Hi—Bogert! where's Mike?"

"Sir, he was right here jus' before quarters went."

Presently there was dismay on the gun-deck where the Marines live. The captain and the lieutenant stood by Gun 7, and they were angry men. The non-coms and the second-cruise fellows raged all together. And a pimply-faced recruit who had toted his sea-bag aboard an hour before sailing said helpfully:

"If you-all's lookin' for that little black dawg, I saw a gunn'ry-sergeant stick him in his overcoat just when we-all went up-stairs."

"So you did, hey, you—"

"Well, seh, I never knowed—he said it was all right when he seen me lookin' at him, an' he told me to go fall in; besides, he was a gunn'ry-sergeant"—for the recruit was just from Parris Island, where a gunnery-sergeant is the peer of kings . . .

"And," concluded the captain of Marines, when he could think of no more words, "old Murph put it over. The lousy scalawag! An' I make you my compliments, you bladder-headed animals, you, that let one man come aboard in the daytime an' get what he wants an' walk off with it—thank the Lord he didn't happen to want one of my five-inch guns or something, besides Mike. Police sergeant—take this—this—this critter here"—indicating the distressed recruit—"an' instruct him about ladders an' hatches an' so forth. Up-stairs, good Lawd! Have I got a flag-ship guard or a bad dream?" And the cruiser went out into winter weather on the western ocean at its worst.

The destroyer people, whose little tin boats run up and down continually on all the seas, say that the Atlantic, between Bar Harbor and Crooked Island Channel, is the worst water you'll find. This day there were hurricane signals up from Barnegat to Palm Beach, and the cruiser bucketed south through all of it. Her new drafts were a moaning tangle of misery on gun-deck and berth-deck and every place a man might lie, and not until she raised Cat Island Light and saw a great golden dawn break over the white beaches of San Salvador did things abate enough to open the gun-shutters. She anchored in Guantánamo Bay with salt crusted to her stacks, and her bluejackets swarmed at once over the side and all about to scrub her clean again, and the Marines went off as soon as her boats were in the water, to make a camp for rifle practice.

Guantánamo is where the ships do their annual small-arms training. It is a hot and windy dent on the south coast of Cuba, toward the eastern end, where barren hills come down to water incredibly blue, and mirages flicker and dance across the rifle ranges so that your target, at five hundred yards, appears to be doing a dance over your sights. The Marines are always delighted, in their wrong-headed way, to get ashore on their own; besides, rifles are their mission in life, and a man gets five dollars a month extra for expert rifleman qualification and three dollars for sharpshooter. The bluejackets fire also, and have inducements to excel, but they hate stretching their duck-legs on the beach, and they abhor standing in ranks with leggings on, and they despise rifles.

"Damn!" said the files in the first motor launch, shoving off. " 'Member how proud Mike was to get ashore las' cruise? Up in the bow wit' the automatic rifles, he was."

The croakers of the guard harped on the theme. They were frank:

Mike was the luck of the outfit; look at the weather we've had. An' how slow the new replacements are, snappin' into it—every one of them wit' two left feet. Not like last cruise. Gonna be some cruise, this is!

"Aw—knock it off!" growled the hard-headed lieutenant of Marines. "Murph and some of you crooks stole Mike year before last from Fish Point yonder—go steal his brother. And you will pipe down that croaking, or—"

But the guard was in no mood for dog-stealing. Another dog in Mike's place would be worse than no dog at all. Mike had come aboard a small and impudent puppy. He had taken amazingly to seagoing—more apt in learning, said his messmates, than the smartest Marine the Norfolk Sea School ever sent to salt-water. Knew all the drills, had his station, billet number, and rating. After that affair at Puerto Dios his proper seniors elevated him to the rank of sergeant, and he patrolled the streets of South American capitals in a tailored overcoat of fine blue cloth, adorned with brass buttons and collar ornaments and bearing sergeant's chevrons of golden silk. All this was set forth in his service record.

No other dog would live in Spartan simplicity on the gun-deck, scorning ward-room comforts and snubbing all officers save his own. No other dog would ever learn to present arms with the guard.

Even the captain said, when the first sergeant brought Mike's staff returns to be closed out for desertion: "No—we'll just carry him as a straggler. He'll join up again, maybe." And they missed him in the evenings, after chow, when the men sang in front of their tents, and the quick West Indian dark gathered, and the stars blazed blue-white in a velvet sky, brighter than the harbor lights.

For the appointed time the cruiser's people toiled, burning to saddle color in the fierce West Indian sun, and firing prodigious amounts of .30-caliber ammunition. And the cruiser ran southwest across the Caribbean, coaled at Cristobal, visited briefly her base port on the Pacific side, and departed on affairs of state up the south coast of Central America, over a sea where a sleepy wind moves and the decks are wet always with warm rain, and water-spouts run restlessly to and fro between squalls.

Meantime, Mike lived in a flat up beyond the Bronx with the parents of the gunnery-sergeant, until that merry fellow should consider the winter sufficiently spent for Mike to stand the drafty temperatures of Quantico Barracks. For Mike was a warm-weather critter, born close under the line, and his friends feared pneumonia or something. Living so, he grew fat to a disgusting degree. Spoiled like a grandchild by two elderly people who had nobody else to play with, his figure lost its lean, efficient lines, and he came in from his turn around the block with his red tongue slavering out and his wind quite gone.

This was the only exercise he took. He had been accustomed to twenty-mile hikes over tropic trails, finishing strong on his own legs, unlike that fox terrier of *U. S. S. Austin's* guard, who had to be toted after the third hour ashore. He had been wont to carry out all evolutions aboard ship at the double, as regulations provide; now he always waited at the foot of the stairs—it being a walk-up place—for transportation. Like many seafaring people who come ashore, he at once became soft and extremely lazy.

Such a life was pleasant in the winter-time. Snow was not in Mike's previous experience, and he hated it. His blanket-coat barely kept him warm, and his toes, spread by habit to grip a smooth deck, had a way of picking up slush that distressed him. It was infinitely more comfortable to doze in front of the fire, and partake languidly of elegant rations, brought him on a plate. It is doubtful that, through cold February and March and the raw, wet April of the Bronx, he gave a thought to his shipmates of the flag-ship guard.

May, after a brutal winter, was lovely in the North that year. To Mike, drowsing grossly over a terrific breakfast of pork chops, before a dead fireplace one morning, came a breath of perfumed air, a hint of growing things. Something forgotten stirred in him; his nostrils twitched. He remembered the green that follows the first of the rains, and seas of turquoise-blue, and the white decks and the bright work in the tropic sun, and all the color and ardor of the southern seas. He remembered the guard, drawn up in starched khaki at the quarter for ceremonies, with parade polish on belts and rifles; and he saw himself, groomed until he was shining ebony, by the left guide.

He remembered runs ashore, over trails cool in the dawn, with the guard swinging at adventure behind him, and something interesting ahead. He remembered the fascinating alleys you poked into, and the odd folks you met, ashore with the beach-patrol. And he raised his head and felt again salt spray on a little dog's tongue, and the steady heave of the fo'c's'le when you put to sea; and he saw the rainbow that runs in the spray off the bow, when the wind is on the quarter and the bow wave breaks in foam. And he remembered his Marines, and he thought he would go and look for them.

Mike rose and yawned and stretched himself. The door was open, and he went below. On the street, he twisted his nose into the moist air and turned downtown, for spring comes up from the South. He had tremendous adventures at street crossings, and some brutal treatment at the hands of an elderly gentlewoman who was walking out with a little lady-dog of high degree; she—the elderly gentlewoman—smote him with an umbrella. In the afternoon, he found salt-water. He was tired when he found it, and his tail was dragging, for he was appallingly out of condition from his winter of soft living. He limped up the first gangway he came to and looked around hopefully. Remembered things had driven him all day; he noted sadly that there were no navy uniforms on deck, and he further observed that this was not, by navy standards, a clean ship. But he was very tired, and it was a ship, and that was what he wanted.

It was a busy ship; winches were squealing and cargo hoists clattering, and nobody paid him any attention. His stomach sounded a persistent mess call, and his instincts took him to the crew's galley, forward. He entered this place with confidence—there was, in his experience, no unkindness; when a little dog was hungry between meals, they always found something for you in the galley. In a dark place full of smells he came upon a greasy cook, cutting up dubious meats and casting them into a pot. Mike loved meat. The man did not look; Mike nuzzled his calf. Then he stood on his hind legs and barked once, politely, deferentially: "I say, Jack, how's it for a piece of chow?" And Alfred Tupper, fo'c's'le cook on S. S. *Benlothian*, whirled with a twitter, for the condition of his nerves was deplorable—that Yankee gin he'd been so incautious as to drink last evening, with certain American chaps.

He was not an attractive person, this Alfred Tupper. He was bottle-shouldered, with a pendulous stomach and a pasty face, and his long nose overhung a mean little mouth. For the rest, he was smothered in hair; an unpleasant mass of it grew to his eyes, and bristled in his ears, and showed startlingly black against the fish-belly white of his forearms. He was the sort of fellow who always has a woman or a dog attached somewhere for mistreatment—a woman usually, for dogs have a surer instinct about such things. Mike would have cut him dead anywhere else, not caring much for the run of sailors and civilians under the happiest circumstances; but just now he was hungry, and he was a dog of practical mind. He barked again, with a note of impatience. Manners are manners, but this egg had no call to stare at him so pop-eyed, like.

"Cripes," said Alfred Tupper, and worse than that. "Strike me blind if it ain't a tike. Now, wot the bloody—"

His first idea was to kick the tike through the bulkhead; Mike was a small dog, and it looked safe. Then he noted that the tike stood on his hind legs with an air, a certainty, that denoted education. Alfred Tupper was a chap always on the make; he had known good things to come out of dogs before this. He gave Mike a piece of meat, and he took advantage of Mike's interest in this victual to make him fast to a stanchion. Then he appraised his capture.

No visible marks of ownership—Mike's neck had grown too fat ashore for the ornamental collar, suitably engraved with his name, rate, and ship, that the black gang had made for him, and a new one had not been supplied. Smart-lookin' tike, with a bright eye to him. Belonged to somebody, surely. Question was, would they come lookin' for him?

In view of the fact that S. S. *Benlothian* was a mean ship, on the back side of an obscure dock, Alfred Tupper didn't think so. Sailing in an hour, anyhow. Just take him along; Alfred Tupper was for the moment without a pet. They presently dropped down East River with Mike still fast to the stanchion.

S. S. *Benlothian* was a ship of no special character. She carried the flag of a little house, on leisurely runs between Liverpool, New York, Havana, Panama, and Valparaiso, with intermediate stops. One degree above a tramp, she took freight and such passengers as were not particular. What happened on her fo'c's'le was no concern of any person's, and being reasonably fond of dogs, I will not dwell upon it. Alfred Tupper, in the course of a misspent life, had served with an American dog and pony show, and he knew the mysteries of that trade.

He started out with the lavishing of a new collar on Mike, which was very fine to see, if you didn't know what the inside of the collar was like. Mike, even after he joined up with his own folks again, never carried his head quite the same. For Alfred Tupper took up his education in a serious way. There was nothing gentle about his methods, but they were effective. The first officer, who was a hard man, with no sweetness in him, observed them one afternoon on the well-deck forward, and kicked Alfred into the runways by way of showing how he felt about it.

From a sleek, arrogant fellow, looking every man in the eye, Mike was transformed into a wretched, cringing little brute. All the curl went out of his tail, and the look of him was pitiful. But he knew what he must do when Alfred Tupper played "God Save the King" on a mouth-organ, and he knew how to sit up and ask for a drink, and jump through arms, held so, and balance Alfred's cap on his nose, and to die for his country, and a lot of other pretty capers. By the time S. S. *Benlothian* made Port Limón, Mike was a success in every cantina Alfred Tupper visited. A man may pick up a flock of free gin from the slightly boiled if he can inject some small entertainment, like a performing tike, into an evening, and Alfred considered that Mike was worth all the trouble he caused him.

S. S. *Benlothian* transited the Canal and ran down the Rainless Coast, following her occasions in and out of roadsteads like Mollendo and Arica and Iquique and Antofagasta, all the way to Valpo; and came back North again. She had much business, including coal, at Balboa, and she tied up to Pier 16, just inshore of the American squadron anchorage by the canal mouth. This day the flag-ship and a gunboat were riding to their buoys there, and S. S. *Benlothian* swung across them, dipping her red ensign to the Stars and Stripes.

Alfred Tupper, on the fo'c's'le, was giving Mike a bath preparatory to a run ashore. He looked briefly at the gray ships and swore at Mike, who for some reason was all worked up. A bugle sounded on the flag-ship, and Mike barked furiously. This was insubordinate, and Alfred wrung his slim muzzle. Mike, with a flash of his old spirit, slashed savagely at his hand, and Alfred, inexpressibly shocked at such baseness, took steps. The bout ended with Mike properly subdued and half drowned. "Tike the bloody starch out uv any uv 'em if y' hold they heads under water a bit," observed Alfred genially, and he presently went ashore with Mike under his arm and laid a course for the flesh-pots of Panama.

He noted incuriously that Mike was restless and contrary beyond his wont, but he was not the sort of trainer who tries to figure what a dog is thinking about; he had never given a thought to Mike's background. As they passed, in a jitney, the landing at Pier 18, two motor launches full of sailors and Marines on liberty were standing in.

For the flag-ship's guard was going to have a party, with a month's pay in their pockets. It was a sort of an occasion; they had done a good job of work up the south coast of Central America, and they felt high. All hands except the guard of the day, from the top-sergeant down, were present. Even the junior music, miraculously unrestricted for misdemeanor, was along, and they all assembled at Billie Bean's place. Each man had chipped in according to his rank, and Billie Bean was furnishing sandwiches and the use of the arbor back of his dance-hall, for he esteemed the guard. There was any amount of beer, and the ship's band had been invited, so that music would not lack; and the guard's favorite hospital corps man and the big ship's cook, who always went ashore with the Marines, were present.

In this squadron, they take the liquor question calmly. It is always available, and astonishingly little drinking is done, considering. Lots of files, these days, honestly prefer ice cream. For the rest, they make it a point of honor to carry their drinks; a man who came back from the beach out of control would be effectively dealt with by his messmates, even if his officers failed to observe and take steps. And it was the pleasant custom of the guard to throw parties as a unit when suitable occasion offered.

Unofficially, and in cits, their officers might drop in during the evening, to hear a song and wish them well and see how things were going. Patrol officers were tranquil on party nights, because they knew where all the Marines were, and they knew that any possible disorder would be suppressed by particularly heavy-handed sergeants who were zealous not to abuse privileges. And the arbor behind Billie Bean's was, this night, a happy place.

It would be between nine and ten, with two hours of liberty yet to go, when Alfred Tupper and the melancholy Mike got down that far; they had started at the other end of town. Mike had been ugly all evening, and both he and Alfred showed wear. Alfred had found it necessary to carry him; he wouldn't lead at all, in spite of his collar. But this far, luck had been mighty kind to Alfred; in Panama, where Mike was known for two cruises, no person had recognized him. They raised the lights of Billie Bean's and paraded to the bar.

It was a good night at Billie Bean's. Besides the regular customers, a big English boat was in, carrying some hundreds of Irishry out to Australia, on a settlement scheme. The fo'c's'le of a Norwegian was present in a body, large, crop-headed fellows drinking *aquavit*. Most of the *Benlothians* were there, and other merchant chaps were represented. The front bar was rather crowded, and the dance-hall behind was paying for itself.

Alfred Tupper set Mike upon the bar and did something secret, and Mike got on his hindquarters and barked. "Hi, mite," said Alfred to the gentleman in the white jacket, heartily, "me little friend 'ere, 'e says 'e'll 'ave a spot o' Old Tom. An' a spot fer meself, eh? No fears bout tiltin' the bottle—right-o!" Alfred flung small coins on the bar and shot his slug down. "Ow, ye don't fancy yours, wot? No fear, I'll tike it—never waste good 'Ollands, wot?" And he wiped his mouth and began a long account of his little friend. "Mite, hit would bloody well hastound you, the store I set by that there tike. Like brothers, we are—like brothers. There's few tikes like him—"

"Where'd you get the mut?" cut in the bartender, with a narrowed eye; he was a busy man, but he stopped to listen.

"Mite, I'll tell you. Last run, there was a lidy—bleedin' lidy of quality, she was—Alfred Tupper nimes no nimes," began Alfred with a smirk, "on our little packet, an' she—"

"Huh!" said the bartender, and served a customer.

Mike, still erect, kept an uneasy eye on Alfred. From the arbor came a gust of song—a hundred men yearning thunderously for "Sweet Adeline." Mike rolled his eye that way and shivered violently . . . And a fellow lounged alongside and said:

"Man, it's a grand tike ye have, that same. Meself, I'm all for the beasts. Sittin' on his hunkers like that, would he be knowin' any tricks, now?"

Later Mike sat in the center of a table, among beer-mugs, and wretchedly made sport. And two petty officers drinking near by said:

"Amoosin' mut, that. Kinder like the mut the Marines uster have, aboard—they lost him sommers. What was that mut's name, now?"

Private Jones was not one of the big men of the guard; when the guard formed for ceremonies, his squad was more than half-way down from the right, where the first squad ran six-feet-three or so. But what there was of him was very compactly put together. He had been out for air; the property-sergeant had said to him, like a father:

"Now, listen, Jones—you're gettin' tight. Now you just get outer here an' run around the block a couple times."

He was returning with his head cleared. He passed the group at Mike's table—Mike had muffed one, and was being corrected—and he came to a full halt.

"Say, guy, where'd you get that dawg? I said, where'd you get 'im?"

Mike had been standing stiffly with Alfred's cap on his nose; now he whirled around. Alfred caught him a cuff and cursed. He told this sunburnt bloke in khaki where he could go, him an' his tight pants an' his tin-pot Nivy, too—blowin' in on a hartistic ak like this here.

"Lissen," repeated Private Jones earnestly, overlooking personal insults, "that's our dawg. That's Mike. Of the Marine Guard, U. S. S.—"

Mike whined very pitifully and quivered; Alfred Tupper snatched at his collar and Jones saw.

The closest way to Alfred was across the table, and Jones took it. The table overturned, with other matters; Mike barked, one of the dance-girls screamed, and Alfred said nothing whatever, because Private Jones himself was using his windpipe. The jolly merchant seamen at the table picked up chairs and danced around the pair on the floor, watching for an opening; they didn't care about Alfred Tupper, but they resented militarism. Others jammed in, catching up chairs, bottles, steins, anything; especially the Irishry. They didn't know what it was all about, but they had hopes.

It was the narrow-eyed bartender who whispered to the bar-boy; that volatile Jamaican scuttled back to the arbor, and immediately thereafter a wave of Marines rolled silently through the door at the flank of the long bar, and waded in. The fo'c's'le of the Norwegian finished their *aquavit* and rose to a man, baring huge freckled arms. People crowded in from the dance-hall; odds and ends from the harbor bore a hand, and the girls took refuge behind the bar, squealing.

In an instant, the place was a perfect hell; pacifists there present went away; *Rhon Istmeño* is no friend to peaceful folk. Bottles sung through the air; chairs and tables crashed into ruin; a stool flung by a huge Marine ripped down the array of bottles behind the bar, from an enfilading direction, smashed the big mirror, and caught Billy Bean, entering from the dance-hall to investigate, square on the bows. Billie Bean, a robust person, roared like a lion, caught up a bung-starter and came into action with complete impartiality.

The astute bartender, from under the bar, sent his Jamaica boy for the police, the naval patrol, and the Special Service Squadron, if the last happened to be available. All at once there were uniforms in the street doors; a naval lieutenant with a black arm-band blew piercingly on a whistle. And the gunnery-sergeant of the guard, who had climbed on the bar for observation, thought fast; he made a dive at the switch behind the bar and pulled the lighting. In the breath of comparative silence that followed the sudden dark, a great voice spoke:

"All right, M'rines—get clear—hold everything—patrol's aboard—back to the ship, all hands!"

There is nothing like military discipline, even in a bar-room row. When the furious Billie Bean found his lights again, all the patrol officer netted were two or three Marines who had been engrossed in their work to such an extent that they had not heard their orders. The Marines stated that they had been attacked and were defending themselves; would the patrol officer please take care of them? The Panama police made numerous captures, and the fine new bastille of Panama city was a populous place that night.

It is just a dash from Billie Bean's place to dry and orderly Balboa, as you go down to the docks. The first sergeant shepherded his men on the Balboa road, and squad leaders checked up.

"We'll just shove on back," said the first sergeant, nursing his knuckles. "Any casualties? And did anybody find out what it was about?"

"Word was passed some of these here merchant marines beatin' up a gyrene, all I heard."

"Well, it was a good scrap, anyway. Who was it, gettin' beat up—an' how come?"

"Damifino. Tell you what I did. 'You Scowegian bastard,' I says, an' wit' that I hit him."

"Say, one guy was all set to massage your dome wit' a table leg, an' I kicked the seat of his pants right up between his shoulders, I did. Say!"

"Jam like this, chair makes the best weapon in the worl'. Not too heavy, an' you hit a guy wit' a chair, you're bound to land somewhere—can't guard off a chair."

"Sargunt, sleeve's tore right out of my new blouse—English khaki—survey it for me, line of duty, will you?"

"Wait till skipper sees it—skipper'll be mad as——."

"Aw, the skipper! First thing he'll say'll be, who licked—"

"Jus' the same, better get back an' tell the lootenant about it first, an' let him tell the skipper."

"Hi! Who's that there?"

Private Jones had withdrawn early, and with a reason. He stood up now under a street-light, where he had been effecting running repairs, and he yelled: "Gang—it's ole Mike! I got ole Mike back, right here —lookit! Know who had him? That Limey son of a ——."

The yell that followed brought all the motorcycle-cops in Balboa. And shortly thereafter the flag-ship guard went down the road in column of squads, closed up and keeping step under their non-commissioned officers, all present, including Sergeant Mike, and roaring out: "From the Halls of Montezuma":

> If the Army and the Navy
> Ever win to Heaven's scenes,
> They will find the streets are guarded
> By United States Marines. . . .

S. S. Benlothian entered the Canal on the first run next morning. The fo'c's'le-cook was in his galley, trying to carry on with two ruined deadlights and a throat that was almost ruined for practical purposes, besides other bruises and contusions of a painful nature. He had lost his dog, and his shore-going duds were fit only for brass rags. He is still wondering just what happened, and why, and he will always cherish a sense of injury against those bloody Yankee Marines, one of whom assaulted him, all for nothink, mind you—just for nothink, the bleedin'— He didn't notice, when *S. S. Benlothian* swung across the flag-ship's bows, a little black dog among the people on her fo'c's'le, trying hard to tell his folks how glad he was to be back in his own place . . .

WHEN THE BOMBS FELL

They Also Serve

DOROTHEA ST. HILL BOURNE

During the German bombings of London in the Second World War, dogs often saved the lives of people and animals buried alive in the ruins. Time and again it was their keen instincts that located victims beneath tons of debris, victims who would have perished from suffocation or in the spreading fires if the dogs had not shown the rescue squads where to dig. Numbers of the dogs received the Dickin Medal, the animals' award for valor. The "P.D.S.A." referred to in the piece was the "People's Dispensary for Sick Animals." "A.R.P." stands for "Air Raid Precautions."

MANY Civil Defence Units had mascots, two of whom were awarded the Dickin Medal. For that reason, and because they were pioneers in the rescue of air raid victims by dogs, it is right that their stories should introduce the record of the official Rescue Dogs whose forerunners they were.

These two dogs were Beauty, wire-haired terrier mascot of a P.D.S.A. Animal Rescue Squad and Rip, mascot of Southill Street A.R.P. Post, Poplar, London. It is claimed for Beauty that she was the very first dog to do rescue work and that, moreover, it was entirely on her own initiative that she started life-saving. It was her own kind and not human beings for whom she worked.

At the beginning of the war the P.D.S.A. converted all its caravan dispensaries and ambulances into animal rescue vehicles to work with the National A.R.P. for Animals Committee. These rescue squads stood by at strategic points all over the country. Working closely with the Civil Defence authorities the squads would follow up the A.R.P. workers, and once the human casualties had been dealt with the animal rescuers went into action.

They searched empty and shattered houses, went into areas evacuated because of time bombs, and dug in debris. One of their most important jobs was the care of homeless animals. After an air raid every

From *They Also Serve*, by Dorothea St. Hill Bourne. Reprinted by permission of the author.

bombed site would be haunted by the cats and dogs who had once lived there, searching hopelessly for their lost homes and owners. The squads also gave first aid to injured animals and painlessly destroyed those who were badly injured or unwanted.

The work of these squads has never been publicly recognized. But the Civil Defence officials with whom they worked again and again expressed their appreciation of their collaboration. The squads handled problems, often at great personal risk, which the overworked A.R.P. workers had no time to tackle and which, if left unsolved, might have created a serious situation. Had London been over-run by thousands of homeless, starving and often injured and diseased animals it is not difficult to imagine what the results might have been.

Besides relieving the suffering of the animals, the rescue squads also brought comfort to their owners. The gratitude of householders, who, having lost almost all they valued, were comforted by the return of a beloved cat or dog, had to be seen to be believed.

Tipperary Beauty—to give her full name—belonged to Mr. "Bill" Barnet, a Superintendent of the P.D.S.A. who was leader of one of the Animal Rescue Squads. Beauty used to accompany the Superintendent in his searches among the wrecked houses of East London.

One night in 1940 when the squad was busy digging in some debris Beauty wandered off and started a little digging on her own. Faster and faster, and deeper and deeper she dug until she attracted the attention of her master and his mates. Struck by the little dog's eagerness and determination the squad decided to continue her excavation. After some tough work, they discovered a cat trapped under a damaged table and still alive.

That was the beginning of Beauty's work. From that time onwards the squad had the greatest respect for her intuition—if intuition it was. Through her efforts no fewer than sixty-three animals which might otherwise have died a lingering death from starvation or suffocation, were rescued alive from bomb ruins. Beauty's admirers presented her with little leather boots to protect her paws which became raw and bleeding in her efforts to reach the victims of air raid disasters.

Beauty was the pioneer of this grand work of rescue. That was why the P.D.S.A. awarded her its Pioneer Medal, usually given only to human beings. She became a very well-known character. She took part in many War Savings parades, sitting perched beside her master on a big animal rescue van. She received a silver mounted collar from the deputy Mayor of Hendon (Alderman C. Beaumont Teare) from which hung a medal engraved "For Services Rendered." This was presented to her by the Mayor of Salford where she was living at the time, as her master had been transferred to that area. She was also given the Freedom of Holland Park, Old Trafford—which meant she was the only dog allowed to run loose in it!

The greatest day in Beauty's life was a cold snowy day in January 1945. She travelled to London, which was still under rocket bombardment, to meet Admiral Sir Edward Evans ("Evans of the Broke," now Lord Mountevans) who was at the time Regional Commissioner for Civil Defence in London. From his hands she received, as the reward of her gallantry, the Dickin Medal—the highest award any animal can win.

While Beauty was engaged in her pioneer rescue work another dog was also doing a magnificent job with a Civil Defence unit. The story of Rip—for that was his name—is best told by his owner, Mr. E. King.

Rip was found, homeless and hungry, after a heavy raid in September 1940. I did not know who owned him and I thought that after a feed he would have gone away. But he attached himself to me. As my post was in the dock area we had many bad incidents, and Rip soon proved his worth.

He was very valuable in helping us to locate persons trapped in the debris. During the alerts, heavy gunfire, and incendiary raids Rip was always out on duty—never in the way, but always eager to do his bit.

After blackout Rip always accompanied me on my nightly rounds of the street shelters. He was always sure of a tit-bit from one or other of the occupants.

Official dogs are now trained for this kind of work, but Rip was the first dog to locate trapped persons. He had over five years' active service to his credit.

Rip's training was gained the hard way. When I came across Rip sniffing around on the job, I always knew that there was someone trapped in the ruins.

No one knew how old Rip was when he wandered into the lives of the Southill Street wardens, but he cannot have been young. In 1946 he began to fail and develop dropsy. In the autumn of that year he died, and was buried in the peaceful little animals' cemetery at the P.D.S.A. Sanatorium at Ilford. On his headstone are the words "We also serve," the motto inscribed on the Dickin Medal which was presented to Rip in 1945 when his story became known to the Mascot Club.

When Beauty was decorated in 1945 with the Dickin Medal, two of the official Rescue Dogs who were doing such valuable work at that time were on parade with the little terrier. They were the Alsatians Jet and Irma who took part in the great London Victory March of 1946. London showed, by the roar of welcome it gave those gallant dogs, that their work had not been forgotten.

One of the worst and most haunting terrors of the air raids was the dread of being buried alive. The men of the Civil Defence Forces did magnificent work after each incident, searching every inch of ground for buried raid victims. But with the best will in the world the men had to rely on sight and reason. They lacked the unerring instinct and wonderful natural gifts which made the co-operation of dogs effective when at last they were called in to help. Unfortunately it was not until near the end of the war that it was decided to use dogs in raid rescue work.

A number of dogs, already trained in anti-sabotage and patrol work at the Ministry of Aircraft Production Dog School in Gloucestershire, were selected for trial. After a short spell of special training they were sent to London to work with the Civil Defence rescue squads. During the bombardment of London by V-weapons the dogs were at work night and day. So useful did they prove that the authorities regretted that trained dogs had not been used earlier in the war.

Fourteen dogs were used in rescue work in London. Of these five were awarded the Dickin Medal. All the dogs were under the command of Lieutenant Colonel W. W. Dove, T.D., who took the keenest interest in all of them.

Jet of Iada, first of the dogs attached to the Civil Defence Forces, was a large and beautiful black Alsatian, bred in Liverpool by Mrs. Babcock Cleaver, a well-known dog breeder. Jet had already distinguished himself in anti-sabotage work in the service of the Government.

One September afternoon in 1944 he arrived in London with his handler, Corporal C. Wardle, R.A.F., after a journey of over one hundred miles by lorry. Never a good traveller, Jet had been ill much of the way. But less than two hours after his arrival a call came for help at an incident in the London suburb of Edmonton. Immediately he and his handler went to the spot where a missing person was thought to be buried. Through Jet the casualty was located. The dog was again called out the next night and was continually in action until the end of air attacks on London.

Many people owe their lives to Jet, and many bodies were located by him which might have remained long undiscovered.

When a call was received from an incident the dogs would report with their handlers to the Incident Officer. The dogs would then be set to search over the area where people were thought to have been trapped. They would quarter the ground methodically until the whole site was covered. In spite of the grim circumstances it was fascinating to watch the care and eagerness with which a dog worked. It was rarely that no indication was given and even more rare for a dog to be at fault.

One of the outstanding personalities of the dog rescue squads was Mrs. M. B. Griffin who was awarded the B.E.M. for her work.

For many years Mrs. Griffin had been a well-known breeder and trainer of Alsatians. It was therefore not unnatural that as soon as the call came for "dog power" she should give up her home to become the chief trainer at the Ministry of Aircraft Production Dog School.

One of her Alsatians, Crumstone Irma, was Jet's companion both at the presentation of Dickin Medals by Admiral Evans and in the Victory March. The Crumstone strain is one which produced dogs whose intelligence and devotion to duty led them to play an important part in the war.

Their outstanding qualities were probably inherited from Echo, Irma's grandmother, whom Mrs. Griffin brought from New Zealand. Although nine years old when war broke out, Echo did a year's service as patrol dog. During that year she was only absent from duty on one night, and that was on doctor's orders as she had a badly lacerated eye. At the age of ten she went into honourable retirement and her place was taken by a granddaughter.

Other outstanding dogs of the Crumstone family were Psyche, Storm (who was Irma's father) and Drift, another of Storm's daughters.

Of nearly all Mrs. Griffin's dogs fascinating stories can be told. Storm, one of Echo's sons, was well known as a film-actor for he starred as "Black Wull" in the film *Owd Bob*. Before joining the R.A.F. he and Irma acted as emergency messengers for the Leatherhead A.R.P. Unit. They were trained to carry messages from the A.R.P. Post to the Report Centre if ever the telephone lines were put out of action. At first there was prejudice against using the dogs. But they proved their worth and Civil Defence officials admitted it. Storm once covered three and a half miles in thirteen minutes fifty-eight seconds.

When Storm went with Mrs. Griffin to the Dogs' Training School he was soon marked out for his cleverness. It was during his stay at the school that he helped the Somerset police to trap a criminal. After travelling 160 miles to Yeovil in a car he followed the trail of a wanted man (although the scent was twelve hours old) to within a few yards of his hiding place in a thick wood. As dusk was falling and the man was known to be armed, it was decided to call Storm off and wait till daylight. All approaches to the wood were guarded, unknown to the criminal, who, trying to make a getaway, succeeded only in running into the arms of hidden constables.

Mrs. Griffin often found time to send reports of her dogs' rescue work to the Mascot Club. Here is a letter written in February 1945:

I know you will be pleased to hear that Psyche and Irma both indicated at a spot at an incident recently. A girl of seventeen was missing so operations were begun on the pile of debris indicated by the dogs. The first thing the rescue men found was a little dog. He was quite all right and so thankful for his release after seventeen hours. He was about five feet below the surface but hiding in a cavity.

Curiously enough this dog was quite silent. The rescuers only realized he was there when they broke into the little cavity. The dog rushed into the open, wagging his tail like mad and shaking himself violently to free his coat of the dust.

Another letter written in March 1945 said:

I was called out in the morning following an incident as persons were still missing. Irma and Psyche *together* suddenly ran to a point in the debris. Beneath this rubble we found a collapsed floor. A woman was trapped there between two floors. She had been there over nine hours and was still conscious. We got her out and, after examination, the doctor said she had a good chance of recovery.

This was a wonderful find, as the position of the floors was quite hidden by a mound of rubble and the woman's presence was quite unsuspected. The rescue and other workers were walking about over the very spot where this unfortunate woman was sandwiched with her small son dead beneath her feet. At this same incident these two dogs indicated another live victim. On digging out the place we got a small collie who was little the worse for his experiences.

At a later incident Irma gave the position of victims under a collapsed house and although there was some doubt in the minds of the men who were working on the ruins, excavations were made. As a result they discovered two girls, both alive. Charlie, Mr. Murray's dog, also found a live casualty at this incident in another part of the ruins. So we felt that our hours of work were well spent that morning.

I hope soon the bells of peace will be ringing out and there will not be any more of these tragic scenes for us to witness and our dogs to work upon.

As will be gathered from this letter, the rescue dogs and workers did not ignore animal casualties. Another rescue of this kind was recorded in one of Mrs. Griffin's letters:

Recently, while working Psyche, I went over the debris of a collapsed building supposed to be quite clear. She indicated and while trying to find out the exact spot I heard a small sound. I listened but heard nothing more. I encouraged Psyche and she sniffed down into the debris. I listened again—and sure enough heard a whine. A nice red setter dog was badly trapped under a collapsed floor. He was jammed against a fireplace in which a fire was still burning. It took quite a while to get at him and when we first got him out I feared his heart would peter out. He was terribly exhausted and could not stand. We gave him some hot tea, wrapped him in blankets, left him quiet and telephoned for the P.D.S.A. van.

In another letter in March 1945, Mrs. Griffin wrote:

Psyche and Irma have indicated several animal victims to me. In one big incident recently the rescuers were searching for an old lady and began their excavations on the dogs' indication. Our first find two and a half feet below the surface was a lovely cat, completely trapped by debris. The men thought this was all the dogs had found, so desisted from further work. I was at that moment in another part of the incident. On my return to this section I tried that part over again and the dogs gave further indication though not so strongly as before. Further excavation there gave us three bodies—an old lady, her daughter and her sailor fiancé all dead. They were found six or seven feet further down below the debris, so the first very keen indication was largely on the cat.

On another incident, while working my dogs on blast "bits and pieces" round the perimeter, they indicated under some light debris. On searching I found a cat with a broken back. I got a policeman, and led by Psyche, we found our poor victim. Putting a sweater over him I carefully lifted him up and the policeman took him away for painless destruction.

In one of these letters it will be noticed that mention is made of "live" indications. This was Irma's speciality. She always seemed to know if the victim she was tracing was alive or dead and would indicate this clearly. On one occasion when she had barked the "live" signal the casualty was recovered apparently lifeless. Later on the victim recovered consciousness, and Irma proved to be right. When anyone located by Irma was brought out dead, she would try to lick the lifeless face or a hand and look up at her handler as if entreating that something should be done about it.

In the midst of all this tragic work there were moments of a lighter kind. There was for example the day when Peter—a collie who later won a Dickin Medal—and his handler Mr. Archie Knight were badly hoaxed. While searching a ruin Peter gave a strong indication and tunnelling was started. Suddenly from under the ruins came a voice uttering strings of curses. Relieved that the casualty was evidently very much alive, Mr. Knight called out, "It's all right, we're coming"—and sent for the ambulance men. After further digging they came upon a smashed parrot cage. Sitting amid the wreckage and vigorously cursing was a large and irate parrot!

Another time Psyche indicated a casualty and, after tunnelling, Mrs. Griffin groped in the darkness searching for what might be there. She could see nothing and called for a light. When it arrived it showed a completely naked chicken, whose feathers had been blown off, sitting sadly on a waterpipe.

It is interesting to note that in times of great danger animals which might naturally be antagonistic to each other often keep a truce. On one occasion a large bomb had fallen at night in the Hendon area, wrecking several streets. The animal rescuers commandeered a private car and filled it with homeless animals of many sorts and housed them all together in a large room until arrangements could be made for their proper accommodation. Not one fight occurred and cats and dogs mixed amicably.

Of Taylor, a rescue dog from Chelsea, an amusing story is told by his handler Mr. W. T. Rowe. It is a story which shows there can be labor troubles among canine as well as human workers!

It was right at the end of the war and the incident was caused by one of the very last rockets to fall. Taylor was sent to the spot in company with Peter, the collie. On arrival at the site both dogs sat squarely down and refused to take any interest in the proceedings. Their handlers called them off, tried them at different points and did everything they could to encourage them. But they were unsuccessful. Finally thinking the dogs must be ill, the handlers withdrew them. But as both appeared to be in perfect health no one could give a satisfactory explanation of their behaviour.

At last Mr. Rowe had an inspiration. Every evening the dogs received their rations—three pounds of horsemeat and two pounds of biscuits. Unfortunately no meat had arrived for three days owing to enemy action. The dogs had had to put up with biscuits. The handlers could only conclude that a strike had been organized by way of protest. No meat— no work! That was, however, an isolated experience.

When the time came for Taylor to be demobilized there was a farewell party before he returned to his old home in Glasgow. Mr. Rowe said afterwards: "Do I miss him? Every day I think of him. He was a pal any man could be proud of. In fun, in fear, in danger he was always beside me and always ready to help mankind. What more could one ask of any animal?"

Gallant rescue dogs! Londoners can never realize all that they owe to them.

Part Three
STORIES OF BREEDS

Ay, in the catalogue ye go for men;
As hounds and greyhounds, mongrels, spaniels, curs,
Shoughs, water-rugs and demi-wolves, are clept
All by the name of dogs: the valued file
Distinguishes the swift, the slow, the subtle,
The housekeeper, the hunter, every one
According to the gift which bounteous nature
Hath in him closed, whereby he does receive
Particular addition, from the bill
That writes them all alike . . .

Shakespeare: Macbeth

FROM CAVE TO PENTHOUSE

Man's Ancient Companion

EUGENE KINKEAD

Fascinating stories of dogs and the breeds of dogs—
their characteristics, feats, and services to mankind—
fill this article.

The Canine Family Tree

THE ancestor of the dog is believed to be the wolf, or a cross between
the wolf and the jackal. Dogs breed freely with either animal and the
progeny is fertile. In most cases, however, the present race of dogs is
far from the ancestral type. By constantly crossing bloodlines man has
produced a staggering number of varieties. They range in size from the
tiny Chihuahua weighing as little as a pound to the St. Bernard which
is over 200 pounds. And they vary in coat from the shivering Mexican
hairless to the furry Eskimo dog that sleeps in the snow. In fact, from
the great reservoir of breeds now existing, any known type that has become extinct can be restored. This was conclusively proved in the case
of the Irish wolfhound. This animal, the world's tallest dog, was a famous competitor in the ancient Roman arena, and the stadium crowds
cheered him long and loud. They were the only dogs used there with
recorded victories over the lion and the elephant. Three of them were
a match for a bear and four for a lion. On their hind legs the creatures
towered well over the head of a six-foot man. In pre-Christian Ireland
they were used singly for wolf, and any such dog must be stout indeed.
Of all the animals employed today for that purpose, none tackles the
wolf in less than a pack with the exception of the borzoi, the Russian
wolfhound. These are trained to attack in pairs and hold the quarry
until their master arrives to dispatch it, each dog simultaneously grab-
bing an ear so the wolf cannot use its tremendous jaws. The logic of
this is sound. One snap of a wolf's jaws may break any bone in a man's
frame, and its neck is so strong that it can throw a sheep over its back
and walk off like a fox with a chicken. Although the last czar's kennel
is said to have contained at least one dog that could handle a wolf alone,
the Irish wolfhounds constantly turned this trick offhandedly. When

First appeared in *Holiday Magazine*, November 1947. Reprinted by
permission of the author.

civilization caused the disappearance of wolves in Ireland, the breed dwindled and declined until in the middle of the last century it could be said to have vanished. At that time its revival was undertaken by a Captain Graham, of Dursley, England. Employing the degenerate remainders of the race, he mated them with Scottish deerhounds, great Danes and borzois. Before long he had produced a breed that answered to all the descriptions of the earlier dog and which persists today.

Actually all our purebred, blue-blooded dogs are really stable types of mongrels. Many instances in kennel-club history illustrate this. The popular and well-known Airedale up to about 1885 was simply a nondescript and highly variable terrier, a clever and dependable stray prized by poaching gangs that operated in the north of England for its ability to kill quickly and silently. After that date, public interest in the animal arose, and supervised breeding crystallized the class. Another illustration is the Doberman pinscher. Now one of the Continent's leading police dogs, it was produced arbitrarily some fifty years ago by Louis Dobermann (sic), a German dogcatcher, who was out to breed the perfect watchdog, and who blended four different grandparents, one of which was a black-and-tan terrier. The rule of selective breeding also applies to the matter of diminishing size. The Pomeranian arrived in the English-speaking world over a hundred years ago, a creature somewhat larger than a sheep dog; today, because of popular demand, its average weight is seven pounds and this figure, in all likelihood, could be further substantially reduced by careful propagation.

Fashion in Dogs

Of course, some breeds have remained virtually unaltered through the centuries. One of these is now probably the most fashionable dog in America, the boxer. Its numbers in this country have increased enormously within the past decade, and last February at the Westminster Kennel Club Show at Madison Square Garden a specimen was adjudged best dog in show. So far as pictures show, the boxer—originally called the *Bullenbeisser*, or "bull biter"—has since the Middle Ages looked much as it does today, a heavy German chase dog, as traditionally conspicuous for agility, courage, and dignity then as now. Like everything else connected with man, the preference in dogs changes. A few years back, a spate of Scotties, immortalized in drawings by Marguerite Kirmse, clogged the walks and sofas of the land. A little earlier, the collie had its day. Before that, there was another favorite, the quizzical pug. This fat, flat-faced emigrant from China with the double-curled tail was the omnipresent dog of the Victorian world, one out of every three exhibits in the New York dog shows then being a member of this comical clan. It was an artful and engaging beggar with an amazing capacity for food, invariably satisfied by its kindly owners, and to all intents and purposes it ate itself to death. As a result, today it is practically nonexistent in this country.

Just what dog has changed the least over the years has not been definitely established, but two prominent contenders for the honor are miles apart in habitat. One, the Norwegian elkhound, is a gray, short-bodied, wolfish-looking dog whose remains have been found with those of prehistoric Vikings in graves dating back 6000 years. Hard-muscled and square, it is said to have few equals for elk or bear, whose body scent it can take at two to three miles. The other contender is the saluki, whose likenesses were engraved on the tombs of ancient Egypt and whose mummified bodies have been found in them. Living in the Mediterranean regions of Africa and in upper India, it resembles a shaggy greyhound, is used for coursing game and is the only dog admired by the Arabs who, as Mohammedans, generally regard the species as unclean.

At present the arbiter of dogdom in this country, the American Kennel Club, recognizes 111 different breeds, and among them are, naturally, some interesting animals. The bloodhound, for example, one of the most ancient kinds of hound, is also one of the rarest, being seldom exhibited, as it is too delicate to stand much carting around. Far from being savage, as its name might imply, it is in fact the height of docility and would be more apt to lick the hand of a fugitive it had cornered than to attack him. The greyhound is the fastest dog (it has been clocked at 40 miles an hour, or almost 20 yards a second). The famous pointer is a relative newcomer. It was born only after the wild-fowling habits of English sportsmen had changed and they had stopped aiming at birds on the ground and had started shooting them in the air. When English sportsmen aimed at birds on the ground they used a heavy Spanish trailing dog to help them locate game. Now for shooting at birds on the wing they needed a much faster assistant and one that could scent through the air as well as on the ground. So they crossed the Spaniard with the greyhound and foxhound. The result was a speedy, rugged, far-ranging creature whose nose-up attitude has probably been the subject of more popular art than any other phenomenon in the sporting field.

Not included in the Kennel Club's recognized varieties are a number which, nevertheless, have at one time or another been shown in this country, but which are so uncommon that their names are not even known to the average person. Some of them have such exotic labels as Australian terrier, Chinese crested dog, Rhodesian lion hound, and Russian owtchar. Briefly, the Australian terrier is like a toy Yorkshire with a short coat; the Chinese crested dog is a naked little fellow with a tuft of hair at about where hair grows on a human being's head; the Rhodesian lion hound is a large gawky beast whose short back fur has a curious pattern like watered silk; and the Russian owtchar is a big, rough-coated sheep dog. It's possible that the last might have been much better known in this country. An American master of foxhounds imported some a while back and they did well except that the males arrived castrated, a Russian practice to keep them from straying after bitches, and so propagation of the breed here never got started.

Aristocrats and Laborers

For the convenience of judges at dog shows, the American Kennel Club has divided its recognized breeds into six categories: sporting, working, hound, terrier, toy, and nonsporting classes. Originally, of course, all dogs were working dogs; all were bred and employed either to help man hunt and kill game or to prevent other animals from killing livestock that was the source of food. To a marked degree they retain this faculty. Not long ago a champion poodle, fresh from the prize ring, entered a spaniels' field trial on Long Island. To the amazement of almost everyone, it performed magnificently. Work dogs can't be too much praised for both their determination and ingenuity. For instance, one of the great problems of bird dogs recently has been pheasants. Dogs trained to point grouse or quail find pheasants puzzling. Instead of staying put when they're pointed, the birds run quietly away. One indignant setter trailed pheasants for thirty-six hours, never finding one that would settle down. Finally the resolute dog changed its style. Following a hot scent, it would suddenly break off, make a wide circle, and, coming around in front of the astonished bird, force it to flush.

MASTIFF

Rab and His Friends

JOHN BROWN

In writing the classic dog story, a chapter of which follows, Dr. Brown remembered that Robert Burns once declared, "Man is the god of the dog." And the doctor added as postscript: "Did we serve our God with half the zeal Rab served his, we might trust to sleep as peacefully in our graves as he does in his."

FOUR-and-thirty years ago, Bob Ainslie and I were coming up Infirmary Street from the High School, our heads together, and our arms intertwisted, as only lovers and boys know how, or why.

When we got to the top of the street, and turned north, we espied a crowd at the Tron Church. "A dog-fight!" shouted Bob, and was off; and so was I, both of us all but praying that it might not be over before we got up! And is not this boy-nature? and human nature, too? and don't we all wish a house on fire not to be out before we see it? Dogs like fighting; old Isaac says they "delight" in it, and for the best of all reasons; and boys are not cruel because they like to see the fight. They see three of the great cardinal virtues of dog or man—courage, endurance, and skill—in intense action. This is very different from a love of making dogs fight, and enjoying, and aggravating, and making gain by their pluck. A boy, be he ever so fond himself of fighting, if he be a good boy, hates and despises all this, but he would have run off with Bob and me fast enough: it is a natural, and a not wicked interest, that all boys and men have in witnessing intense energy in action.

Does any curious and finely-ignorant woman wish to know how Bob's eye at a glance announced a dog-fight to his brain? He did not, he could not see the dogs fighting; it was a flash of an inference, a rapid induction. The crowd round a couple of dogs fighting, is a crowd masculine mainly, with an occasional active, compassionate woman, fluttering wildly round the outside, and using her tongue and her hands freely upon the men, as so many "brutes"; it is a crowd annular, compact, and mobile; a crowd centripetal, having its eyes and its heads all bent downwards and inwards, to one common focus.

Well, Bob and I are up, and find it is not over: a small thoroughbred, white bull terrier is busy throttling a large shepherd's dog, unaccustomed to war, but not to be trifled with. They are hard at it; the scientific little fellow doing his work in great style, his pastoral enemy fighting wildly, but with the sharpest of teeth and a great courage. Science and breeding, however, soon had their own; the Game Chicken, as the premature Bob called him, working his way up, took his final grip of poor Yarrow's throat, and he lay gasping and done for. His master, a brown, handsome, big young shepherd from Tweedsmuir, would have liked to knock down any man, would "drink up Esil, or eat a crocodile," for that part, if he had a chance: it was no use kicking the little dog; that would only make him hold the closer. Many were the means shouted out in mouthfuls, of the best possible ways of ending it. "Water!" but there was none near, and many cried for it who might have got it from the well at Blackfriars Wynd. "Bite the tail!" and a large, vague, benevolent, middle-aged man, more desirous than wise, with some struggle, got the bushy end of Yarrow's tail into his ample mouth, and bit it with all his might. This was more than enough for the much-enduring, much-perspiring shepherd, who, with a gleam of joy over his broad visage, delivered a terrific facer upon our large, vague, benevolent, middle-aged friend, who went down like a shot.

Still the Chicken holds; death not far off. "Snuff! a pinch of snuff!" observed a calm, highly-dressed young buck, with an eye-glass in his eye. "Snuff, indeed!" growled the angry crowd, affronted and glaring. "Snuff! a pinch of snuff!" again observes the buck, but with more urgency, whereon were produced several open boxes, and from a mull which may have been at Culloden, he took a pinch, knelt down, and presented it to the nose of the Chicken. The laws of physiology and of snuff take their course; the Chicken sneezes, and Yarrow is free!

The young pastoral giant stalks off with Yarrow in his arms, comforting him.

But the bull terrier's blood is up, and his soul unsatisfied; he grips the first dog he meets, and discovering she is not a dog, in Homeric phrase, he makes a brief sort of *amende*, and is off. The boys, with Bob and me at their head, are after him: down Niddry Street he goes, bent on mischief; up the Cowgate like an arrow—Bob and I, and our small men, panting behind.

There, under the single arch of the South Bridge, is a huge mastiff, sauntering down the middle of the causeway, as if with his hands in his pockets: he is old, gray, brindled, as big as a little Highland bull, and has the Shaksperian dewlaps shaking as he goes.

The Chicken makes straight at him, and fastens on his throat. To our astonishment, the great creature does nothing but stand still, hold himself up, and roar—yes, roar; a long, serious, remonstrative roar. How is this? Bob and I are up to them. *He is muzzled!* The bailies had proclaimed a general muzzling, and his master, studying strength and economy mainly, had encompassed his huge jaws in a home-made apparatus, constructed out of the leather of some ancient *breechin*. His mouth was open as far as it could; his lips curled up in rage—a sort of terrible grin; his teeth gleaming, ready, from out the darkness; the strap across his mouth tense as a bowstring; his whole frame stiff with indignation and surprise; his roar asking us all round, "Did you ever see the like of this?" He looked a statue of anger and astonishment done in Aberdeen granite.

We soon had a crowd; the Chicken held on. "A knife!" cried Bob; and a cobbler gave him his knife; you know the kind of knife, worn away obliquely to a point, and always keen. I put its edge to the tense leather; it ran before it; and then!—one sudden jerk of that enormous head, a sort of dirty mist about his mouth, no noise,—and the bright and fierce little fellow is dropped, limp, and dead. A solemn pause: this was more than any of us had bargained for. I turned the little fellow over, and saw he was quite dead; the mastiff had taken him by the small of the back like a rat, and broken it.

He looked down at his victim appeased, ashamed, and amazed; snuffed him all over, stared at him, and taking a sudden thought, turned round and trotted off. Bob took the dead dog up, and said, "John, we'll bury him after tea." "Yes," said I, and was off after the mastiff. He made up the Cowgate at a rapid swing; he had forgotten some engagement. He turned up the Candlemaker Row, and stopped at the Harrow Inn.

There was a carrier's cart ready to start, and a keen, thin, impatient, black-a-vised little man, his hand at his gray horse's head, looking about angrily for something. "Rab, ye thief!" said he, aiming a kick at my great friend, who drew cringing up, and avoiding the heavy shoe with more agility than dignity, and watching his master's eye, slunk dismayed under the cart,—his ears down, and as much as he had of tail down too.

What a man this must be, thought I, to whom my tremendous hero turns tail! The carrier saw the muzzle hanging, cut and useless, from his neck, and I eagerly told him the story, which Bob and I always thought, and still think, Homer, or King David, or Sir Walter alone were worthy to rehearse. The severe little man was mitigated, and condescended to say, "Rab, ma man, puir Rabbie," whereupon the stump of a tail rose up, the ears were cocked, the eyes filled, and were comforted; the two friends were reconciled. "Hupp!" and a stroke of the whip were given to Jess; and off went the three.

Bob and I buried the Game Chicken that night (we had not much of a tea) in the back-green of his house, in Melville Street, No. 17, with considerable gravity and silence; and being at the time in the Iliad, and, like all boys, Trojans, we called him Hector of course.

BLOODHOUND

You Don't Kid Bloodhounds

C. B. COLBY

True stories of feats of trailing by the big, melancholy-looking dogs are told in this article.

I DIDN'T have much time. Dashing across the hot concrete of Route 100, I made the edge of an open field on the other side. My old cap fell off, but there was no time to pick it up. Thick bushes grew along the edge of the field, and I kept close to them at a fast trot. Better save my running wind for later.

Another parkway loomed ahead of me, and under it bored a dark tunnel big enough to walk through. It was heavenly cool on such a hellish hot day, but a guy in my shoes didn't stop to enjoy it. I panted out of the cool gloom into another broad, sun-baked field behind a boys' school, pounded along its edge, and turned down a narrow woods road. No dice this way; it led to a pond. Jumping to one side into tall grass, I plunged back to the well-worn playing field, keeping close to the woods along its edge, dodging between the trees . . . I'd better double back —too much open country ahead. It might be too late to make the woods again, but I started across the clearing at a dead run, my heart pounding too hard for my age . . . It *was* too late.

Out of the tunnel across the field burst a huge, rust-colored bloodhound, deep chest heaving as he followed my scent in great bounds. Behind him, leash wrapped around his sweaty wrist, strode a tall New York State Trooper, urging him on.

The tree behind which I crouched grew smaller and more transparent by the second as I watched the trooper and hound make short work of my trail. It might just as well have been fitted up with flashing neon directional arrows, for all the trouble that the massive animal had had with it. With never a pause or a moment of doubt, he skirted the bushes, untangled my puny trickery by the pond, and zigzagged along the edge of the woods toward me.

Halfway across the clearing the trooper bent down, the sunlight flashing on his revolver holster, and slipped the hound's leash. With head high, the dog raced ahead. Trailing by scent alone, rather than by eye-

Reprinted by permission of the author.

sight, he passed close to me on a loop of the trail, up the ridge; and then straight as a long-eared lance he raced down the slope to my ridiculous hiding place behind the tree. It was all over, and as an escaping "criminal" I had failed miserably.

Technical Sergeant William Horton, Troop "K," New York State Police, snapped the leash back onto Dapper Dan's trailing harness and wiped the sweat from his chin. "Hell of a convict *you'd* make!" he grinned, handing me a paper cup full of horse-meat scraps to reward the hound with. "That magazine ought to be ashamed of you."

Dan, one and a half years old and eighty-odd pounds of cold-nose cop, gulped the horse-meat and chewed disgustedly on the paper cup. I was thankful that he had no personal comments to add to those of the tall trooper.

Walking back to the State Police "suburban" for the ride back to the barracks, I learned a lot more about the Troop "K" hounds. Back in 1935 when the troop's first dogs came up from the South, Sergeant Horton was sent into New York to pick them up. Bill had never had a dog of his own, but he liked the looks of the huge, sad-faced beasts and so began to take care of them.

The first week they had the dogs at "K's" barracks at Hawthorne, New York, a call came in to see if they could find an old lady who had wandered off into the woods. Horton snapped a leash onto one of the dogs, and with mingled feelings of hope and doubt picked up the woman's trail.

An hour or so later the old lady was back home, and so were Bill and the dog—Bill with a new job. Since that time the dogs have been the sergeant's assignment. From the way Bill talks about them and to them, you gather it hasn't been too rough on either.

The Troop "K" hounds are as famous as they are feared—famous for the hundreds of missing persons they have tracked successfully, and feared by the many criminals that have had them on their trail, when neither Bill or the hounds have been kidding.

To lost persons, particularly children, they have been big, friendly, face-licking rescuers. To criminals they have been stubborn, ruthless, and (upon command) vicious trailers. Unless otherwise directed, they are tail-wagging good-will advertising for the troopers, as tickled to find a lost youngster as their trainer.

No parent who has need for calling the bloodhounds should ever hesitate because of their name or Uncle Tom's Cabin reputation, if a child is lost. As a matter of fact, for several years, Sergeant Horton has been using his young son Fred as a training quarry.

There are four of these thoroughbred bloodhounds on the Troop's horse-meat payroll: Rusty, late of the K-9 Corps, and Melody, both six years old; Old Smarty, ten years old, born in the service and now nearly blind ("he can still trail mighty well," according to the sergeant) and Dapper Dan, the kid of the kennels. All are big, strong, deep-chested, and tough. That does pretty well for their trainer too.

The dogs are kept in rugged steel and wire-mesh enclosures at the barracks. When they rear up their five feet and a hundred pounds against the mesh for a head scratch, even the steel posts are apt to give a bit; and when they brush against your legs in a chummy gesture, it's tough on weak joints.

All were trained by the sergeant, and all are usually good-natured, even when they indulge in their own peculiar form of roughhousing. They even have a sense of humor—of sorts. Every so often there's a terrific uproar from the kennels: bellows, yelps, barks, and growls, as though the whole pack of them was tearing each other to bloody bits. Bill used to grab anything handy and leg it for the kennels—to find them just sitting around looking as sad and bored as only a bloodhound is capable of.

Sergeant Horton has learned a lot from them, as they have from him. As a recognized authority on their use, he alone takes over when a "dog job" comes in over the teletype.

They travel about from case to case (the troop receives about fifty "dog calls" a season) in the troop's suburban, stretched out on well-worn mattresses. No stuffy traveling cases for these guys. One of their first lessons as a pup is to like to ride, for a bloodhound that arrives on the case tired and upset from traveling is almost worthless, and poor travelers are eliminated in the early stages of training.

They have journeyed hundreds of miles to a case, yet arrived fit and rarin' to get to work. In one year they covered as widely separated places as the shore of Lake Ontario, and Maryland. They and their trainer fly if the case is urgent. In that Maryland case, short work was made of it.

For two weeks a Negro had held a white girl captive in a patch of wilderness. She finally slipped away during an unguarded moment and escaped, but the officials were hesitant about going into the woods after her captor. He might be armed, and they had no idea where he might be holed up. The Maryland State Police got in touch with Troop "K," and off went Bill and the dogs.

Once on the scene they quickly trailed him through the thick scrub pine. He set off in a pretty straight line for some definite destination across the wilderness. While the hounds kept him going ahead, the word raced faster to the only spot he *could* be heading for—the shack of his estranged wife. Not knowing how far ahead of the dogs the Negro was, they surrounded the shanty just as the man burst out of the door, breakfast still in hand . . .

Most of the cases are missing persons, but even these can have an odd twist, and Bill and hounds seldom have a chance to be bored while on a

job. For example, up at Ellenville, New York, an old man nearly eighty
went berrying. He didn't come back. His son-in-law and daughter finally
called the troopers. Bill and his charges hit the road and were soon at
work. They worked part of that night, and went at it again the next
day, finally locating the old chap, sprawled out exhausted by his full
berry pail, miles from home.

Sergeant Horton picked up the old man and, in the trooper's usual
thorough manner, the pail of berries too, and started back. Reaching
the rest of the searchers, including the son-in-law, he deposited the old
duffer on the grass and set down the pail of berries alongside of him.
Routine case, up to that point, but the novel twist happened right then.
The son-in-law walked over to the old man, stood looking down at him
for a moment without a word, then with a vicious kick of his hiking
boot, sent the berries, pail and all, scattered all over the clearing—and
walked off without opening his mouth. The sergeant still doesn't know
the answer to that one.

In the South, bloodhounds trail without leashes and are taught to
bay so that they can be followed, but the "K" hounds, which quite
often are worked through traffic, city blocks, and even saloons, are almost always kept at the end of the six-foot leather-and-chain leash. They
are silent trailers, working in heavy wide leather trail-harness that will
keep them in check without restricting their breathing or movements.
At the kennels, however, they are plenty articulate, particularly when
visitors leave. They bay dolefully, moan and yelp like lost souls when
their trainer stops scratching their high-domed scalps and walks off.
They love company, and hate to have another dog taken on a case in
preference to themselves. That very quirk of bloodhound nature has
been used to catch criminals.

The sergeant well remembers the fool who shot a New Jersey trooper
and then fled into the wilderness with a couple of guns and a "You lousy
so-and-so's won't get me alive!"

That was more or less quite okay with the troopers, but for the sake
of a trial they wanted to get him alive. The woods were thick, and he
was well armed and hidden—and a many-times offender from the South.
They got in touch with Troop "K," and off rolled the suburban, with
Bill tramping a heavy foot on the accelerator. "Shoot a trooper, eh! Let's
get over to Jersey, dogs."

At the scene, with all stretches of the surrounding woods roads covered with the guns of the police, Bill looked over the situation, his
mind balancing one fact against another: hidden gunman, valuable dogs,
all roads covered, old offender from the South. The *South!* That gave
the sergeant a clue. The pieces of a plan began to fall into place and
the pot began to boil.

One of the dogs was securely tied to the tailboard of the suburban, and off went Bill with his eager running mate straining at his harness. The underbrush closed behind them. Straining at his chain, the remaining hound looked reproachfully at the rest of the troopers, and burst into a spine-chilling lament of frustration, jealousy, disgust, and despair that should have been heard for miles. It was.

Deep in the wilderness the crazed killer leaped to his feet, staring about him. Bloodhounds—after *him!* He'd seen how they worked them in the South. He'd have to do something, and fast. Sending the hounds in after him, were they? He'd show 'em. They weren't going to just come in and find him. Not him!

Working his way through the thickets from cover to cover, he finally made a last dash across a clearing into a woods road—and right into the front sights of the murdered trooper's buddies.

Back at the Troop "K" suburban, the word was received a few moments later; and strangely enough, out of the bushes stepped Bill and the trailing hound. That was as far as they had been, a few feet out of sight of the other tied-up animal! No sense in taking chances with a good four-legged trooper, the best trainer in the business, and some other fine officers, when the jealous howl of a frustrated trailer and the imagination of the killer would do the trick.

Thick woods, open fields, highways, or old buildings are all the same to the fantastic noses of the trained "K" hounds. Some conditions make trailing easier, of course. Certain kinds and conditions of roads make trailing tough; others fairly scream, *"He went that way!"* Which does which is a trade secret; Horton wouldn't tell, and the hounds just look wise.

Green foliage is good either for actual tracks or the quarry having brushed past in flight. Damp and overcast days are tops for trailing. Bright sunny days are said to be tough, but if my experience with Dapper Dan was a "tough" day for trailing, I'd like to see them work on an ideal day! Heavy night frosts make a day-before trail hard to keep track of, for it glazes it over with a smell-deadening coat. When that happens, the dogs and trainer just wait until the sun wipes off the glaze of frost and then go to work.

Some fox hunters have looked down their smug noses at the sergeant's technique of handling frost, and point out that their dogs can track a fox the morning after a heavy frost with no trouble. They fail to consider that a fox runs at night on *top* of the frost, leaving a fresh spoor, while the human track may have been made hours or perhaps days before *under* the frost.

With conditions ideal, Bill's hounds can follow a fairly fresh trail at a gallop. The human scent drifts down from the quarry to leave a broad "band" or road before them. Bill has clocked them in a car at nearly ten miles an hour over certain types of roadbed. That's really puppy stuff for the veterans at the kennels now.

It's not even necessary for the quarry to have walked along the road for the veterans to trail him. Riding a bicycle won't sneak you past Horton's charges either. Human scent is heavy and drifts downward to the ground after your passing. The wind may drift it to one side as much as several yards, but that won't save you either. The dogs just follow where the wind blew "you," and stick to the trail like leeches. They almost never go from footprint to footprint.

Bill trains the dogs to stick to one scent alone, no matter how many distractions and other scents cross and confuse the issue. A rolled-up newspaper or leafy branch, noisy but not bruising, train the younger dogs to keep to the all-important scent, ignoring all others. The playing field where Dan found me this morning must have been crisscrossed by a hundred other human scents, but he never faltered once, taking my every turn at a gallop. City traffic and pavement offers no serious problem for the dogs' educated noses. The sergeant has trailed his own youngster through the school playground, candy stores, town traffic, and straight to where he was "hiding" in a recreation building full of amazed and delighted playmates.

Once they have the scent clue to follow, from a hat, cap, socks, or other article of clothing from the quarry, it's all over but the little matter of catching up to the real thing at the other end of the smell. Pajamas or bed clothing are the best, provided the quarry has slept alone. As one chap put it: "The virtuous get caught." Sometimes the feats of the dogs startle even their trainer, who has begun to take their amazing noses as routine. One of their most tricky trailing jobs was on Long Island a few years ago.

A man had been murdered along a road; no tracks, no weapon, no motive. Just a well-hacked corpse. It looked like a hatchet job. There was only one feeble suspect, and a mighty poor one; a Negro who just happened to live a few miles from there. They had nothing on him, but were holding him for the routine "Where were you on the night of—?" stuff.

Sergeant Horton was called over to the Island to see if his dogs could perhaps find where the murder weapon might have been thrown away in the woods. That might give a clue.

The hound sniffed about the scene of the crime and then instead of heading into the thick bushes, started slowly off down the highway. Bill and the other officers looked at each other. How come? There were no tracks except a few auto-tire marks, and no signs of anyone having been down that way for days.

The bewildered officers sauntered behind (the hounds are never hurried on a tough trail) while the animal meandered from side to side of the road, sniffing the air, the bushes and occasionally the trackless road-bed itself. For three miles the posse straggled along; then the dog turned up the drive to an old shanty. He was sure now. His pace quick-ened, and he trotted straight to a dilapidated, old, open roadster, sniffed about it and then walked to the shack—the shack where the lone Negro suspect lived, and where he parked his open roadster.

Confronted with the evidence of the solemn-faced bloodhound from Troop "K," the Negro confessed and admitted having driven home from the scene of the murder in the battered roadster, spreading a trail that only a Hawthorne hound could follow. That takes a good hound, well trained, and in the pink of hound condition. Bill keeps them never less.

They are all inoculated against every kind of disease dogs are subject to and have the best of care. Anyone who likes dogs as their trainer does would see to that. Sergeant Horton is a pretty good "vet" himself, but if he can't handle a situation, no expense is spared to have a top veterinarian there in a hurry. They are fed once a day with about two pounds of horse meat, plenty of kennel rations, vegetables, and petting.

They also get rewards of meat after tracking down a practice quarry and, if at all possible, after finding a lost person or other object of their search.

The dogs and their trainer are on call whenever there is a real need for their services and talent. Many requests have been received (and re-fused) to find anything from a pet monkey to a snake. Not that the hounds *couldn't* find them, their trainer hastens to assure you; but those years of patient training to track only humans might be ruined in a few moments if they are permitted to trail anything *but* a human quarry. Sometimes their quarry seems almost *un*human at the time.

Take, for example, the time the Army called the barracks and wanted the dogs in a hurry. Matter of life and death. Over on Fishers Island, off the Connecticut shore, a GI had gone haywire. He'd stolen about a hundred and fifty dollars and a .45 pistol and had set out to do the town and then commit suicide. He'd left a note to that effect, and the Army was worried. Might be a hoax, and then again—"Could you please hurry those hounds over here?"

The dogs trailed the GI from one saloon and gin mill to another, to the amazement of the more sober customers, and then down to the gloomy beach. They picked their way slowly across the sand to an old, half-buried barge. Right there the dogs sniffed about, wagged their tails and looked at each other and the officers. As far as they were concerned, that was all—period.

The troopers were a bit embarrassed and the Army was more than skeptical. They searched the beach, dragged the water and went over the old barge with a fine GI combing . . . No soldier. Trainer Horton was frankly stumped, but he trusted his fine dogs. He suggested that perhaps the GI might have gone A.W.O.L. Well—could be; time might tell.

It did, several months later, when they moved the old barge to clear the beach. Out floated the body of the missing GI with a neat .45 hole in his head. Neither he nor the hounds had been bluffing.

Sergeant Bill Horton has been with the New York State Police going on twenty years. Nearly fifteen of those twenty have been spent working the bloodhounds. He's tucked a lot of tricks up his gray uniform sleeves during that period. The dogs of Troop "K" do all right without sleeves; they carry their tricks in those cold crystal balls they wear for noses.

POODLE

Rivals

FAIRFAX DOWNEY

We love the same fair lady.
   The two of us she dangles,
Though she and I are married.
   It's one of those triangles.
"You dog!" I dub my rival
   (He thinks me just a noodle),
But he takes the name I call him,
   For he is a dog—a poodle.

She says that his attentions
   The hardest heart would soften.
Does he just sit home reading?
   No, he takes her out quite often.
He sits up, begs so nicely,
   While I, she keeps retorting,
Have never bothered begging
   Since the days when I was courting.

The depth of my affection,
   Which vies with any ocean,
Seems shallow when compared to
   His sheer, dog-like devotion.
I greet with wry expression
   Of one who bites persimmons
That statement that the dog is
   A man's best friend. . . . He's women's!

DALMATIAN

The Complete Dog Book

AMERICAN KENNEL CLUB

Fervent praise of each breed, by the club devoted to it, is contained in the American Kennel Club's *Complete Dog Book*. Although it is difficult, not to say invidious, to select any one, the panegyric on that famed fire engine and coach dog, the Dalmatian, is here chosen as one of the most lyrical examples.

No breed has a more interesting background or a more disputed heritage than that dog from long ago, the Dalmatian. His beginning is buried so deep in the past that researchers cannot agree as to his origin. As to the great age of the breed, and the fact that it has come through many centuries unchanged, investigators are in complete agreement.

Models, engravings, paintings, and writings of antiquity have been used with fair excuse but no certainty to claim the spotted dog first appeared in Europe, Asia, and Africa. Perhaps some of the divergencies in opinion as to the original home of the Dalmatian can be accounted for by the fact that the dog has frequently been found in bands of Romanies, and that like his gypsy masters, he has been well known but not located definitely in any one place. Authoritative writers place him first as a positive entity in Dalmatia, a province of Austria on the Eastern shore of the coast of Venice. Though he has been accredited with a dozen nationalities and has as many native names—he is nicknamed by the English, the English Coach Dog, the Carriage Dog, the Plum Pudding Dog, the Fire House Dog, and the Spotted Dick—it is from his first proved home that he takes his correct name, the Dalmatian. We find references to him as Dalmatian in the middle eighteenth century. There is no question whatsoever that his lineage is as ancient and his record as straight as that of other breeds.

His activities have been as varied as his reputed ancestors. He has been a dog of war, a sentinel on the borders of Dalmatia and Croatia. He has been employed as draft dog, as shepherd. He is excellent on rats and vermin. He is well known for his heroic performances as fire-apparatus follower and fire-house mascot. As a sporting dog he has been used as bird dog, as trail hound, as retriever, or in packs for boar or stag

Reprinted by permission of the American Kennel Club.

hunting. His retentive memory has made him one of the most dependable clowners in circuses and on the stage. Down through the years the intelligence and willingness of the Dalmatian have found him in practically every role to which useful dogs are assigned. Most important among his talents has been his status as the original, one-and-only coaching dog.

The imaginative might say that his coaching days go back to an engraving of a spotted dog following an Egyptian chariot! Even the practical minded will find no end of proof, centuries old, of the Dalmatian, with ears entirely cropped away and padlocked brass collar, plying his natural trade as follower and guardian of the horse-drawn vehicle.

He is physically fitted for road work. In his make-up, speed and endurance are blended to a nicety. His gait has beauty of motion and swiftness, and he has the strength, vitality, and fortitude to keep going gaily till the journey's end. The instinct for coaching is bred in him, born in him, and trained in him through the years. The Dalmatian takes to a horse as a horse takes to him, and that is to say, like a duck to water. He may work in the old way, clearing the path before the Tally Ho with dignity and determination, or following on with his ermine spottings in full view to add distinction to an equipage. He may coach under the rear axle, the front axle, or, most difficult of all, under the pole between the leaders and the wheelers. Wherever he works, it is with the love of the game in his heart and with the skill which has won him the title of the only recognized carriage dog in the world. His penchant for working is his most renowned characteristic, but it in no way approaches his capacity for friendship.

There is no dog more picturesque than this spotted fellow with his slick white coat gaily decorated with clearly defined round spots of jet black, or, in the liver variety, deep brown. He does not look like any other breed, for his markings are peculiarly his own. He is strong-bodied, clean-cut, colorful, and distinctive. His flashy spottings are the culmination of ages of careful breeding.

His aristocratic bearing does not belie him, for the Dalmatian is first of all a gentleman. He is a quiet chap, and the ideal guard dog, distinguishing nicely between barking for fun or with purpose. His courtesy never fails with approved visitors, but his protective instinct is highly developed and he has the courage to defend. As a watch dog he is sensible and dependable. He is not everyone's dog—no casual admirer will break his polite reserve, for he has a fine sense of distinction as to whom he belongs. Fashion has not distorted the Dalmatian. He is born pure white, develops quickly and requires no cropping, docking, stripping, or artifices of any sort. He is all ready for sport or the show ring just as nature made him. He is extremely hardy, an easy keeper, suited to any climate. He requires only the minimum of care, for he is sturdy and neat and clean.

SLED DOGS

The Devil Pups

JOHN BEAMES

Alaskan Huskies are tough customers, and the annual
sled race is won by the toughest of a fighting breed.

"JUST my cursed luck," grumbled Don Pauley, nursing his swollen knee.
"I got to go and twist this here so I can't run, and the big race comin'
up in only three days. Garry, I guess it's up to you."

The sandy hair on Garry March's head seemed to stick up more spik-
ily than ever.

"Oh, my gosh, Don, I never drove in a race."

"Well, a feller's always got to start sometime. Who'll I get to drive
'em else? The pups would tear a stranger limb from tree. Flash, he won't
do a thing for nobody he don't like; and Pep, he can be awful ugly."

"And Snookums needs watchin' too," observed Garry. "Timmy and
Tommy ain't no angels, neither."

"But you have run 'em—they know you," insisted Don. "And what a
feller has done once, he can do again. I'll go on up and put in your
name as drivin' for me."

The public announcement that Don Pauley, famous double winner
of the Northern classic, would be replaced by an unknown, caused a
sensation in town.

In the afternoon Don said to Garry, "You best take the pups out for
a run on the river; they'll get stale, tied up in the barn."

"I hate facin' all them people," sighed Garry. "But I guess the dogs
got to have their exercise."

He hitched in the seven. First Flash, black with silvery blue markings,
diabolical green eyes set aslant, tough, tireless and savage. Paired behind him were Pep and Snookums—Pep gray and black, Snookums a
dingy yellow; both ready to fight or to bite anything, human or animal.
Tommy and Timmy came next, gray and buff, well-matched, young but
learning fresh deviltry every day. The runner pair, Hick and Heck, were
sour old veterans of five.

As the train went down the main street of Greenstone toward the
frozen river, the keen eyes of many Northern mushers were upon them.

Reprinted by permission of Marguerite Beames.

"The dogs sure look good," said one. "But that long-geared, homely-lookin' lad what's drivin'—" He shook his head and spat in the snow.

"He acts like he was half-scared of 'em," said another. "Mind you, it ain't everyone can handle them devil-pups of Don Pauley's. I wouldn't want to monkey with 'em myself."

"Well, here's where I hedge that bet I put on Don," said a third man. "That boy will likely get eat alive on the trail some place. He can't handle 'em. Now, just look at that."

A small boy, with that determination to get himself killed that seems to actuate most small boys, had run right in the path of the train. Flash had him by an arm in an instant.

Garry rushed up, yelling: "Here, hey, quit! Flash, let go."

Flash scornfully obeyed, and the small boy ran off screaming. Garry pursued him, the team at his heels. Just as Garry caught up with the youngster, Flash saw a stray dog and swung off after him.

Garry had to let the boy go and race to rescue the stray from being torn to pieces. By the time the yelping animal had gone rocketing up the street, the team was twisted around a telephone pole, and the carriole turned upside down.

They had to be disentangled; and the small boy, with a torn sleeve but otherwise none the worse, as well as twenty more like him, had to be shooed away. Garry's face was crimson to the roots of his hair by the time he got the train straightened out and down to the river. Here he ran them hard for an hour. There was more trouble getting back through town, and he was in a state bordering on collapse when he finally came in to where Don was.

"My gosh—oh, my gosh, Don," he groaned. "They wanted to eat every dog and kid they seen. Flash near had the arm off one little lad. I don't know, Don—I don't think I'm goin' to be much use to you in this."

"Aw, forget it, them damn kids is always gettin' themselves bit," said Don. "You can't keep 'em out of the road. Once you get out of town, you'll be all right. Look, Garry, I'm asking you to drive the pups as a favor to me. The folks wants to see my dogs run. You ain't goin' to let me down, are you?"

"If you put it that way," agreed Garry mournfully.

The morning of the big day arrived; the whole population of Greenstone, together with some hundreds of visitors from the mines, trooped down to the area on the river that had been cleared by snowplows and decorated with evergreens and bunting.

It was what the North calls a "cool" day, about twenty below, without wind enough to freeze anybody—much. But the folk were well bundled up, and the sun shone brilliantly.

As each racing team drove up, it was tethered to a post in the ice, so that the excited dogs were free to bark defiance at their rivals but not to start a general massacre.

Don rode down to the starting line in the carriole, where he got out and stood leaning on a stout stick. "Take her easy and don't worry," he advised Garry. "If you can win, okay, but don't kill the dogs to do it—and don't let 'em kill you."

"Oh, I'll take care of 'em," promised Garry earnestly.

The order came to cast off all ties, and the drivers had now only the spiked drag at the rear of each carriole to restrain their teams.

The starter lifted his pistol, but the report was hardly heard in the clamor that broke out. The drivers pulled up their drags, and the trains broke with a scrambling rush, yelling like fiends, the long whips flickering over them.

The plowed expanse at the starting line steadily narrowed, and the teams jockeyed to be first on the out trail. A train of light dogs swung out diagonally in front of Garry.

An experienced driver would have tried to go over and through, as he had the right of way, but Garry put his weight on the drag instead. The devil-pups promptly seized the golden opportunity for mass murder.

The two drivers pried them apart with shouts and whip butts, but not before ugly gashes had been inflicted on both sides. The other dogs, however, had suffered the more.

"I'll report you," raged the other driver.

"Okay," said Garry meekly. "You report me, but meantime I got to get goin'."

The field had passed and were far up the trail. Garry cracked his whip and called: "Cha-way, pups, cha-way! We lost a lot of time. Got to mush now and keep out of fights. Cha-way, little fellers!"

The trail was good, and the dogs soon settled into the long swaying trot that made them the great team they were. It was not long before they had passed two tail enders.

"That's a bunch of murderers you got there," one of them bawled after him. "They'll eat you alive."

Then he caught up with Sam Sorrel, a galloping bone rack who was trying to make up for an indifferent train by running all the way. Sam gave him a wide, gap-toothed grin.

"Watch out for Shandy and Mook—they want to win this race awful bad," he cried.

The train left the river and pulled on through deep forest and occasional ponds. Visibility was limited, and Garry saw nothing of the trains ahead.

He reached Charley Bell's stopping place at the foot of Raggy Lake, an irregular body of water full of spits and islands.

"You're in fourth place," said Charley. "Shandy's way out ahead, but Mook and Piper ain't gone by very long. Say, you're drivin' Don Pauley's dogs, eh? What 'come of him?"

"Hurt his knee," replied Garry.

Out on Raggy Lake, day was closing. The sun laid down a level golden pathway on which they traveled for a few minutes, then winked out behind a high bluff. Gray shadows stole out across the ice, and the temperature dropped fifteen degrees in as many minutes.

A curl of smoke went up from a point ahead, and dogs yelled at them as they drew in to it.

Gus Mook and Slim Piper were sitting by a fire. Mook was tall, and had a flat face with a nose like a wart in the middle of it. He stuck out a lower lip like a scoop shovel and said in a hoarse voice: "Well, if this here ain't the boomer!"

Slim had a hatchet-face and a thin smile that lifted only one corner of his mouth. "Don's dogs brung him this far, anyway," he commented.

Garry flushed but did not trouble to reply. He tethered his dogs and started a fire of his own.

"It's a pity Don Pauley couldn't get nobody better'n him to mush a fine team like them," went on Mook, his voice purposely raised.

"Must be pretty hard on the dogs, too," added Piper, and they laughed loudly.

Garry prepared hot food, and began to distribute it. Taking his eye for a second off Snookums, he had a finger nipped. At the same time Timmy reached out stealthily and tried to bite his heel.

"You know well you didn't ought to do that," said Garry in gentle reproof.

Snookums merely showed a scornful fang.

"Seemin'ly nobody thinks a hell of a lot of me around here," remarked Garry sadly. "I'd ought to had more sense than bring out a bunch like you."

Mook and Piper got their dogs under way. "See you in town if them there don't eat you first," mocked Mook.

It was now full night, a purple sky studded with diamond-hard stars. A vicious wind had risen too, as Garry found when he took the train out of the shelter of the bush again.

The dogs did not like it and wanted to head back. Garry coaxed and shouted and cracked his whip. They only snarled contemptuously.

"I got to take you around the course, whether you like it or not," he said at last. "Come on, I'll lead you."

He reached out to take Flash by the collar. The brute, hackles lifted, eyes glaring, every tooth bared, lunged at him.

Garry jerked back; man and dogs faced one another. If the man did not prevail now, he would have to sneak back to town, beaten.

He rubbed his chin, shook his head and went in again. Up went Flash on his hind legs, mouth wide open. Garry hit him a heavy clout on the head with his mittened hand, and Flash dropped on all fours in astonishment.

"I don't want to be rough with you," said Garry, "but we got to move." He smiled. "No hard feelin's."

Sleigh dogs know who is afraid of them, and despise him accordingly. The devil-pups looked at Garry with a new respect. He was not their mighty master, but he was not to be imposed on, it seemed. Reluctantly but obediently they put their noses down and bored into the bitter wind.

Garry fed again just before he pulled over the height of land and coasted down to Blueberry Portage, halfway point on the race.

"You're Number Four," said the checker. "Slower time than last year. They tell me there was a bad headwind on Raggy Lake."

"About as bad as I ever seen," said Garry. "How far are the others ahead?"

"Shandy's got quite a bit on you. Said he wanted to make the Gander Lake crossing before a blizzard got up. Wants to do it in daylight."

"Think there's goin' to be a blizzard?" asked Garry.

"The weather's thickenin', and it's warmin' up," was the reply. "Liable to be some kind of a storm."

The way now led up Blueberry River to Gander Lake. The wind had died away, and the air was thick and hazy. The dogs were uneasy, looking back over their shoulders and snarling when Garry spoke to them. .They had been traveling generally northward until the turn, but were now headed east of south, which would bring them back to Greenstone on a wide curve.

It began to snow very gently, large, soft flakes drifting slowly down. Dawn was on its way, but the place where the sun ought to rise showed instead a leaden gray mass that advanced and enveloped them.

With it came the wind. The snowflakes stopped drifting and began to whirl. It was as though a heavy, damp blanket had been thrown over them. It bore down man and dogs, and pinned them to the ice. For some minutes they crouched there helpless. They could not see, hardly even breathe. The dogs pawed their noses continually and snorted, and Garry held his mitten before his face.

The flurry passed, but it continued to snow, the flakes skimming in straight lines before a strong breeze. There was nothing in sight but the trail, represented by a broken string of snow nodules appearing between the drifts. To Flash, however, this was as good as a highway, and he followed it unerringly.

An hour or so later he lifted his head and gave a short, high bark. Out of the smother loomed a wooded islet, and as they drew in, a fire twinkled and dogs yelled at them.

Dick Shandy, Gus Mook, and Slim Piper were sharing a single fire.

"Why, I thought you'd be a long ways from here," said Garry.

Mook jerked his head at Shandy. "That's the kind of young damn fool he is," he said.

Shandy was stocky and long-armed. He had a jaw like a plowshare, a broken nose, and narrow eyes. His expression was morose and his voice harsh.

"You can keep on goin' if you want," he growled at Garry.

"But I never been over this trail before."

Shandy flapped a hand. "Just keep on headin' east, and you'll land someplace. It's only fifty mile across."

"But I can't see nothin' with this blizzard blowin'."

"Nor nobody else can't."

"Well, my dogs need a rest," said Garry. "Maybe she'll ease up by the time we're ready to pull on."

Piper came over to look at the train. "You ain't drove 'em very hard," he said.

"No, I'm more interested in gettin' 'em back to Don in good shape," replied Garry.

"You ain't in any hurry?"

"No, I got lots of time."

"That be damned for a yarn!" snapped Shandy. "You been nursin' them dogs along so'd they'd be fresh to cross the lake. Tryin' to play us for suckers?"

Garry looked at him in astonishment. "I don't know what you're talkin' about," he said.

"Never mind that guff," snarled Shandy. "What you want is for us to break trail for you till you're ready to pass and go into the lead. Well, that don't go. You'll do your share, you young four-flusher."

"Say, I'm willin' to do my share any time," protested Garry angrily.

"We'll hold you to that," was Shandy's grim retort.

Garry fed himself and the dogs and curled up in the carriole for a nap. But it was not long before Shandy was shaking him by the shoulder.

"Hey, the sun's comin' out. If we want to get across before dark, we better get goin'."

A misty sun, low in the south, gleamed faintly through scudding clouds.

"We head due east till we raise the bald hill," said Shandy. "The trail goes up the bank a half mile south of the hill."

The going was very patchy. Large areas had been swept by the wind almost to ice level, and the dogs could travel fast. But at frequent intervals drifts lay diagonally across their path, hard and sharp-edged on the eastern side, but soft and deep on the west. The team breaking trail had to flounder through each of these in turn.

Plunging into one such, Flash suddenly broke through. Garry grabbed the trace and hauled him back. Out of the hole left, water bubbled and spread across the ice.

Garry snatched up a cloth and began to wipe the dog's legs and feet.

"What's holdin' you up?" demanded Shandy.

A little spark lit in Garry's eye. "He broke through in a blowhole, and I'm not havin' his feet froze."

After crossing a few more drifts, Garry halted his train again. "Somebody else's turn now," he said firmly.

"Oh, so you're gettin' smart," sneered Mook. "You ain't goin' to break trail, eh?"

"When it comes around to my turn again, but not until."

"But if the three of us says you got to break trail?" inquired Shandy in his most arrogant tone.

"That don't make no difference."

"Stubborn as hell, eh? Look, you ain't goin' to win this race. Get that notion right out of your head. You can take any stuff they're handin' out for fourth place, but us three is gettin' the big money. Savvy?"

Garry shook his head. "I'm makin' no dicker. If these here dogs can win, they're goin' to win."

"Okay, then—now we know where we stand," said Shandy. "Not that we'd trust you, anyway. Either you break trail from here on, or we fix you and your dogs so you can't go too damn fast."

Garry looked from one to another of the hostile faces, and then out across the ice.

"And you can't get away from us," added Mook. "We'll catch up with you the first drift you come to."

Garry bent swiftly and whipped the harness off the devil-pups. Then he stood up, gripping his whip defiantly. The dogs scattered, rolling over and rubbing themselves in the snow, and then bunched at a little distance and stared curiously at what was going on.

"What the hell did you do that for?" demanded Mook.

"Do you know what you done?" warned Shandy. "You put yourself right out of the race. It might take you hours to catch 'em—if you ever do. What's more, if you're left alone with them man-killers, they're liable to have you tore to pieces before mornin', and we ain't goin' to stop and help you catch 'em."

"Well now," said Slim, with a sinister smile, "didn't he do this his own self? We never touched him nor his dogs. So we'll just leave him to do whatever he wants, and get movin'."

Shandy gave an abrupt laugh. "That's so," he agreed. "He can't blame us now for anythin' that happens to him. All right, boys, mush!"

Garry was left alone with the devil-pups, who sat and stared at him, moving their forefeet and licking their lips.

"Well, I saved you from havin' to break trail all the way," he said, "but be darned if I know what to do now. Have to try and get you back in harness. Here, Flash!"

The black leader looked at him insolently and did not stir.

Garry advanced, and the dogs separated until they formed a semicircle about him. Snookums was on the extreme left, his yellowish coat blending with the snow, and Garry kept an uneasy watch on him out of the corner of his eye.

At the same time he was aware that Timmy and Tommy, on the other flank, were watching Snookums' movements and preparing to copy them. He coiled his whiplash in his hand, and pursued Flash, who kept sullenly just out of reach.

The yellow dog ran in, his belly almost touching the snow, and rose to spring. Garry's loaded thong caught him across the chest. He rolled over on his back with a yelp, regained his feet and scurried away. Timmy and Tommy flinched and jumped back.

"Down, Flash!" cried Garry peremptorily. "Down, or I'll cut the liver out of you."

Growling deep in his throat, Flash dropped in the snow, and Garry flung the looped whiplash around his throat. "Come on, now," he said irritably. "I'm gettin' sore with you. Cut out the foolin'."

He dragged Flash back to the carriole and pulled the lead collar over his head, but though the other dogs approached, they ducked away whenever he reached out to catch one of them.

"All right," said Garry. "I guess I got to go without you."

He picked up Pep's trace, and walked along behind Flash, pulling on the trace with one hand and holding his whip in the other. The sun had faded out completely by now, and a faintly luminous mist prevailed, but Flash had no difficulty in following the trail.

The dogs followed, and as darkness increased they closed in, running behind or on either side, just out of whiplash range, alert for any stumble or sign of weariness on Garry's part.

Suddenly Pep leaped into the carriole to try and get at the food. Garry turned with a shout, and he jumped out. But an instant later, Timmy imitated him. Garry got a good cut at him, but glanced around to see Snookums crouched for a spring right behind him. He slashed right and left, and the dogs scattered, snarling, only to wheel and return.

"This ain't good enough," said Garry. "I don't know why you want to kill me, but I ain't goin' to let you."

He made Flash lie down and brought the carriole up beside him. Its high back provided protection from the rear.

"May as well eat," said Garry. "And seein' as you've been a good dog, I'll give you somethin'. The rest of these bums can go hungry."

He brought out a piece of meat and gave it to Flash. Instantly the others set up a frantic yelling, but the crackling whip kept them back.

Finally, Heck came cringing up, wagging his tail and whining. "Oh, so you're not goin' to be tough any more," said Garry. "Well, get in your place and I'll feed you." Heck meekly obeyed.

One by one the others followed his example, until only Snookums was left. "Get out of here, go away," shouted Garry. "I don't want you any more—you're no good."

Snookums sat down, threw up his head and howled with misery. Then he flung himself on his back, all four feet in the air, writhing his body and making a snuffling whimpering.

Garry jerked him to his feet by the scruff of the neck, gave him a cuff on the ear, and pushed him into his place. "No more funny business," he said sternly. "I put up with enough from you fellers. From now on, you got to do what I say."

He surveyed the train with a satisfied expression. "Well, I got you all back in harness again. I guess we're out of the race, but I'll hand you all back to Don in good shape, and that's the last I want to see of any of you. Get up in the collar there. Cha-way! Cha-way!"

The temperature was falling again, and the ice began to talk, as it does on the big lakes of the North. There were heavy reports, near and distant, followed by ripping, tearing noises. Through the cracks of all sizes thus opened, water welled and spread across the surface under the snow.

Flash, pattering along nose to trail, halted suddenly. Garry, going forward, found their road blocked by a lead that had evidently opened since the others had passed that way. He followed the lead down until it pinched out, crossed and came back up the other side, hoping to cut the trail.

But in a little while they came to wet ice that would carry no tracks. The position was dangerous: there might be four or five feet of solid ice under them, or only a skin. If they remained where they were, the feet of the dogs would freeze. Garry picked up his trail axe and tested the ice, the dogs following.

Somewhere out of the foggy darkness a dog gave tongue. Immediately Flash and his mates flung back their war cry.

A voice bawled: "Who in hell's that?"

"Me," answered Garry. "Who's that?"

"It's the boomer," came Mook's raucous voice. "Where are you at?"

"Be damned if I know—I'm just here."

"Well, there's open water between you and us, anyway. This here's like a nightmare. We seem to be goin' around in circles and comin' up against bad ice every place. How is it over your way?"

"Just the same. I'm goin' to try and find dry ice before my dogs freeze their feet. Mine are soakin' too."

"Well, see you in town tomorrow if any of us ever get there," shouted Mook.

Moving cautiously through the slush, on the watch for open water, Garry went forward until he found dry snow under his feet. He halted, dried off the dogs, and quickly changed his wet socks.

The dogs curled up in the snow, tail over nose, and Garry rolled into the carriole, pulling a blanket over himself. He was wakened presently by a rising wind and a violent snow flurry. As that passed, it tore the veil off the face of the sky and showed a moon in its last quarter hanging low in the sky.

It gave light enough for a fairly extensive view. Garry stood up on the carriole and looked in all directions. On the lake itself were indeterminate shadows that might indicate drifts, leads, or wet ice. He could not see anything that moved, but he was startled to see something gleaming white a little above the horizon. Then he made out that it was the summit of a bald hill of which the rest lay in shadow.

"If that's east," he mused, "and I guess it must be, I'm turned right around. It's likely the hill Shandy was talkin' about, and the trail goes ashore about half a mile south of it. So I got to head southeast. Get up in there, pups! We're in sight of land, anyway."

The light strengthened gradually until the eastern sky was crimson, gold, and a deep, pure green, though the sun would not rise for another hour.

Garry glanced to his right and saw the other three trains moving rapidly on a converging course.

"Well, it seems we are in the race again after all," remarked Garry. "Cha-way, pups!"

As the teams approached, Garry saw that there was an open lead several feet wide between. In a few minutes they were all moving on a parallel course separated only by the open water.

"You think you're pretty smart," jeered Shandy. "I think it's just damn-fool luck."

Garry nodded with a grin. "That's right," he agreed.

"Well, you ain't goin' to win this here race," shouted Mook. "And you better get wise."

The lead made a half turn that brought it squarely across Garry's path. The others howled with triumph and mockery, as they swung away toward shore.

"Seemin'ly," commented Garry, "once more we ain't in the race."

He had to follow the curving lead to land, work around it in deep soft snow, then down along the shore until he came to where the trail went up the bank. He hustled up it for a short time, then pulled his dogs down.

"Take it easy, pups," he said. "We're not breakin' any more trail. They asked to do the hard work and we're goin' to let 'em."

Day broke bright and not too frosty. They had only fifteen miles to go now. The dogs were weary but still capable of a burst of speed. Garry helped them by running most of the way, riding only on the downgrades.

The trail dipped to the river valley. Not much over a mile away the buildings of Greenstone came into view. A scout had already gone racing back to town to call the people to watch the finish.

"Cha-way!" cried Garry and cracked his whip. "No foolin' now, boys —I want all you got."

There was a new note in his voice; it was that of a man no longer anxious and afraid, but one who had confidence in himself and a purpose to pursue. The dogs heard it, understood it, and responded as they would have responded to the mighty Don Pauley himself. They went down the riverbank with a rush and out across the ice.

Here was Shandy's train, overdriven, too tired to keep the pace. Garry went by fast, and without turning his head to look at the scowling face of his beaten enemy.

Such a thing as a three-way finish had never been known before, and had not been provided for. The out trail was wide, but the in trail had been plowed only to a width that would allow two trains to race. On either hand was a high snowbank.

Mook and Piper were racing neck and neck, but Garry gained on them fast. They looked back at him and then at each other.

"Don't let him by," cried Mook.

Piper nodded. "Hold her the way she is, and we got him beat."

The finishing post was in sight. The trail widened a little. To attempt to pull out and around would be foolish, but there was a gap of about two feet between the carrioles ahead. Garry made his decision.

He flung his whip out over the heads of the train and roared: "Cha! Cha! Cha!"

Into the narrow gap hurtled the devil-pups. Like a wedge they split the teams and forged forward.

Mook yelled with fury and lashed out at them with his whip. Piper took a cut at Pep, who yelped but kept on.

Then they both turned on Garry. He warded off a slash from Piper on his arm. Mook was aiming at his head with the butt of his whip. He struck a backhand with his own butt that landed on Mook's button nose and sent the blood spurting.

With his cap knocked off and blood trickling down his neck from a gashed ear, he went flying across the finishing line, first by half a length.

ST. BERNARD

"Wanted: a Job for Experienced St. Bernard!"

IB MELCHIOR AND WILL SPARKS

The wonderful rescue dogs, of which Barry was the
most celebrated, saved many lives in the Swiss Alps.
In recent years improved travel conditions have less-
ened the need for them, and it was thought that a new
field for their work might be found in the mountains
of Tibet. But that was before the country's conquest
by the Red Chinese who do not specialize in errands
of mercy.

PROWLING alone through a snow-filled pass in the mountains, the young
dog was suddenly drawn by an inexplicable sense toward a small, almost invisible mound in the dazzling white expanse. Cautiously he
sniffed, then began to dig urgently. Buried in the snow, sleeping the
heavy sleep of near-death, lay a little ten-year-old girl, lost by an ill-
starred party of travelers in a storm the night before.

Unhesitatingly the great dog lay down beside her, licking her face
with his warm tongue until she revived. Sensing with uncanny wisdom
that if he left to get help—as he had been trained to do—the weakened
child would not survive, the dog somehow managed to place her on
his back and muster up the super-canine strength to carry her to safety.

So began the fabulous career of *Barry der Menschenretter*—the Savior
of Man—credited in his day with the saving of forty human lives. Barry
was the world's first famous St. Bernard. For many years after his death
the great gentle dogs of his breed were called, not St. Bernards, but
"Barry Hounds." An inscription on his memorial tells of his murder by
a man who was to have been his forty-first rescue—a soldier who mis-
took his benefactor for a beast of prey, and stabbed him with a hunting knife. Actually, Barry lived to the ripe old age of fourteen years and
finally died in Berne, Switzerland, where his likeness stands today in the
Museum of Natural History.

Barry's home, and the source of all St. Bernards, is the Great St. Bernard Pass high up in the Swiss Alps. A treacherous route stretching
fifty-three miles across the Alps from the village of Martigny in Switzerland to Aosta, Italy, the pass is covered for at least nine months of the

Reprinted by permission of Ib Melchior.

year with snow that often reaches a depth of more than fifteen feet. Below-zero temperatures, frequent sudden snowstorms, perilous snow-

disguised precipices, and avalanches add to the dangers of travel. But toward the middle of the pass stands the Great St. Bernard Hospice, offering food and shelter to the weary traveler, and seeking out those lost along the way.

No member of the animal kingdom is surrounded with more heroic and romantic legends than the friendly giant dog who works alongside the monks of the Hospice. His instinct for rescue work is one of nature's most fascinating mysteries. In their three hundred years of existence the St. Bernards have saved nearly three thousand persons from death in the perilous pass.

Most people are surprised to learn that despite their famed instinct the dogs undergo a rigorous training before they are allowed to wander about the Alpine pass. For their work to be effective, they must be schooled in awakening and reviving victims, moving them without injuring them, and summoning help from the Hospice. Above all, they must learn teamwork.

The monks take the young pupils, along with some of the experienced dogs from whose example the trainees learn, out into the mountains where there is always snow. One of the monks will separate himself from the group, lie down and cover himself with snow, and the dogs are sent out to find him.

On actual rescue missions the dogs work in packs of four. When a victim is found, he is first dug out of the snow. Then two of the dogs lie down beside him to warm his body. A third licks his face to revive him. The fourth dog rushes back to the Hospice to summon help. It is only the fourth dog who carries that famous little cask around his neck, fastened on *after* the dog reports back to the Hospice. The monks want it clearly understood that the dogs never wander about the mountains by themselves carrying brandy.

The casks are made of oak staves and bound with brass hoops, and they hold a pint and a half. For fifty years these little barrels were absent from the heavy St. Bernard necks. But in the last year so many persons lost themselves in the Alps that the monks decided to restore the liquor casks. But it isn't brandy they carry. It's *marc*, a distillation of grapeskins made by the monks.

If a lone dog chances upon someone in the snow, his first duty is to revive him. Then, if the victim is able to walk, the dog leads him to the Hospice. If not, the dog barks to call aid. If out of earshot, he tries to drag the victim to where the barking will be heard.

Once a party of Italians seeking jobs in France attempted to negotiate the pass. They underestimated the rigors of the crossing and were hopelessly stranded. When the monks arrived with stimulants, in response to an insistent summons from the dogs, all thirty of the men were in bad condition. They can thank the faithful dogs that they are alive today.

No visitor to the famous Hospice has ever met with hostility from the even-tempered dogs—none, that is, except Elysabethe Dalrymple.

When Elysabethe walked into the courtyard a few years ago, her arrival brought all of the rescue dogs, young and old, rushing toward her furiously, with howls of suspicion and protest. The monks were able to calm their charges before any harm was done, and they are inclined to forgive this one instance of strange, unorthodox behavior. Nothing like her, they point out, had been seen in the Alps for over two thousand years; and the dogs wanted, quite understandably, to discover which end of her was which. Elysabethe Dalrymple was an elephant.

When Hannibal, great general from ancient Carthage, was at war with mighty Rome, he led his army from Africa to Spain, then across France and over the Alps through the Great St. Bernard Pass, chosen because it was so dangerous the Romans left it unguarded. With Hannibal went a herd of three dozen elephants, on the backs of which rode majestic Carthaginian officers.

More than two thousand years later, in 1935, adventurer Richard Halliburton retraced Hannibal's route with an elephant of his own, Elysabethe Dalrymple—Dally for short. Like all travelers, this unique pair was given food and lodging at the Hospice, to the grand amusement of monks and dogs alike.

The Hospice was founded in the middle of the tenth century by Bernard de Menthon, an Italian monk who ventured into the pass after hearing stories of highwaymen who robbed Rome-bound pilgrims along the way and held back every tenth man in slavery. The valiant Bernard went into the perilous mountains with a small band of courageous men, taking the fateful tenth position for himself. The little group proceeded, chanting Christian hymns and songs, when suddenly they were set upon by the bandits. Bravely, with invincible faith, Bernard held forth his crucifix, and as by a miracle the robbers became terror-stricken and fled. Falling to his knees and thanking God, the monk vowed to set up a hospice on that very spot to succor all who traveled the pass. Today an impressive monument to Bernard de Menthon overlooks this settlement in the pass which bears his name.

At first the monks, members of the Order of St. Augustine, worked alone in their dangerous task of mercy. Each morning they diligently searched the pass for travelers who might have become lost during the night; and finding them, they brought them to the Hospice for help and care. To break the monotony, the monks fell into the habit of taking with them the dogs from the valley below, and they soon discovered the uncanny ability of these animals to find people lost and buried in the snow. From then on the dogs played an important and permanent part in the famed rescue work of the Hospice. These first dogs belonged to a common local breed known as Thalhund, or Dog of the Valley.

It was not until 1865 that the dogs, whose extraordinary exploits then were told in the four corners of the earth, became commonly known as St. Bernards.

Modern innovations have eased the burden of travel across the pass, diminishing the usefulness of both Hospice and dogs. Autos have shortened the length of time it takes to cross the pass, and radio and telephone communications at either end keep the monks posted on the number of people en route. If a modern traveler hasn't turned up at the Hospice within a given length of time, searching parties and the dogs are sent out.

Until 1924 the St. Bernard Hospice was supported by gifts left in the alms box by those who stopped. But charity was not what it might have been, and in that year the monks were forced to place a small charge upon their hospitality; but even now the poor may still enjoy it gratis. Since the war the famous old Hospice has found itself in financial straits. This despite the fact that summer traffic on the Great St. Bernard Pass has become so heavy that a special traffic officer is needed. Unable to extend their hospitality to such a great number of guests, the monks have converted a wing of one of the buildings into a hotel, and now cater to tourists.

In 1930 the monks began casting about for a more remote place where they and their dogs might continue their historic charity. Eventually they made a branch settlement on the Li La Pass in Tibet, 13,-780 feet up in the Himalaya Mountains. There they appear to have escaped, for a time, the inexorable march of technology.

SPRINGER SPANIEL

Choice of the Litter

RODERICK LULL

As reward for a service, the boy was given his choice of pups from a wealthy man's kennel. He trained the dog until it possessed the makings of a champion in the hunting field. But there were grave complications before the fine springer could come to his own.

It was to him a very simple thing and the wonder was that the others, the older ones, were so stupid and confused. It was only a matter of going back a few years to when he was ten and her age, and thinking as he had thought then.

The old urges and desires and faiths came back, and along with them the memory of the path, half-forgotten now, that followed down the tiny stream through the woods and came at the end to the cave. It was there, he decided firmly, that the lost girl had gone.

He stood a little distance from the group of men, watching the captain, noting his taut face and nervous hands.

He had always thought of the captain and of the captain's daughter as beings apart—as, somehow, Olympian people, with whom he and his kind had little or nothing in common. He had felt that way for years, ever since the time his uncle had left him the fifty dollars and he had gone, nervous and hesitating, to his father and said that he meant to spend it for one of the captain's fine springer spaniels.

He could remember still his father's dark, bloodshot eyes looking at him with infinite weariness, and he could still hear his father's voice saying, "So you're getting big ideas. Well, you'll get over them before you're much older. Them fancy dogs is for people like the captain. Not for our kind. Keep that in your mind, if you got one. We ain't like the captain—we only work a piece of his land."

The money had been spent for clothes for the family and a much-needed new stove, and the little that was left had gone into the meager budget.

So it was a strange thing to see the captain now as only a worried and indecisive man, a man like other men, gesturing and shaking his head and saying over and over, "We've got to find her before another night comes. You sure you asked at every house along the Toll Road, Tom?

Copyright © 1941 by The Curtis Publishing Company. Reprinted by permission of the author.

I'm not satisfied with the way we combed that hill country, Jim." He looked at them with bright, agonized eyes.

Ben Frazier went down the road then, tightening the loose knot in the rope that served him for a belt. The captain sure set a mighty store by his daughter, he thought.

He pulled the old straw hat down against the sun and walked faster. Soon he turned off on the little, abandoned, logging road and, a hundred yards along, left that to fight his way through brush to the forgotten trail. He saw a strip of bark torn from a log, broken branches, and a shoe print in the mud made by a small spring. He smiled. He had been right; he knew where the lost girl was.

He found her at the old cave, as he had expected, and she was too tired and frightened to answer when he told her shortly that they were going home. They walked side by side up to the house.

He was about to leave her, when he heard a call and saw the captain coming toward them.

He shifted uncomfortably from one foot to the other while the captain bent and held his daughter close. Then the captain, clinging to the girl's small limp hand, rose and turned to him, the tightness gone from his face now, the lines fewer and not so deep. He said, "I've seen you around—you're Frazier's son, aren't you?"

"Yes, sir."

The captain ran a hand through his hair. "What do you want, boy? You've got something coming."

He shook his head and turned away. "That's all right."

The captain laughed. "Maybe she would have come home by herself today. But saving me an hour or two of the worry is worth plenty. Tell me what you'd like, boy."

He drew a sharp breath. He thought of the kennel back of the house and of the fine new litter. The captain was a dog man. He raised the best springers in the state. The captain owned the greatest springer that had ever lived, and this dog had sired the new litter. But dogs like that were rich men's dogs.

He settled his feet in the roadbed. "I'd like a dog. One of your dogs. Only I know it's too much to be asking."

The captain looked at him for a moment, then nodded and said, "Nothing's been sold out of the new litter. You can have your choice of it. I didn't plan to sell for two weeks. If you want to wait you'll be able to make a better pick. I'm promising you I'll sell nothing until you've had your pick."

He had to think the words over in his mind before they had any meaning. Then he had to look into the captain's face again to make sure he wasn't having the cruelest kind of sport that any man had ever had. And when the words came out of his throat at last, they came in a voice he had never heard before. "If you mean it—if it's all right, I'll pick now."

It was a litter of eight; he knelt and ran his hands over them lovingly. He looked at their tremendous feet and their bright sad faces; he watched the eternal movement of their sterns and thought that surely he was dreaming. After a long time he stood up and saw that the captain, whom he had forgotten, was still leaning against the fence.

The captain smiled at him. "If you want my advice, I'd take that big fellow. I never saw a better chest, and if he turns out gun shy I'll eat him."

The captain's advice was honest; Ben had watched dogs all his knowing life, and this was the likeliest specimen. Most men would take him. Only there was another of the males that he had been watching. A little small, maybe, and he certainly didn't stand out in a litter fine as this. He couldn't have told why he preferred him to the rest. It was something felt, something beyond and alien to words.

"I'd like him," he said.

The captain looked puzzled. "He's seemed to me a little on the nervous side. But it's your choice, not mine; and I've made my mistakes."

"I'll take him along now, if it suits you."

The captain nodded and he picked the dog up. He heard the captain telling him to come back in the morning and they'd make a deal about food—he wouldn't have a dog fed wrong, and feeding right was an expensive business for a man who didn't own a kennel.

Ben said, "Thank you, sir," and started home. A little wind had come up and he put the dog gently inside his shirt against his skin, and very soon its frightened trembling stopped.

He did not go directly home. He knew with grim certainty what would be said when he arrived there carrying the dog.

He went into a field where the clover was deep and soft as an animal's pelt and put the dog down. The dog looked up at him, pricking his ears, his muzzle quivering and eager. Even in his great-footed awkwardness was a grace, a fineness of movement that was surer proof of his breeding than the writing on his pedigree. The dog came to him when he called and he stroked him for a few moments, then stood up, suddenly austere. You could harm the finest dog ever born with an excess of attention.

He went home then, and when he met his father he spoke first. "This is my dog," he said softly. "The captain's girl got lost. I found her. He gave me the dog."

His father looked at the dog with fathomless eyes. "So the captain did. I guess you're about one of the captain's buddies. No doubt you'll be going into the city soon to buy yourself some of those swell clothes like he wears. A blooded dog like that expects a lot of a man, all right. Why, he wouldn't lower hisself to bark at anyone like me."

Ben said nothing. The dog lay at his feet on his back, the four immense paws waving. And while he looked at him he changed from a puppy into a grown dog, all grace and power and sureness and intelligence—the finest sight any man's eyes had ever seen. It was as if the dog's whole great career had been graphed out, right down to his final victories in the great National trials that rich men spent thousands trying to win and failed a hundred times for each time they succeeded. He started to turn away.

His father said slowly, "You take that dog back."

"I'm not taking him back." He said the words without passion, the way you say a fact beyond denial.

When his father turned suddenly on his heel and went into the house he knew he had won the first round. He took the dog to the barn, where there was old wire and boards, and started the job of building an enclosure and a doghouse.

It seemed to him that each day really began at evening, when he was done with his work and could have some time for the spaniel. He was prepared for his father's giving him more and more jobs to do. He made no complaint. He worked harder than ever in his life and knew no weariness. The most onerous work was easy when you knew that once it was finished you could do what was closest to your heart. He and his father talked little. His mother had nothing to say concerning the dog; it was obvious that she thought of him as only a creature that ate food and barked at nothing and tried to come into the house where he wasn't wanted.

He thought a great deal about a name for the dog. You couldn't call one of the captain's spaniels Bill or Pete or Boy. He had to have a dignified name, with style. It came to him in the middle of one night. The nearest town was Derrydale, and the captain had given him the dog. Derrydale Captain. Derry for short.

He worked slowly, patiently, first teaching the dog obedience. He taught Derry to come to him, to walk at heel, and to sit at his feet without jumping on him. After each lesson he lay on the ground and let the dog run about as he pleased, watching him all the time.

Often he talked to Derry, telling him in short, definite words what his life was to be. He held him by the scruff of his neck, and tried to make him understand all that was wanted of him, all that he must do. Once his father came up to him at such a time and announced his arrival by a laugh.

"That must be a wonderful dog you got. Talks English just like a human, I see. Or maybe you're a little cracked in the head."

He stood up and faced his father, feeling an impotence, a harsh knowledge of his inability to say in words the thoughts that boiled within him. When he turned away without answering, his father laughed again, a long laugh. He wondered, his blood pulsing hotly, that any man could be so unfeeling. Then his father walked away almost jauntily, as if he had achieved a victory. He had no heart for more training that evening and put Derry into his kennel. He awoke in the middle of the night feeling deep shame that he had let himself be so disturbed by nothing. His father was only a man who did not see as he did.

Twice each week he went to the big house to get food for Derry. He didn't feel that this was charity; he and the captain knew that such a dog must have certain foods and that was all there was to it. Sometimes one of the hands would get the food for him. Other times the captain would be there and they would talk.

"How's he coming along? Taught him anything yet?"

"He's coming pretty good."

"Bring him up next time you come. I'd like to see him."

"Yes, sir," he always said. But he didn't bring the dog next time. He didn't intend to. He didn't want the captain or anyone else to see Derry until he was right.

One night Derry looked poorly. His eyes were watery, the underlids half closed. He felt a surge of fear like a knife between his ribs and he stayed up all night keeping the dog warm, watching and waiting, feeding him warm milk. In the morning Derry was definitely improved. It wasn't distemper, after all—just a slight cold.

His father was waiting for him. "Did you go to bed last night?"

"No."

"You stayed up with that dog. I suppose he coughed or something. Well, I'm telling you this—I'm not letting any dog interfere with the work around here. I've let you keep him so long as you held your end up. This is too much. No man's fit to work without sleeping. And—"

He said, "You'll have a better idea when the day's over what I can do."

He drove himself to the most productive day's work of his life. When his eyes were burning and half blind for lack of sleep and muscles fairly screamed for rest he increased his exertions. His father said nothing.

The next morning Derry was in perfect fettle, jumping at the wire and crying to get out for a run. He allowed himself to pet him a little longer than usual that morning.

Derry took to retrieving quickly, but he had a naturally hard mouth and many hours of work with a feather-covered ball in which needles were cunningly placed, were needed to break him. When Derry was six months old it was late summer and time for him to know the sight and sound and scent of pheasant.

Ben took him into the remote corn patch one Sunday morning. He fastened a long line to the round collar of saddle leather that he had bought with money long saved for another purpose. Then they started slowly through the corn, Ben speaking softly to Derry now and then to restrain his bouncing eagerness. A young hen flushed five feet ahead and rose cackling into the air. Derry broke and Ben called to him, not raising his voice. The dog rushed on, barking now, oblivious of everything but the bird soaring toward the shelter of the woods. Ben held the line firm and Derry tumbled over backward, gave a small cry, more of surprise than pain, and came trembling to his feet.

Ben went on as if nothing had happened. The same thing happened half a dozen times. After that Derry stopped dead in his tracks when his name was spoken, even when three birds were flushed at once, not ten feet from him.

They went home at noon and Ben himself was trembling with excitement. His father was sitting smoking in a rickety chair in the sunshine, and Ben was so eager to talk to someone that he blurted out the news as soon as he reached him. "You should have seen him with the check line—he got onto it in no time. I know it took weeks to break some of the captain's good dogs. I tell you this dog's got something no other dog I ever saw has."

His father blew a spiral of gray smoke into the clear air. "Wonderful," he said. "Maybe he can smell out a gold mine. I hate to remind you of it, but we're poor people and we're supposed to work at things that make a little money."

"A good bird dog's worth money," he said. "Big money."

"That may be," his father said. "I don't doubt it. Now, if you think your high-toned dog's worth something—"

Ben spoke over his shoulder, "There's not enough money in the world to buy this dog."

His father made no answer. Ben walked quickly away. He had been burdened suddenly with a dark fear that clung to him stubbornly, try as he might to shake it off.

He felt his heart beating hard and too fast the day he first went into the field with his old hammer gun and a pocketful of shells he had loaded himself with light charges. He let Derry go a good way off, then fired. Derry started, looked about and cowered, belly to the ground. Ben walked toward him, firing twice as he came; the dog broke and ran out of sight into the woods. He called him, but Derry was a long time coming back.

When the dog returned to him, shaking as if with fever, he stroked him lightly until the fear had passed. Then they returned home.

For five days each evening at feeding time he put the tin plate of food down and waited until Derry came for it. Then he fired into the air. The dog ran into his kennel and Ben took away the plate. On the fifth day the dog's flanks, to Ben's agonized eyes, were thin as paper. He wanted to give in, to let Derry eat in peace and afterward to sit by him and let him lick his hands and look up at him worshipfully with his great spaniel eyes. But he steeled himself and waited.

The sixth day Derry ate, though he trembled still. Ben praised him extravagantly and after that there was no trouble.

He worked until darkness made work impossible, the week before the opening of the pheasant season. He walked the five miles into town and back one Sunday to buy his license, then stayed up late that night to load shells and clean the old shotgun. The evening before, he told his father he wanted the day off.

"I been working extra," he explained quietly. "I've done a good day's work ahead and more."

"And if I said no—"

"I'd go anyway. I have to go. This is my first chance to see what he can do. Only—I'd rather have your say-so."

His father shrugged. "Do what you like. If you're as crazy—dog crazy —as that, there's nothing I can do to help it."

He chose a place where no others were apt to go. He was there before dawn broke, waiting with Derry pressed against his knees. He didn't expect many birds. It was not a good place. If he could only bring one or two down he'd be satisfied. Then he'd know where Derry stood.

They worked two hours, the dog crossing and quartering the ground, before a bird was raised. It was a fine shot, going away, and he made a clean kill. He saw the cock fall and the dog go forward to it. He stood still, his hands shaking so he could hardly support the gun. Then, through misty eyes, he saw Derry coming to him, the pheasant in his jaws. He straightened and waited; the dog sat down before him and placed the bird lightly in his hand.

He drew a long breath. He'd seen the captain's dogs work, and only one of them handled a bird in handsomer fashion. That dog was the champion who had sired Derry.

He said aloud, "You know, you, there's no dog young as you in the world that's in your class. And some day there won't be any dog in the world as good as you, no matter how old and smart he is."

He got his last bird just before it became too dark to see. Derry raised it out of a small corn patch and Ben swung and brought it down with a side-angle shot. A moment later Derry retrieved. It was then that he felt someone watching him.

He turned, and fifty feet away saw a dark figure. The captain's voice came floating across to him, soft-syllabled and obviously excited.

"That was good," he said. "That was fine. I enjoyed seeing that."

"I didn't know you were here, sir."

"Heard shooting and thought I'd wander down and see who it was. Truth is, I'd an idea it might be you."

The captain approached and stooped to touch and examine Derry. "And I would never have picked this one," he said. "I always pride myself for picking 'em young and picking 'em right too. I congratulate you."

"I guess I was lucky."

"Maybe. But there wasn't any luck about the way you trained your dog. You did train him yourself?"

"Yes, sir."

"Have any help at all?"

"No, sir. My father don't care about dogs." He was sorry at once for saying that; to tell a man like the captain that another man didn't care for dogs was to brand him an outcast.

"I see. What's his name?"

Ben felt his face redden as he told it. But the captain laughed and clapped him on the back and said that was a mighty fine compliment. He'd never had a finer one, the captain said, and he was grateful and happy for it. Then he said, and there was a serious note to his voice, "I'd like you to stop in at the house a minute. There's something I want to talk to you about."

Ben said, "Yes, sir." As they walked along in silence he felt a sharp quick sense of foreboding that robbed him of all the pleasure of the day. But he told himself it was ridiculous—the captain was his friend . . .

The captain led him to a small study. "Ben," he said, "I'm looking for a good young dog. A real field-trial dog. A dog that has a chance to win the National. That dog of yours, that Derry, might be what I'm looking for. I've a hunch he is."

Ben looked at the captain, then away. He felt real fear now, cold and hard, and wished desperately that he hadn't come. He drew a breath that hurt his chest and said, "Yes, sir."

"Now I don't want you to think of how you got your dog at all. Don't think you owe me any favors. You don't, and that's a fact. He's your dog, just as much as if you'd come to my kennel and paid a big price for him. But I'm going to make you a proposition. I'm going to offer you five hundred dollars for that dog. And on top of it, the choice of any other pup I've got. You're perfectly free to take it or leave it."

Five hundred dollars meant riches such as Ben had never known. It meant lifting the ceiling of fear that pressed his family down. But Derry. He could not let himself think of Derry. It seemed now as if this had been predestined from the beginning. If he had only been wiser he could have seen it coming, sure and certain as the procession of the days. He could, of course, refuse. For a moment he clutched at the thought as if it were a sturdy, floating plank and he a boy drowning. But no matter what, you always knew what you had to do. There was something that made you do it out of respect for your own self.

He said, "Yes, sir, captain."

"It's a deal," the captain said. He opened a desk drawer, found a checkbook and wrote a check. He handed it to Ben. "Now we'll go out to the kennel and you can have your pick again. And, boy, I'll bet you pick right."

Ben stood up. He said quietly, "Thank you, sir, but I don't want another dog. I'll be going now."

"Then you're entitled to a hundred more."

He didn't answer that. He turned and hurried away. He heard the captain's voice with a worried note to it, "Well—then I'll send it down to you."

Outside he did not look at Derry. He told him roughly to stay where he was and did not look back as the captain led him away.

At home he put the check on the table and told his father what had happened. His father picked up the check and examined it, holding it as delicately as if it were some fragile bit of china. Then he laid it down.

Ben said, "It's yours. To do with what you want."

His father shook his head. He looked past the boy, above his head, as if there were something of great interest on the wall opposite. "Thanks for your favors. I don't want no part of them. I got along and I always will. Maybe you'll want to be buying a car with it, like your rich friends have."

Ben stared at his father for a long time. His father's eyes never lowered. A sudden gust of wind came through the open window and blew the check to the floor. His father picked it up and put it in the drawer of the table. "It'll stay there, for all of me and your mother," he said. "You'll know where it is when you want it."

The days went by leadenly. At first it seemed that not having Derry was more than he could bear. Then one day he tore down the enclosure he had made and chopped the kennel into kindling. After that it was not so hard; it was as if with ax and hammer he had destroyed something that never should have been, and so, in a strange sense, set himself free from a harsh bondage.

Half a dozen times he met the captain. Always he escaped as soon as he decently could, not asking about Derry. The captain mentioned the dog once. That was soon after the sale, and the captain asked if he'd like to come up for a hunt. He made some palpably false excuse and the captain, nodding his head, said gently, "As you like, Ben. I know. But he's doing what he was made to do and that's what any being should." The captain did not speak to him of Derry again.

He worked a day for a neighbor and earned enough cash to subscribe for a magazine devoted to field trials; the check still lay in the table drawer, untouched, and with it the check for the additional hundred which the captain had sent down by a servant. He read the magazine with infinite care, line by line, analyzing the dogs pictured, and finding none which had the grace and power and perfection that was Derry.

The first time he saw Derry's name the print seemed to leap from the page. It was in an article covering a tri-county trial and it simply said that Derrydale Captain, owned by Captain Richard Harmon and handled by Joe Bleecher, had placed second. Derry, the article went on, "ranged nicely and obviously had an excellent nose, but was not too well controlled."

He felt anger at the criticism, then wonder that Derry had come in but second. Yet Bleecher was a famous trainer and handler, to whom the captain sent many of his most promising dogs. It was ridiculous to think that the outcome would have been different had he been the handler that day, but that night he slept badly and dreamed of hunting with Derry, and the dog was the great champion of all the great champions of the world.

Derry's name appeared frequently after that—a third here, another second there, a first in one or two county trials where the competition was entirely unworthy of him. In the Western he did not place at all. Once there was a picture, a small, one-column cut taken at a bad angle. He stood for minutes looking at it, miserable with the pictorial injustice of it.

He kept the magazines from his father's sight. He was always first at the mailbox around the period when they were due to arrive. Once his father caught him as he was reading one in the barn. His father's shadow fell across the page and he looked up.

His father's eyes were wide and bright. "So our gentleman is improving his mind," his father said. "It must be fine to be born to the purple."

Ben stood up, holding the words back that wanted to gush out. He rolled the magazine and stuffed it in a pocket. "I'm doing my work," he said.

His father smiled. "When you getting that car? The money's still in the drawer."

"It'll be there forever, far as I'm concerned."

"And me too. I guess the captain's ahead a nice piece of change. Well, if you can spare a minute I can use you. If you can lower yourself to help."

The State Field Trial was coming up and he read in his magazine that the captain had three dogs entered. Derry was one. He was hoeing the kitchen garden a day or two later when the captain's car came down the road and stopped near him.

They shook hands gravely and the captain stuffed tobacco into his pipe. "Ben, Derry's not going like I hoped. I don't know whether you know."

"I know. I been reading about it."

"I figured him for maybe a National champion one day. And he couldn't win even those little trials. It's hard to blame Bleecher. He's got a record back of him."

Ben put the hoe down. "Bleecher ought to know as much as anybody."

"There's such a thing as a dog working right for only one man," the captain said. "It doesn't happen often, but it does happen."

He saw what was coming and wanted desperately to dodge it. He never wanted to see Derry again. That was one thing of which he was dead sure. And all he could do was to stand cowlike before the captain and wait for him to say what he knew he was going to say.

The captain put his pipe in his jacket pocket. "I want you to handle Derry in the State. I'll pay you the same as I would Bleecher—"

Ben broke in angrily, "I wouldn't take pay for a thing like that."

The captain eyed him curiously. "Well, we can argue that later. It's a detail. The point is—will you do it?"

He looked away from the captain, seeking hastily for excuses. There was but one he could hit on that was at all valid. "We're busy now. I got to help. You know how it is this season."

"I know," the captain said. "I can send a man down to take your place."

"And my father—well, he wouldn't like it. He doesn't think much of things like dog trials. For me, that is. And so I guess I'd better—"

"I can fix that with your father."

There was a way the captain said that, as if he thought his father nothing more than the servants that waited on table, or the milch cows in the fine pastures. Ben stiffened and looked away stonily, his whole being an intense discomfort.

The captain watched him for a moment, then said, a different tone to his voice, "I'd think he'd be mighty proud of you handling a dog— maybe a winning dog—in that trial. After all, it's second only to the National. Yes. I've a feeling you'll be out there with Derry."

He could find nothing to say. The captain left him then, striding away to his car, and Ben watched him drive off. When he looked toward the barn he thought suddenly, his heart beating painfully hard, that he could see the wire enclosure and the doghouse within. He had to run his hand across his eyes to banish the strange illusion.

The captain came for him early and they drove off into the cold, clear morning. His father had said good-by to him calmly, without comment, as if he were going off on some ordinary errand.

The captain drove fast, humming a tune, keeping his short brier pipe going like a furnace. Ben sat huddled in his ancient overcoat, his body a bundle of active nerves.

The trial was held at one of the great farms, twenty miles away, and long before they reached it the traffic grew thick. There were little cars and big cars, old cars and new, and the men who drove and rode in them were the big, smiling kind of men whose lives were given largely to their interest in sporting dogs.

They arrived and the captain got out, stretched, and pointed to a dog trailer hitched to a big coupé parked under a clump of trees. "That's Bleecher's rig," he said without emphasis. "Derry's there."

Ben walked toward the trailer slowly, wondering if the dog would recognize him, hoping in one breath that he wouldn't and in the next knowing that it would be the cruelest blow he had ever suffered. Then Bleecher's boy, at the captain's nod, was opening the trailer back and Ben was saying, "Hello there, Derry," and the dog was hurling himself upon him. The dog barked twice, a high-pitched, staccato sound, and his eyes were blazing with eagerness. Ben said, "Charge, Derry," and the dog hesitated, then dropped. He could resist no longer. He knelt and ran his hands lovingly down the smooth flanks, his head close to the dog's ears, so that he could talk to him without being overheard.

Afterward he took him away into an empty field and gave him orders. He had him cross and quarter the ground and threw a rubber ball for him to retrieve. He was still busy with this when the captain appeared. "You're going out in twenty minutes," the captain said. "How's he doing?"

"He's fine," Ben said. "He can win this."

"He's got tough competition. It's the best lot the State ever saw, to my mind. There's a dog here—shipped west by plane with her handler. She's been taking everything."

"He can win," Ben said again. The feel of the captain's hand on his shoulder was warm and pleasantly intimate, and he was glad that the captain said nothing more.

Afterward, he tried to remember the day in full detail, and he failed. He remembered the beginning of it, when his own clothes seemed horribly shabby beside the fine boots and breeches and jackets of the big handlers. Then he put this firmly out of mind and concentrated on Derry. He never looked at another dog, and he never allowed himself to think that another dog might be going better. When he came to the trailer in the early afternoon the captain spoke to him for the first time since the start. "Well done," the captain said.

He really saw the eastern dog for the first time when it was announced that she and Derry were to go out together—the judges had not been able to decide between them for first honors. She was a liver-and-white dog, delicately but beautifully made, with the fine eyes and full muzzle of a great line. He saw her handler looking at him, smiling curiously; he drew his shoulders back and made a little speech of resolution to himself. Then the guns were ready and the judges were down the field in a little knot.

They were to have three birds each, and before Derry found his first a shot to the left meant the other dog had scored. Then Derry found two in quick order and they were brought down and perfectly retrieved. The other dog found her second a moment later. Both found their third birds almost together—the shots came hardly a second apart.

It was over. As Ben walked back, Derry at heel, the sweat was dripping down his back and chest, though the day was not warm. The captain had his arm and was saying, "I don't care which wins, I'll never forget this. You even had Bleecher amazed. By the way, your father's over there. He arrived a couple of hours ago."

Ben turned quickly and saw his father standing alone, dressed in his ancient Sunday best, the dust thick on his heavy, carefully polished shoes. There was about him an immense pride, as if it were his protection against a world full of humiliating and inimical things. He stood very straight and he looked like a man who was alone because it was the way he wished to be, not because he had no one to whom to turn for companionship.

Ben walked quickly toward him, thinking of how his father must have come because he could not bring himself to ask for a ride with Ben and the captain. The five-mile walk to town, the search for a lift to reach the farm. . . . Ben felt a strange, soft emotion that was entirely new to him. He said, "Hello."

His father said, "Hello. I guess you did all right out there."

Now he could almost feel the pride—as if it were a stone wall between them. He said, "Listen—I want to tell you—I want to tell you I'm mighty glad you came. That makes it a good day—sort of caps it off, as they say."

It seemed to Ben that a little of the ramrod stiffness went out of his father's posture. "You mean that, Ben? You mean that, like you said it?"

"Of course I mean it."

His father smiled then, a wide, free smile that was reflected in his eyes. "I'm glad I came too. I guess there's a lot more to these dog things than I knew."

The loud-speaker rumbled then and a metallic voice roared out, "The judges wish it announced that this was one of the closest and most brilliant contests in their experience. The winners are: first, Derrydale Captain, owned by Captain Richard Harmon and handled today by Ben Frazier. Second—"

He heard no more, for there was a pounding as of surf in his ears and his father and the captain were slapping him on the back and shouting. His mind was a spinning wheel of many colors that he thought would never stop.

It seemed a long time later that the captain was saying, "I've something to tell you. I'll make it short. It takes you to handle Derry. He's your dog. I'm giving him back to you, no strings attached. He won't work right for Bleecher or me or anyone else. I'm doing this because I want to, Ben."

The world was a calm and silent place now and he looked up at the captain, knowing at once what his answer had to be—as if it had been all prepared by some portion of his mind that had the gift of anticipation. "I can't do that, sir."

The captain didn't answer, but waited.

"Because of Derry. He—he's got to do what he's supposed to do. Win the National. He can do it. It wouldn't be right not to give him the chance to do that."

"You mean," the captain said slowly, "there's a sort of absolute justice involved?"

"I guess that's it. I can help Mr. Bleecher so Derry will work for him. Derry'll do what I want. And I want him to be champion."

"I see." The captain looked away and when he looked back his eyes were soft and moist as a spaniel's. "Only—the way you feel about Derry —I thought—"

"It's something I've got to work up to. To earn, I guess you'd say. And I will. I don't care how long it takes. I'm going to work and save for it."

The captain looked at him for a long time, then ran a big hand across his face.

"Well. Well. Anyway—you go get your father. We're having a victory dinner tonight at the house. And I'm going to see to it your mother comes up too."

He found his father and they went along to the car. His father walked slowly, his head down. Ben took hold of his arm. "I had an idea," he said. "About you and me and what to do with that money the captain paid for Derry. Maybe we could use it to start a little place of our own. We could work it on the side, to begin with. I could help with all the work and then maybe get a pup cheap from the captain and start raising dogs and—well, I thought something like that might be all right."

His father's shoulders bent forward a little and he did not lift his head. "That was no thought of mine," he said slowly. Then words came out with a sudden burst, as if a dam had broken. "You could use that money for schooling. You'd ought to have more than just eighth grade. You could go to high school in town—the money would buy clothes and books and I could make out here without you maybe, if I worked Sundays and a little extra evenings. I never wanted—I never wanted you should grow up ignorant like me."

Ben stopped short and faced his father with blazing eyes. "What a thing to say!" For the first time in his life he felt grown up, felt that he and his father were men together. "No man's ignorant that can farm the way you can. No man's ignorant that can train dogs right. But any man that don't know what he can do and has to go to high school to try to find out—that is awful ignorant!"

He stopped talking, suddenly conscious of his father's eyes. They were looking straight into his own with a warm, awakening understanding. "All right," his father said.

They walked on toward the car, keeping step, heads up, feet coming firmly and rhythmically down on the ground.

Part Four
FAMOUS DOGS OF
FAMOUS PEOPLE

The misery of keeping a dog, is his dying so
soon; but to be sure, if he lived for fifty
years, and then died, what would become of
me?

Sir Walter Scott

BAN ON BIRDS

The Spaniel, Beau, and His Reply

A poet chides his dog but lets him make an answer.

ON A SPANIEL, CALLED BEAU,
KILLING A YOUNG BIRD

A Spaniel, Beau, that fares like you,
    Well-fed, and at his ease,
Should wiser be, than to pursue
    Each trifle that he sees.

But you have kill'd a tiny bird,
    Which flew not till to-day,
Against my orders, whom you heard
    Forbidding you to prey.

Nor did you kill, that you might eat,
    And ease a doggish pain,
For him though chas'd with furious heat,
    You left where he was slain.

Nor was he of the thievish sort,
    Or one whom blood allures,
But innocent was all his sport,
    Whom you have torn for yours.

My dog! what remedy remains,
    Since, teach you all I can,
I see you, after all my pains,
    So much resemble man!

BEAU'S REPLY

Sir! when I flew to seize the bird,
    In spite of your command,

A louder voice than yours I heard,
    And harder to withstand:

You cried—Forbear!—but in my breast
    A mightier cried—Proceed!
'Twas nature, Sir, whose strong behest
    Impell'd me to the deed.

Yet much as nature I respect,
    I ventur'd once to break
(As you perhaps may recollect)
    Her precept for your sake;

And when your linnet, on a day,
    Passing his prison-door,
Had flutter'd all his strength away,
    And panting press'd the floor,

Well knowing him a sacred thing,
    Not destin'd to my tooth,
I only kiss'd his ruffled wing,
    And lick'd the feathers smooth.

Let my obedience then excuse
    My disobedience now,
Nor some reproof yourself refuse
    From your aggriev'd Bow-wow!

If killing birds be such a crime,
    (Which I can hardly see)
What think you, Sir, of killing Time
    With verse address'd to me?

CANINE CURSE

The Hound of the Baskervilles

A. CONAN DOYLE

A celebrated case of a famous character in fiction, Sherlock Holmes, concerned a "hound of hell," which had haunted generations of the Baskerville family. In the following chapter of the novel, Holmes and his companion, Watson, hear of apparitions of that "great, black beast, shaped like a hound." Holmes would finally unmask the clever criminal who made use of the legend for his ends.

"I HAVE in my pocket a manuscript," said Dr. James Mortimer.

"I observed it as you entered the room," said Holmes.

"It is an old manuscript."

"Early eighteenth century, unless it is a forgery."

"How can you say that, sir?"

"You have presented an inch or two of it to my examination all the time that you have been talking. It would be a poor expert who could not give the date of a document within a decade or so. You may possibly have read my little monograph upon the subject. I put that at 1730."

"The exact date is 1742." Dr. Mortimer drew it from his breast-pocket. "This family paper was committed to my care by Sir Charles Baskerville, whose sudden and tragic death some three months ago created so much excitement in Devonshire. I may say that I was his personal friend as well as his medical attendant. He was a strong-minded man, sir, shrewd, practical, and as unimaginative as I am myself. Yet he took this document very seriously, and his mind was prepared for just such an end as did eventually overtake him."

Holmes stretched out his hand for the manuscript and flattened it upon his knee.

"You will observe, Watson, the alternative use of the long *s* and the short. It is one of several indications which enabled me to fix the date."

I looked over his shoulder at the yellow paper and the faded script.

From *The Hound of the Baskervilles*, by Sir Arthur Conan Doyle. Reprinted by permission of the Estate of Sir Arthur Conan Doyle and John Murray, Ltd.

At the head was written: "Baskerville Hall," and below, in large, scrawling figures: "1742."

"It appears to be a statement of some sort."

"Yes, it is a statement of a certain legend which runs in the Baskerville family."

"But I understand that it is something more modern and practical upon which you wish to consult me?"

"Most modern. A most practical, pressing matter, which must be decided within twenty-four hours. But the manuscript is short and is intimately connected with the affair. With your permission I will read it to you."

Holmes leaned back in his chair, placed his finger-tips together, and closed his eyes, with an air of resignation. Dr. Mortimer turned the manuscript to the light and read in a high, crackling voice the following curious, old-world narrative:

Of the origin of the Hound of the Baskervilles there have been many statements, yet as I come in a direct line from Hugo Baskerville, and as I had the story from my father, who also had it from his, I have set it down with all belief that it occurred even as is here set forth. And I would have you believe, my sons, that the same Justice which punishes sin may also most graciously forgive it, and that no ban is so heavy but that by prayer and repentance it may be removed. Learn then from this story not to fear the fruits of the past, but rather to be circumspect in the future, that those foul passions whereby our family has suffered so grievously may not again be loosed to our undoing.

Know then that in the time of the Great Rebellion (the history of which by the learned Lord Clarendon I most earnestly commend to your attention) this Manor of Baskerville was held by Hugo of that name, nor can it be gainsaid that he was a most wild, profane, and godless man. This, in truth, his neighbours might have pardoned, seeing that saints have never flourished in those parts, but there was in him a certain wanton and cruel humour which made his name a byword through the West. It chanced that this Hugo came to love (if, indeed, so dark a passion may be known under so bright a name) the daughter of a yeoman who held lands near the Baskerville estate. But the young maiden, being discreet and of good repute, would ever avoid him, for she feared his evil name. So it came to pass that one Michaelmas this Hugo, with five or six of his idle and wicked companions, stole down upon the farm and carried off the maiden, her father and brothers being from home, as he well knew. When they had brought her to the Hall the maiden was placed in an upper chamber, while Hugo and his friends sat down to a long carouse, as was their nightly custom. Now, the poor lass upstairs was like to have her wits turned at the singing and shouting and terrible oaths which came up to her from below, for they say that the words used by Hugo Baskerville, when he was in wine, were such as might blast the man who said them. At last in the stress of her fear she did that which might have daunted the bravest or most active man, for by the aid of the growth of ivy which covered (and still covers) the south wall she came down from under the eaves, and so homeward across the moor, there being three leagues betwixt the Hall and her father's farm.

It chanced that some little time later Hugo left his guests to carry food and drink—with other worse things, perchance—to his captive, and so found the cage empty and the bird escaped. Then, as it would seem, he became as one that hath a devil, for, rushing down the stairs into the dining-hall, he sprang upon the great table, flagons and trenchers flying before him, and he cried aloud before all the company that he would that very night render his body and soul to the Powers of Evil if he might but overtake the wench. And while the revellers stood aghast at the fury of the man, one more wicked or, it may be, more drunken than the rest, cried out that they should put the hounds upon her. Whereat Hugo ran from the house, crying to his grooms that they should saddle his mare and unkennel the pack, and giving the hounds a kerchief of the maid's, he swung them to the line, and so off full cry in the moonlight over the moor.

Now, for some space the revellers stood agape, unable to understand all that had been done in such haste. But anon their bemused wits awoke to the nature of the deed which was like to be done upon the moorlands. Everything was now in an uproar, some calling for their pistols, some for their horses, and some for another flask of wine. But at length some sense came back to their crazed minds, and the whole of them, thirteen in number, took horse and started in pursuit. The moon shone clear above them, and they rode swiftly abreast, taking that course which the maid must needs have taken if she were to reach her own home.

They had gone a mile or two when they passed one of the night shepherds upon the moorlands, and they cried to him to know if he had seen the hunt. And the man, as the story goes, was so crazed with fear that he could scarce speak, but at last he said that he had indeed seen the unhappy maiden, with the hounds upon her track. "But I have seen more than that," said he, "for Hugo Baskerville passed me upon his black mare, and there ran mute behind him such a hound of hell as God forbid should ever be at my heels." So the drunken squires cursed the shepherd and rode onward. But soon their skins turned cold, for there came a galloping across the moor, and the black mare, dabbled with white froth, went past with trailing bridle and empty saddle. Then the revellers rode close together, for a great fear was on them, but they still followed over the moor, though each, had he been alone, would have been right glad to have turned his horse's head. Riding slowly in this fashion they came at last upon the hounds. These, though known for their valour and their breed, were whimpering in a cluster at the head of a deep dip or goyal, as we call it, upon the moor, some slinking away and some, with starting hackles and staring eyes, gazing down the narrow valley before them.

The company had come to a halt, more sober men, as you may guess, than when they started. The most of them would by no means advance, but three of them, the boldest, or it may be the most drunken, rode forward down the goyal. Now, it opened into a broad space in which stood two of those great stones, still to be seen there, which were set by certain forgotten peoples in the days of old. The moon was shining bright upon the clearing, and there in the centre lay the unhappy maid where she had fallen, dead of fear and of fatigue. But it was not the sight of her body, nor yet was it that of the body of Hugo Baskerville lying near her, which raised the hair upon the heads of these three dare-devil roysterers, but it was that, standing over Hugo, and plucking at his throat, there stood a foul thing, a great, black beast, shaped like a hound, yet larger than any hound that ever mortal eye has rested upon. And even as they looked the thing tore the throat out of Hugo Baskerville, on which, as it turned its blazing eyes and dripping jaws upon them, the three shrieked with fear and rode for dear life, still screaming, across the moor. One, it is said, died that very night of what he had seen, and the other twain were but broken men for the rest of their days.

Such is the tale, my sons, of the coming of the hound which is said to have plagued the family so sorely ever since. If I have set it down it is because that which is clearly known hath less terror than that which is but hinted at and guessed. Nor can it be denied that many of the family have been unhappy in their deaths, which have been sudden, bloody, and mysterious. Yet may we shelter ourselves in the infinite goodness of Providence, which would not forever punish the innocent beyond that third or fourth generation which is threatened in Holy Writ. To that Providence, my sons, I hereby commend you, and I counsel you by way of caution to forbear from crossing the moor in those dark hours when the powers of evil are exalted.

[This from Hugo Baskerville to his sons Rodger and John, with instructions that they say nothing thereof to their sister Elizabeth.]

When Dr. Mortimer had finished reading this singular narrative he pushed his spectacles up on his forehead and stared across at Mr. Sherlock Holmes. The latter yawned and tossed the end of his cigarette into the fire.

"Well?" said he.

"Do you not find it interesting?"

"To a collector of fairy tales."

Dr. Mortimer drew a folded newspaper out of his pocket.

"Now, Mr. Holmes, we will give you something a little more recent. This is the *Devon County Chronicle* of May 14th of this year. It is a short account of the facts elicited at the death of Sir Charles Baskerville which occurred a few days before that date."

My friend leaned a little forward and his expression became intent. Our visitor readjusted his glasses and began:

The recent sudden death of Sir Charles Baskerville, whose name has been mentioned as the probable Liberal candidate for Mid-Devon at the next election, has cast a gloom over the county. Though Sir Charles had resided at Baskerville Hall for a comparatively short period his amiability of character and extreme generosity had won the affection and respect of all who had been brought into contact with him. In these days of *nouveaux riches* it is refreshing to find a case where the scion of an old county family which has fallen upon evil days is able to make his own fortune and to bring it back with him to restore the fallen grandeur of his line. Sir Charles, as is well known, made large sums of money in South African speculation. More wise than those who go on until the wheel turns against them, he realized his gains and returned to England with them. It is only two years since he took up his residence at Baskerville Hall, and it is common talk how large were those schemes of reconstruction and improvement which have been interrupted by his death. Being himself childless, it was his openly expressed desire that the whole countryside should, within his own lifetime, profit by his good fortune, and many will have personal reasons for bewailing his untimely end. His generous donations to local and county charities have been frequently chronicled in these columns.

The circumstances connected with the death of Sir Charles cannot be said to have been entirely cleared up by the inquest, but at least enough has been done to dispose of those rumours to which local superstition has given rise. There is no reason whatever to suspect foul play, or to imagine that death could be from any but natural causes. Sir Charles was a widower, and a man who may be said to have been in some ways of an eccentric habit of mind. In spite of his considerable wealth he was simple in his personal tastes, and his indoor servants at Baskerville Hall consisted of a married couple named Barrymore, the husband acting as butler and the wife as housekeeper. Their evidence, corroborated by that of several friends, tends to show that Sir Charles's health has for some time been impaired, and points especially to some affection of the heart, manifesting itself in changes of colour, breathlessness, and acute attacks of nervous depression. Dr. James Mortimer, the friend and medical attendant of the deceased, has given evidence to the same effect.

The facts of the case are simple. Sir Charles Baskerville was in the habit every night before going to bed of walking down the famous yew alley of Baskerville Hall. The evidence of the Barrymores shows that this had been his custom. On the fourth of May Sir Charles had declared his intention of starting next day for London, and had ordered Barrymore to prepare his luggage. That night he went out as usual for his nocturnal walk, in the course of which he was in the habit of smoking a cigar. He never returned. At twelve o'clock Barrymore, finding the hall door still open, became alarmed, and, lighting a lantern, went in search of his master. The day had been wet, and Sir Charles's footmarks were easily traced down the alley. Halfway down this walk there is a gate which leads out on to the moor. There were indications that Sir Charles had stood for some little time here. He then proceeded down the alley, and it was at the far end of it that his body was discovered. One fact which has not been explained is the statement of Barrymore that his master's footprints altered their character from the time that he passed the moor-gate, and that he appeared from thence onward to have been walking upon his toes. One Murphy, a gipsy horse-dealer, was on the moor at no great distance at the time, but he appears by his own confession to have been the worse for drink. He declares that he heard cries but is unable to state from what direction they came. No signs of violence were to be discovered upon Sir Charles's person, and though the doctor's evidence pointed to an almost incredible facial distortion—so great that Dr. Mortimer refused at first to believe that it was indeed his friend and patient who lay before him —it was explained that that is a symptom which is not unusual in cases of dyspnœa and death from cardiac exhaustion. This explanation was borne out by the post-mortem examination, which showed long-standing organic disease, and the coroner's jury returned a verdict in accordance with the medical evidence. It is well that this is so, for it is obviously of the utmost importance that Sir Charles's heir should settle at the Hall and continue the good work which has been so sadly interrupted. Had the prosaic finding of the coroner not finally put an end to the romantic stories which have been whispered in connection with the affair, it might have been difficult to find a tenant for Baskerville Hall. It is understood that the next of kin is Mr. Henry Baskerville, if he be still alive, the son of Sir Charles Baskerville's younger brother. The young man when last heard of was in America, and inquiries are being instituted with a view to informing him of his good fortune.

Dr. Mortimer refolded his paper and replaced it in his pocket.

"Those are the public facts, Mr. Holmes, in connection with the death of Sir Charles Baskerville."

"I must thank you," said Sherlock Holmes, "for calling my attention to a case which certainly presents some features of interest. I had observed some newspaper comment at the time, but I was exceedingly preoccupied by that little affair of the Vatican cameos, and in my anxiety to oblige the Pope I lost touch with several interesting English cases. This article, you say, contains all the public facts?"

"It does."

"Then let me have the private ones." He leaned back, put his fingertips together, and assumed his most impassive and judicial expression.

"In doing so," said Dr. Mortimer, who had begun to show signs of some strong emotion, "I am telling that which I have not confided to anyone. My motive for withholding it from the coroner's inquiry is that a man of science shrinks from placing himself in the public position of seeming to indorse a popular superstition. I had the further motive that Baskerville Hall, as the paper says, would certainly remain untenanted if anything were done to increase its already rather grim reputation. For both these reasons I thought that I was justified in telling rather less than I knew, since no practical good could result from it, but with you there is no reason why I should not be perfectly frank.

"The moor is very sparsely inhabited, and those who live near each other are thrown very much together. For this reason I saw a good deal of Sir Charles Baskerville. With the exception of Mr. Frankland, of Lafter Hall, and Mr. Stapleton, the naturalist, there are no other men of education within many miles. Sir Charles was a retiring man, but the chance of his illness brought us together, and a community of interests in science kept us so. He had brought back much scientific information from South Africa, and many a charming evening we have spent together discussing the comparative anatomy of the Bushman and the Hottentot.

"Within the last few months it became increasingly plain to me that Sir Charles's nervous system was strained to the breaking point. He had taken this legend which I have read you exceedingly to heart—so much so that, although he would walk in his own grounds, nothing would induce him to go out upon the moor at night. Incredible as it may appear to you, Mr. Holmes, he was honestly convinced that a dreadful fate overhung his family, and certainly the records which he was able to give of his ancestors were not encouraging. The idea of some ghastly presence constantly haunted him, and on more than one occasion he has asked me whether I had on my medical journeys at night ever seen any strange creature or heard the baying of a hound. The latter question he put to me several times, and always with a voice which vibrated with excitement.

"I can well remember driving up to his house in the evening, some three weeks before the fatal event. He chanced to be at his hall door. I had descended from my gig and was standing in front of him, when I saw his eyes fix themselves over my shoulder and stare past me with an expression of the most dreadful horror. I whisked round and had just time to catch a glimpse of something which I took to be a large black calf passing at the head of the drive. So excited and alarmed was he that I was compelled to go down to the spot where the animal had been and look around for it. It was gone, however, and the incident appeared to make the worst impression upon his mind. I stayed with him all the evening, and it was on that occasion, to explain the emotion which he had shown, that he confided to my keeping that narrative which I read to you when first I came. I mention this small episode because it assumes some importance in view of the tragedy which followed, but I was convinced at the time that the matter was entirely trivial and that his excitement had no justification.

"It was at my advice that Sir Charles was about to go to London. His heart was, I knew, affected, and the constant anxiety in which he lived, however chimerical the cause of it might be, was evidently having a serious effect upon his health. I thought that a few months among the distractions of town would send him back a new man. Mr. Stapleton, a mutual friend who was much concerned at his state of health, was of the same opinion. At the last instant came this terrible catastrophe.

"On the night of Sir Charles's death Barrymore the butler, who made the discovery, sent Perkins the groom on horseback to me, and as I was sitting up late I was able to reach Baskerville Hall within an hour of the event. I checked and corroborated all the facts which were mentioned at the inquest. I followed the footsteps down the yew alley, I saw the spot at the moor-gate where he seemed to have waited, I remarked the change in the shape of the prints after that point, I noted that there were no other footsteps save those of Barrymore on the soft gravel, and finally I carefully examined the body, which had not been touched until my arrival. Sir Charles lay on his face, his arms out, his fingers dug into the ground, and his features convulsed with some strong emotion to such an extent that I could hardly have sworn to his identity. There was certainly no physical injury of any kind. But one false statement was made by Barrymore at the inquest. He said that there were no traces upon the ground round the body. He did not observe any. But I did— some little distance off, but fresh and clear."

"Footprints?"

"Footprints."

"A man's or a woman's?"

Dr. Mortimer looked strangely at us for an instant, and his voice sank almost to a whisper as he answered:

"Mr. Holmes, they were the footprints of a gigantic hound!"

AN AUTHOR'S PETS

Our Dogs

The bloodhounds of *Uncle Tom's Cabin*—the fierce
creatures which pursued Eliza across the ice—always
come to mind when one thinks of dogs in the writings
of Mrs. Stowe. Far less known are her moving true
stories of household pets in "Our Dogs," selections
from which follow.

WE who live in Cunopolis are a dog-loving family. We have a warm
side towards everything that goes upon four paws, and the consequence
has been that, taking things first and last, we have been always kept in
confusion and under the paw, so to speak, of some honest four-footed
tyrant, who would go beyond his privilege and overrun the whole house.
Years ago this began, when our household consisted of a papa, a
mamma, and three or four noisy boys and girls, and a kind Miss Anna
who acted as a second mamma to the whole. There was also one more
of our number, the youngest, dear little bright-eyed Charley, who was
king over us all, and rode in a wicker wagon for a chariot, and had a nice
little nurse devoted to him; and it was through him that our first dog
came.

One day Charley's nurse took him quite a way to a neighbor's house
to spend the afternoon; and, he being well amused, they stayed till after
nightfall. The kind old lady of the mansion was concerned that the little
prince in his little coach, with his little maid, had to travel so far in the
twilight shadows, and so she called a big dog named Carlo, and gave the
establishment into his charge.

Carlo was a great, tawny-yellow mastiff, as big as a calf, with great,
clear, honest eyes, and stiff, wiry hair; and the good lady called him to
the side of the little wagon, and said, "Now, Carlo, you must take good
care of Charley, and you mustn't let anything hurt him."

Carlo wagged his tail in promise of protection, and away he trotted,
home with the wicker wagon; and when he arrived, he was received with
so much applause by four little folks, who dearly loved the very sight of
a dog, he was so stroked and petted and caressed, that he concluded that
he liked the place better than the home he came from, where were only
very grave elderly people. He tarried all night, and slept at the foot of

the boys' bed, who could hardly go to sleep for the things they found to say to him, and who were awake ever so early in the morning, stroking his rough, tawny back, and hugging him.

At his own home Carlo had a kennel all to himself, where he was expected to live quite alone, and do duty by watching and guarding the place. Nobody petted him, or stroked his rough hide, or said, "Poor dog!" to him, and so it appears he had a feeling that he was not appreciated, and liked our warm-hearted little folks, who told him stories, gave him half of their own supper, and took him to bed with them sociably. Carlo was a dog that had a mind of his own, though he couldn't say much about it, and in his dog fashion proclaimed his likes and dislikes quite as strongly as if he could speak. When the time came for taking him home, he growled and showed his teeth dangerously at the man who was sent for him, and it was necessary to drag him back by force, and tie him into his kennel. However, he soon settled that matter by gnawing the rope in two and padding down again and appearing among his little friends, quite to their delight. Two or three times was he taken back and tied or chained; but he howled so dismally, and snapped at people in such a misanthropic manner, that finally the kind old lady thought it better to have no dog at all than a dog soured by blighted affection. So she loosed his rope, and said, "There, Carlo, go and stay where you like"; and so Carlo came to us, and a joy and delight was he to all in the house. He loved one and all; but he declared himself as more than all the slave and property of our Prince Charley. He would lie on the floor as still as a door-mat, and let him pull his hair, and roll over him, and examine his eyes with his little fat fingers; and Carlo submitted to all these personal freedoms with as good an understanding as papa himself. When Charley slept, Carlo stretched himself along under the crib; rising now and then, and standing with his broad breast on a level with the slats of the crib, he would look down upon him with an air of grave protection. He also took a great fancy to papa, and would sometimes pat with tiptoe care into his study, and sit quietly down by him when he was busy over his Greek or Latin books, waiting for a word or two of praise or encouragement. If none came, he would lay his rough horny paw on his knee, and look in his face with such an honest, imploring expression, that the professor was forced to break off to say, "Why, Carlo, you poor, good, honest fellow,—did he want to be talked to?—so he did. Well, he shall be talked to;—he's a nice, good dog";—and during all these praises Carlo's transports and the thumps of his rough tail are not to be described.

He had great, honest, yellowish-brown eyes,—not remarkable for their beauty, but which used to look as if he longed to speak, and he seemed to have a yearning for praise and love and caresses that even all our attentions could scarcely satisfy. His master would say to him sometimes, "Carlo, you poor, good, homely dog,—how loving you are!"

Carlo was a full-blooded mastiff, and his beauty, if he had any, consisted in his having all the good points of his race. He was a dog of blood, come of real old mastiff lineage; his stiff, wiry hair, his big, rough paws, and great brawny chest, were all made for strength rather than beauty; but for all that he was a dog of tender sentiments. Yet, if any one intruded on his rights and dignities, Carlo showed that he had hot blood in him; his lips would go back, and show a glistening row of ivories that one would not like to encounter, and if any trenched on his privileges, he would give a deep warning growl,—as much as to say, "I am your slave for love, but you must treat me well, or I shall be dangerous." A blow he would not bear from any one: the fire would flash from his great yellow eyes, and he would snap like a rifle;—yet he would let his own Prince Charley pound on his ribs with both baby fists, and pull his tail till he yelped, without even a show of resistance.

At last came a time when the merry voice of little Charley was heard no more, and his little feet no more pattered through the halls; he lay pale and silent in his little crib, with his dear life ebbing away, and no one knew how to stop its going. Poor old Carlo lay under the crib when they would let him, sometimes rising up to look in with an earnest, sorrowful face; and sometimes he would stretch himself out in the entry before the door of little Charley's room, watching with his great open eyes lest the thief should come in the night to steal away our treasure.

But one morning when the children woke, one little soul had gone in the night,—gone upward to the angels; and then the cold, pale little form that used to be the life of the house was laid away tenderly in the yard of a neighboring church.

Poor old Carlo would pit-pat silently about the house in those days of grief, looking first into one face and then another, but no one could tell him where his gay little master had gone. The other children had hid the baby-wagon away in the lumber-room lest their mamma should see it; and so passed a week or two, and Carlo saw no trace of Charley about the house. But then a lady in the neighborhood, who had a sick baby, sent to borrow the wicker wagon, and it was taken from its hiding-place to go to her. Carlo came to the door just as it was being drawn out of the gate into the street. Immediately he sprung, cleared the fence with a great bound, and ran after it. He overtook it, and poked his nose between the curtains,—there was no one there. Immediately he turned away, and padded dejectedly home. What words could have spoken plainer of love and memory than this one action?

Carlo lived with us a year after this, when a time came for the whole family hive to be taken up and moved away from the flowery banks of the Ohio to the piny shores of Maine. All our household goods were being uprooted, disordered, packed, and sold; and the question daily arose, "What shall we do with Carlo?" There was hard begging on the part of the boys that he might go with them, and one even volunteered to travel all the way in baggage cars to keep Carlo company. But papa said no, and so it was decided to send Carlo up the river to the home of a very genial lady who had visited in our family, and who appreciated his parts, and offered him a home in hers.

The matter was anxiously talked over one day in the family circle while Carlo lay under the table, and it was agreed that papa and Willie should take him to the steamboat landing the next morning. But the next morning Mr. Carlo was nowhere to be found. In vain was he called, from garret to cellar; nor was it till papa and Willie had gone to the city that he came out of his hiding-place. For two or three days it was impossible to catch him, but after a while his suspicions were laid, and we learned not to speak out our plans in his presence, and so the transfer at last was prosperously effected.

We heard from him once in his new home, as being a highly appreciated member of society, and adorning his new situation with all sorts of dog virtues, while we wended our ways to the coast of Maine. But our hearts were sore for want of him; the family circle seemed incomplete, until a new favorite appeared to take his place.

Then came a long interval in which we had no dog. Our hearts were too sore to want another. His collar, tied with black crape, hung under a pretty engraving of Landseer's, called "My Dog," which we used to fancy to be an exact resemblance of our pet.

The children were some of them grown up and gone to school, or scattered about the world. If ever the question of another dog was agitated, papa cut it short with, "I won't have another; I won't be made to feel again as I did about Rover." But somehow Mr. Charley the younger got his eye on a promising litter of puppies, and at last he begged papa into consenting that he might have one of them.

It was a little black mongrel, of no particular race or breed,—a mere common cur, without any pretensions to family, but the best-natured, jolliest little low-bred pup that ever boy had for a playmate. To be sure, he had the usual puppy sins; he would run away with papa's slippers and boots and stockings; he would be under everybody's feet, at the most inconvenient moment; he chewed up a hearth-broom or two, and pulled one of Charley's caps to pieces in the night, with an industry worthy of a better cause;—still, because he was dear to Charley, papa and mamma winked very hard at his transgressions.

The name of this little black individual was Stromion,—a name taken from a German fairy tale, which the Professor was very fond of reading in the domestic circle; and Stromion, by dint of much patience, much feeding, and very indulgent treatment, grew up into a very fat, common-looking, black cur dog, not very prepossessing in appearance and manners, but possessed of the very best heart in the world, and most inconceivably affectionate and good-natured. Sometimes some of the older members of the family would trouble Charley's enjoyment in his playfellow by suggesting that he was no blood dog, and that he belonged to no particular dog family that could be named. Papa comforted him by the assurance that Stromion did belong to a very old and respectable breed,—that he was a *mongrel*; and Charley after that valued him excessively under this head; and if any one tauntingly remarked that Stromion was only a cur, he would flame up in his defense,—"He isn't a cur, he's a mongrel," introducing him to strangers with the addition to all his other virtues, that he was a "pure mongrel,—papa says so."

The edict against dogs in the family having once been broken down, Master Will proceeded to gratify his own impulses, and soon led home to the family circle an enormous old black Newfoundland, of pure breed, which had been presented him by a man who was leaving the place. Prince was in the decline of his days, but a fine, majestic old fellow. He had a sagacity and capacity of personal affection which were uncommon. Many dogs will change from master to master without the least discomposure. A good bone will compensate for any loss of the heart, and make a new friend seem quite as good as an old one. But Prince had his affections quite as distinctly as a human being, and we learned this to our sorrow when he had to be weaned from his old master under our roof. His howls and lamentations were so dismal and protracted, that the house could not contain him; we were obliged to put him into an outhouse to compose his mind, and we still have a vivid image of him sitting, the picture of despair, over an untasted mutton shank, with his nose in the air, and the most dismal howls proceeding from his mouth. Time, the comforter, however, assuaged his grief, and he came at last to transfer all his stores of affection to Will, and to consider himself once more as a dog with a master.

Prince used to inhabit his young master's apartment, from the window of which he would howl dismally when Will left him to go to the academy near by, and yelp triumphant welcomes when he saw him returning. He was really and passionately fond of music, and, though strictly forbidden the parlor, would push and elbow his way there with dogged determination when there was playing or singing. Any one who should have seen Prince's air when he had a point to carry, would understand why quiet obstinacy is called doggedness.

The female members of the family, seeing that two dogs had gained admission to the circle, had cast their eyes admiringly on a charming little Italian greyhound, that was living in doleful captivity at a dog-fancier's in Boston, and resolved to set him free and have him for their own. Accordingly they returned one day in triumph, with him in their arms,—a fair, delicate creature, white as snow, except one mouse-colored ear. He was received with enthusiasm, and christened Giglio; the honors of his first bath and toilette were performed by Mesdemoiselles the young ladies on their knees, as if he had been in reality young Prince Giglio from fairyland.

Of all beautiful shapes in dog form, never was there one more perfect than this. His hair shone like spun glass, and his skin was as fine and pink as that of a baby; his paws and ears were translucent like fine china, and he had great, soft, tremulous dark eyes; his every movement seemed more graceful than the last. Whether running or leaping, or sitting in graceful attitudes on the parlor table among the ladies' embroidery-frames, with a great rose-colored bow under his throat, he was alike a thing of beauty, and his beauty alone won all hearts to him.

When the papa first learned that a third dog had been introduced into the household, his patience gave way. The thing was getting desperate; we were being overrun with dogs; our house was no more a house, but a kennel; it ought to be called Cunopolis,—a city of dogs; he could not and would not have it so; but papa, like most other indulgent old gentlemen, was soon reconciled to the children's pets. In fact, Giglio was found cowering under the bedclothes at the Professor's feet not two mornings after his arrival, and the good gentleman descended with him in his arms to breakfast, talking to him in the most devoted manner:—
"Poor little Giglio, was he cold last night? and did he want to get into

papa's bed? he should be brought down stairs, that he should";—all which, addressed to a young rascal whose sinews were all like steel, and who could have jumped from the top stair to the bottom like a feather, was sufficiently amusing.

Giglio's singular beauty and grace were his only merits; he had no love nor power of loving; he liked to be petted and kept warm, but it mattered nothing to him who did it. He was as ready to turn off with a stranger as with his very best friend,—would follow any whistle or any caller,—was, in fact, such a gay rover, that we came very near losing him many times; and more than once he was brought back from the Boston cars, on board which he had followed a stranger. He also had, we grieve to say, very careless habits; and after being washed white as snow, and adorned with choice rose-colored ribbons, would be brought back soiled and ill-smelling from a neighbor's livery stable, where he had been indulging in low society. For all that, he was very lordly and aristocratic in his airs with poor Stromion, who was a dog with a good, loving heart, if he was black and homely. Stromion admired Giglio with the most evident devotion; he would always get up to give him the warm corner, and would always sit humbly in the distance and gaze on him with most longing admiration,—for all of which my fine gentleman rewarded him only with an occasional snarl or a nip, as he went by him. Sometimes Giglio would condescend to have a romp with Stromion for the sake of passing the time, and then Stromion would be perfectly delighted, and frisk and roll his clumsy body over the carpet with his graceful antagonist, all whose motions were a study for an artist. When Giglio was tired of play, he would give Stromion a nip that would send him yelping from the field; and then he would tick, tick gracefully away to some embroidered ottoman forbidden to all but himself, where he would sit graceful and classical as some Etruscan vase, and look down superior on the humble companion who looked up to him with respectful admiration.

Giglio knew his own good points, and was possessed with the very spirit of a coquette. He would sometimes obstinately refuse the caresses and offered lap of his mistresses, and seek to ingratiate himself with some stolid theological visitor, for no other earthly purpose that we could see than that he was determined to make himself the object of attention. We have seen him persist in jumping time and again on the hard bony knees of some man who hated dogs and did not mean to notice him, until he won attention and caresses, when immediately he would spring down and tick away perfectly contented. He assumed lofty, fine-gentleman airs with Prince also, for which sometimes he got his reward,—for Prince, the old, remembered that he was a dog of blood, and would not take any nonsense from him.

Like many old dogs, Prince had a very powerful doggy smell, which was a great personal objection to him, and Giglio was always in a civil way making reflections upon this weak point. Prince was fond of indulging himself with an afternoon nap on the door-mat, and sometimes when he rose from his repose, Giglio would spring gracefully from the table where he had been overlooking him, and, picking his way daintily to the mat, would snuff at it, with his long, thin nose, with an air of extreme disgust. It was evidently a dog insult done according to the politest modes of refined society, and said as plain as words could say,—"My dear sir, excuse me, but can you tell what makes this peculiar smell where you have been lying?" At any rate, Prince understood the sarcasm, for a deep angry growl and a sharp nip would now and then teach my fine gentleman to mind his own business.

Giglio's lot at last was to travel in foreign lands, for his young mistresses, being sent to school in Paris, took him with them to finish his education and acquire foreign graces. He was smuggled on board the *Fulton*, and placed in an upper berth, well wrapped in a blanket; and the last we saw of him was his long, thin, Italian nose, and dark, tremulous eyes looking wistfully at us from the folds of the flannel in which he shivered. Sensitiveness to cold was one of his great peculiarities. In winter he wore little blankets, which his fond mistresses made with anxious care, and on which his initials were embroidered with their own hands. In the winter weather on Zion Hill he was often severely put to it to gratify his love of roving in the cold snows; he would hold up first one leg and then the other, and contrive to get along on three, so as to save himself as much as possible; and more than once he caught severe colds, requiring careful nursing and medical treatment to bring him round again.

The *Fulton* sailed early in March. It was chilly, stormy weather, so that the passengers all suffered somewhat with cold, and Master Giglio was glad to lie rolled in his blanket, looking like a sea-sick gentleman. The captain very generously allowed him a free passage, and in pleasant weather he used to promenade the deck, where his beauty won for him caresses and attentions innumerable. The stewards and cooks always had choice morsels for him, and fed him to such a degree as would have spoiled any other dog's figure; but his could not be spoiled. All the ladies vied with each other in seeking his good graces, and after dinner he pattered from one to another, to be fed with sweet things and confectionery, and hear his own praises, like a gay buck of fashion as he was.

Landed in Paris, he met a warm reception at the pension of Madame B——; but ambition filled his breast. He was in the great, gay city of Paris, the place where a handsome dog has but to appear to make his fortune, and so Giglio resolved to seek for himself a more brilliant destiny.

One day, when he was being led to take the air in the court, he slipped his leash, sped through the gate, and away down the street like the wind.

It was idle to attempt to follow him; he was gone like a bird in the air, and left the hearts of his young mistresses quite desolate.

Some months after, as they were one evening eating ices in the Champs Elysées, a splendid carriage drove up, from which descended a liveried servant, with a dog in his arms. It was Giglio, the faithless Giglio, with his one mouse-colored ear, that marked him from all other dogs! He had evidently accomplished his destiny, and become the darling of rank and fashion, rode in an elegant carriage, and had a servant in livery devoted to him. Of course he did not pretend to notice his former friends. The footman, who had come out apparently to give him an airing, led him up and down close by where they were sitting, and bestowed on him the most devoted attentions. Of course there was no use in trying to reclaim him, and so they took their last look of the fair inconstant, and left him to his brilliant destiny. And thus ends the history of Prince Giglio.

Well, after the departure of Prince Giglio there was a long cessation of the dog mania in our family. We concluded that we would have no more pets; for they made too much anxiety, and care, and trouble, and broke all our hearts by death or desertion.

At last, however, some neighbors of ours took unto themselves, to enliven their dwelling, a little saucy Scotch terrier, whose bright eyes and wicked tricks so wrought upon the heart of one of our juvenile branches, that there was no rest in the camp without this addition to it. Nothing was so pretty, so bright, so knowing and cunning, as a "Scotch terrier," and a Scotch terrier we must have,—so said Miss Jenny, our youngest.

And so a bargain was struck by one of Jenny's friends with some of the knowing ones in Boston, and home she came, the happy possessor of a genuine article,—as wide-awake, impertinent, frisky, and wicked a little elf as ever was covered with a shock of rough tan-colored hair.

His mistress no sooner gazed on him, than she was inspired to give him a name suited to his peculiar character;—so he frisked into the front door announced as Wix, and soon made himself perfectly at home in the family circle, which he took, after his own fashion, by storm. He entered the house like a small whirlwind, dashed, the first thing, into the Professor's study, seized a slipper which was dangling rather uncertainly on one of his studious feet, and, wresting it off, raced triumphantly with it around the hall, barking distractedly every minute that he was not shaking and worrying his prize.

Great was the sensation. Grandma tottered with trembling steps to the door, and asked, with hesitating tones, what sort of a creature that might be; and being saluted with the jubilant proclamation, "Why, Grandma, it's my dog,—a real genuine Scotch terrier; he'll never grow any larger, and he's a perfect beauty! don't you think so?"—Grandma could only tremblingly reply, "Oh, there is not any danger of his going mad, is there? Is he generally so playful?"

Playful was certainly a mild term for the tempest of excitement in which master Wix flew round and round in giddy circles, springing over ottomans, diving under sofas, barking from beneath chairs, and resisting every effort to recapture the slipper with bristling hair and blazing eyes, as if the whole of his dog-life consisted in keeping his prize; till at length he caught a glimpse of pussy's tail,—at which, dropping the slipper, he precipitated himself after the flying meteor, tumbling, rolling, and scratching down the kitchen stairs, standing on his hind-legs barking distractedly at poor Tom, who had taken refuge in the sink, and sat with his tail magnified to the size of a small bolster.

This cat, the most reputable and steady individual of his species, the darling of the most respectable of cooks, had received the name of Thomas Henry, by which somewhat lengthy appellation he was generally designated in the family circle, as a mark of the respect which his serious and contemplative manner commonly excited. Thomas had but one trick of popularity. With much painstaking and care the cook had taught him the act of performing a somerset over our hands when held at a decent height from the floor; and for this one elegant accomplishment, added to great success in his calling of rat-catching, he was held in great consideration in the family, and had meandered his decorous way about the house, slept in the sun, and otherwise conducted himself with the innocent and tranquil freedom which became a family cat of correct habits and a good conscience.

The irruption of Wix into our establishment was like the bursting of a bomb at the feet of some respectable citizen going tranquilly to market. Thomas was a cat of courage, and rats of the largest size shrunk appalled at the very sight of his whiskers; but now he sat in the sink quite cowed, consulting with great, anxious, yellow eyes the throng of faces that followed Wix down the stairs, and watching anxiously the efforts Miss Jenny was making to subdue and quiet him.

"Wix, you naughty little rascal, you mustn't bark at Thomas Henry; be still!" Whereat Wix, understanding himself to be blamed, brought forth his trump card of accomplishments, which he always offered by way of pacification whenever he was scolded. He reared himself up on his hind-legs, hung his head languishingly on one side, lolled out his tongue, and made a series of supplicatory gestures with his fore-paws,—a trick which never failed to bring down the house in a storm of applause, and carry him out of any scrape with flying colors.

Poor Thomas Henry, from his desolate sink, saw his terrible rival carried off in Miss Jenny's arms amid the applauses of the whole circle, and had abundance of time to reflect on the unsubstantial nature of popularity. After that he grew dejected and misanthropic,—a real Cardinal Wolsey in furs,—for Wix was possessed with a perfect cat-hunting mania, and, when he was not employed in other mischief, was always ready for a bout with Thomas Henry.

It is true, he sometimes came back from these encounters with a scratched and bloody nose, for Thomas Henry was a cat of no mean claw, and would turn to bay at times; but generally he felt the exertion too much for his advanced years and quiet habits, and so for safety he passed much of his time in the sink, over the battlements of which he would leisurely survey the efforts of the enemy to get at him. The cook hinted strongly of the danger of rheumatism to her favorite from these damp quarters, but Wix at present was the reigning favorite, and it was vain to dispute his sway.

Next to Thomas Henry, Wix directed his principal efforts to teasing Grandmamma. Something or other about her black dress and quiet movements seemed to suggest to him suspicions. He viewed her as something to be narrowly watched; he would lie down under some chair or table, and watch her motions with his head on his forepaws as if he were watching at a rat-hole. She evidently was not a rat, he seemed to say to himself, but who knows what she may be; and he would wink at her with his great bright eyes, and, if she began to get up, would spring from his ambush and bark at her feet with frantic energy,—by which means he nearly threw her over two or three times.

His young mistress kept a rod, and put him through a severe course of discipline for these offenses; after which he grew more careful,—but still the unaccountable fascination seemed to continue; still he would lie in ambush, and, though forbidden to bark, would dart stealthily forward when he saw her preparing to rise, and be under her dress smelling in a suspicious manner at her heels. He would spring from his place at the fire, and rush to the staircase when he heard her leisurely step descending the stairs, and once or twice nearly overset her by being under her heels, bringing on himself a chastisement which he in vain sought to avert by the most vigorous deprecatory pawing.

Grandmamma's favorite evening employment was to sit sleeping in her chair, gradually bobbing her head lower and lower,—all which movements Wix would watch, giving a short snap, or a suppressed growl, at every bow. What he would have done if, as John Bunyan says, he had been allowed to have his "doggish way" with her, it is impossible to say. Once he succeeded in seizing the slipper from her foot as she sat napping, and a glorious race he had with it,—out at the front door, up the path to the Theological Seminary, and round and round the halls consecrated to better things, with all the glee of an imp. At another time he made a dart into her apartment, and seized a turkey-wing which the good old lady had used for a duster, and made such a regular forenoon's work of worrying, shaking, and teasing it, that every feather in it was utterly demolished.

In fact, there was about Wix something so elfish and impish, that there began to be shrewd suspicions that he must be somehow or other a descendant of the celebrated poodle of Faust, and that one need not be surprised some day to have him suddenly looming up into some uncanny shape, or entering into conversation, and uttering all sorts of improprieties unbefitting a theological professor's family.

He had a persistence in wicked ways that resisted the most energetic nurture and admonition of his young mistress. His combativeness was such, that a peaceable walk down the fashionable street of Zion Hill in his company became impossible; all was race and scurry, cackle and flutter, wherever he appeared,—hens and poultry flying, frightened cats mounting trees with magnified tails, dogs yelping and snarling, and children and cows running in every direction. No modest young lady could possibly walk out in company with such a son of confusion. Beside this, Wix had his own private inexplicable personal piques against different visitors in the family, and in the most unexpected moment would give a snap or a nip to the most unoffending person. His friends in the family circle dropped off. His ways were pronounced too bad, his conduct perfectly indefensible; his young mistress alone clung to him, and declared that her vigorous system of education would at last reform his eccentricities, and turn him out a tip-top dog. But when he would slyly leave home, and, after rolling and steeping himself in the ill-smelling deposits of the stable or drain, come home and spring with impudent ease into her lap, or put himself to sleep on her little white bed, the magic cords of affection gave out, and disgust began to succeed. It began to be remarked that this was a stable-dog, educated for the coach-boy and stable, and to be doubted whether it was worth while to endeavor to raise him to a lady's boudoir; and so at last, when the family removed from Zion Hill, he was taken back and disposed of at a somewhat reduced price.

Since then, as we are informed, he has risen to fame and honor. His name has even appeared in sporting gazettes as the most celebrated "ratter" in little Boston, and his mistress was solemnly assured by his present possessor that for "cat work" he was unequaled, and that he would not take fifty dollars for him. From all of which it appears that a dog which is only a torment and a nuisance in one sphere may be an eminent character in another.

BETTER THAN SUNLIGHT
To Flush, My Dog

ELIZABETH BARRETT BROWNING

"The Flushes have their laurels as well as the Caesars —the chief difference (at least the very head and front of it) consisting, perhaps, in the bald head of the latter under the crown."

So wrote Elizabeth Barrett of her endearing little brown-and-white-breasted spaniel. Flush seldom left his mistress, often an invalid confined to her bed. "He loves me better than the sunlight without," she declared. When poet Robert Browning came courting, Flush jealously bit him. (Finally he became reconciled to their marriage.) Once Flush's mistress and her maid invaded a tough quarter of London and paid ransom to rescue the pet from dog stealers. Years after Flush's death he lived again when a spaniel with his marking played his part in *The Barretts of Wimpole Street.*

Loving friend, the gift of one
Who her own true faith hath run,
　　Through thy lower nature;
Be my benediction said
With my hand upon thy head,
　　Gentle fellow-creature!

Like a lady's ringlets brown,
Flow thine silken ears adown
　　Either side demurely
Of thy silver-suited breast
Shining out from all the rest
　　Of thy body purely.

Darkly brown thy body is,
Till the sunshine striking this
　　Alchemise its dullness;
When the sleek curls manifold
Flash all over into gold,
　　With a burnished fulness.

Underneath my stroking hand,
Startled eyes of hazel bland
    Kindling, growing larger,
Up thou leapest with a spring,
Full of prank and curveting,
    Leaping like a charger.

Leap! thy broad tail waves a light;
Leap! thy slender feet are bright,
    Canopied in fringes.
Leap—those tasselled ears of thine
Flicker strangely, fair and fine,
    Down their golden inches.

Yet, my pretty, sportive friend,
Little is't to such an end
    That I praise thy rareness!
Other dogs may be thy peers
Haply in those drooping ears,
    And this glossy fairness.

But of *thee* it shall be said,
This dog watched beside a bed
    Day and night unweary,—
Watched within a curtained room,
Where no sunbeam brake the gloom
    Round the sick and dreary.

Roses gathered for a vase,
In that chamber died apace,
    Beam and breeze resigning—
This dog only, waited on,
Knowing that when light is gone,
    Love remains for shining.

Other dogs in thymy dew
Tracked the hares and followed through
    Sunny moor or meadow—
This dog only, crept and crept
Next a languid cheek that slept,
    Sharing in the shadow.

Other dogs of loyal cheer
Bounded at the whistle clear,
    Up the woodside hying—

This dog only, watched in reach
Of a faintly uttered speech,
　　Or a louder sighing.

And if one or two quick tears
Dropped upon his glossy ears,
　　Or a sigh came double,—
Up he sprang in eager haste,
Fawning, fondling, breathing fast,
　　In a tender trouble.

And this dog was satisfied
If a pale thin hand would glide
　　Down his dewlaps sloping,—
Which he pushed his nose within,
After,—platforming his chin
　　On the palm left open.

This dog, if a friendly voice
Called him now to blither choice
　　Than such a chamber-keeping,
'Come out!' praying from the door,—
Presseth backward as before,
　　Up against me leaping.

Therefore to this dog will I,
Tenderly not scornfully,
　　Render praise and favor:
With my hand upon his head,
Is my benediction said,
　　Therefore, and forever.

And because he loves me so,
Better than his kind will do
　　Often, man or woman,
Give I back more love again
Than dogs often take of men,
　　Leaning from my Human.

Blessings on thee, dog of mine,
Pretty collars make thee fine,
　　Sugared milk make fat thee!
Pleasures wag on in thy tail—
Hands of gentle motion fail
　　Nevermore, to pat thee!

Downy pillow take thy head,
Silken coverlid bestead,
   Sunshine help thy sleeping!
No fly's buzzing wake thee up—
No man break thy purple cup,
   Set for drinking deep in.

Whiskered cats arointed flee—
Sturdy stoppers keep from thee
   Cologne distillations;
Nuts lie in thy path for stones,
And thy feast-day macaroons
   Turn to daily rations!

Mock I thee in writing weal?—
Tears are in my eyes to feel
   Though art made so straightly.
Blessing needs must straighten too,—
Little canst thou joy or do,
   Thou who lovest *greatly*.

Yet be blessed to the height
Of all good and all delight
   Pervious to thy nature.
Only *loved* beyond that line,
With a love that answers thine,
   Loving fellow-creature!

DIGNITY AND IMPUDENCE

Landseer's Dogs and Their Stories

SARAH TYTLER

To be painted by the celebrated English artist, Sir
Edwin Landseer, gave immortality to a dog, destined
him to live on the glowing canvas even longer than in
a master's memory. The paintings, character studies
of the dogs they depict, seem to ask for the rest of
their stories. These were gathered by Sarah Tytler,
among them that of the two companions in "Dignity
and Impudence": a stately mastiff and a perky little
terrier side by side in the door of their doghouse.

ONE of the most successful and popular of Sir Edwin Landseer's de-
lineations is the picture, "Dignity and Impudence." It is even better
known and more widely prized than his exquisitely comical sick dog,
that is so sorry for itself, while the keeper is examining its paw; and his
deeply pathetic "Last Mourner," in which the shepherd's dog keeps
solitary watch by its master's coffin.

The noble mastiff lies stately and serene, his vast bulk tempered by
his perfect proportions, and by a mien worthy of the king of dogs. His
well-opened hazel eyes look with honest straightforwardness full in your
face. His huge ears hang down quietly. His jaws are closed and over-
lapped by his deep jowl. He is the beau-ideal of strength in restraint
and repose, as he lies there with one paw, like that of a lion's cub, hanging idly over the framework of his couch, and the other half-turned inwards, as if he were about to put it on his heart, in token of the true
gentleman he is.

From within the same pent-house, where he is freely tolerated as a
lively child companion, protrudes the small, confident head—bristling
with hair, the knowing little ears erect, the tongue half thrust out at one
side, equivalent to being stuck in the cheek—of the briskest, most un-
daunted of terriers. I suppose it is because we all know many versions—
both human and canine—of this pair of friends, that we are so fond of
looking at them and admiring their union in diversity.

I can never see "Dignity and Impudence" without thinking of a couple
of dogs belonging to friends of mine, and that were said to bear a striking and exact resemblance to the dogs in the picture. I had not the good

fortune to know this living "Dignity and Impudence," though I long looked forward to the pleasure; but I happened to hear a great deal of them, and registered their traits with interest.

Wallace and Dick were north-country dogs, as is evidenced by the name of the first—he would have been Bevis in England. They dwelt within sight of a purple spur of the Grampians, known as the Braes of Angus. Their home was a hospitable farm-house, among fresh, breezy uplands, with that element of breadth and freedom which belongs to hill countries, where, side by side with the cultivated fields, lies a wide moor and remnant of ancient forest, and where the ground is broken— and now falls gradually in a sunny slope—now dips abruptly into a shady dell, or den, as we call it in Scotland. The last is a place of spreading beeches, feathery larches, waving birks, and a great wealth of ferns and wild flowers in spring and early summer, and with a never-failing wimpling burn threading its recesses. It is quite distinct from a wild heathery glen. The neighbourhood to which I allude has quaint old mansions, some of which existed in the stirring times when the glens and dens served as passes for "John Hielandman," rustling in his plaid and kilt, and bristling with his claymore and skenedhu. He did not bring down cattle—long-horned kylies—like the modern drover, but came, saw, and lifted what "nowt" he fancied on lowland pastures, goading them up among the mountains to the headquarters of the chief and his dhuinnewassels. An ancient town with steep, narrow streets, having a feudal castle on a tree-crowned rock above a brawling river, and the remains of an abbey, is the market town of the district. On the road to this town one has a glimpse from a distance of the silver shield of the German ocean, with a larger town on its brink.

Wallace and Dick could not have been more highly favoured in the matter of locality, though they had been lovers of the picturesque— not the picturesque on a stage scale, but the quality which is large and primitive—and though they had deliberately gratified their aesthetic tastes by pitching their tents in this region, which is fresh on the hottest summer day, and has a bracing keenness, not a chill sluggishness, in its winter cold.

Wallace came first to the farm-house a tremendous puppy, for the most part generous and docile in his conscious power, but not without elements of savageness and danger in him, if he were suffered to grow up undisciplined.

I have heard his master tell that, when Wallace was a young dog, one winter night he took more than his own share of the hearthrug, on which his master's solitary chair was also drawn up. The man, desiring more space to move in, gave the dog an unceremonious push, which roused in him such lurking ill-humor as besets us all at times; only Wallace was a mighty brute, unsupplied with the reins of reason and conscience wherewith to check his passions, and furnished on the other hand with the instinct of quick retaliation and fierce, disproportioned revenge. He gave a low growl, like muttered thunder, and made a half-spring at his master, who recognised on the instant that an unexpected crisis had come, which was to settle whether he was to be the master of the beast or the beast was to be his master, and which placed for the moment his very life in danger. Acting on the impulse of self-preservation, rather than on any deliberate design, he snatched up the poker, and dealt the dog a blow which felled him, and left him stunned and motionless. Quick remorse followed the deed, as the assailant asked himself, had he slain his comrade outright on the spot, and that for the merest ebullition of temper? If Wallace had betrayed some traces of the savage, who else had been cruel in unsparing punishment?

But Wallace came to himself almost before his master could make the compunctious reflection, rose and took himself off with lowered crest and submissive head and tail, clearly acknowledging himself beaten, and as clearly evincing the extreme of shame, for having been guilty of provoking the unequal contest. Unlike man, the dog bore no malice for his defeat; it simply called out in him that unswerving loyalty which has no parallel. From that day to the hour of his death, in a ripe old age, Wallace never again disputed his master's sovereign will, or disobeyed his direct command, but awarded him the most devoted allegiance. The dog's great strength, his solid sense for a dog, his rare magnanimity, were, from the era of his conquest, laid, together with his fervent attachment, at the feet of his conqueror—for the dog is another St. Christopher.

Under the influence of this absolute submission* to his master, rather than from any mere superficial cleverness, such as may be readily found in mere trick-performing dogs, Wallace could be taught a variety of acquirements, and was in the end so accomplished a dog that I fear I cannot call to mind a tithe of his attainments. I believe he could sit up in any attitude or assumption of character, or throw down his body in any required posture, and remain so for a given time. He could mimic swimming at the word of command. He could constitute himself a pony for little children—indeed he was not less than some Shetland ponies—and would carry them decorously round the room or the garden on his back. He could—and this was probably the hardest task of all—at his master's bidding, lie down in a meadow where a herd of cattle fed, and permit the whole of the oxen to gather lowing round him, and even

---

* In addition to the instinct of obedience which in itself rendered Wallace tractable, the great dog had a little weakness, of which I have heard his master say he made use in conducting his four-footed retainer's education. "Wallace wight" "would have gone round the world" for a bit of sugar—the usual reward of a fait accompli.

to lick him with their rough tongues, without his stirring or offering the smallest resistance.

Wallace was somewhat up in years before Dick came on the scene. He also arrived at the farm-house a puppy, but it was not at first intended that he should remain there. The master of the house had kindly procured Dick with the intention of giving him to a friend, when he himself became so enamoured of the little dog's briskness and pluck, and at the same time so persuaded that these qualities would be wasted in the quiet life of the woman for whom Dick had been originally got, that he substituted another and more suitable dog, and kept the little man for his own portion.

As I have been assured, there never was a blyther, bolder, more irrepressible spirit than that which lodged in the body of the small terrier. Like his friend Wallace, he needed to be tamed, and to the last he could not stand teasing for any length of time without a strong inclination to show his fine white teeth in a way which was not play. The fact was, that on these occasions he got into a white heat of rage, in which he was in danger of ceasing to be master of his actions.

Once, when Dick was a young dog, under some provocation he flew at and slightly bit his mistress, who had no resource but to show him the iniquity of the deed in a manner which, I believe, is effectual when it is possible to practise it. According to strict injunctions as to the conduct required in the circumstances, and in the stern necessity of preventing a repetition of the offence, which might have cost the life of the offender, she caught Dick by the refractory cuff of his neck, carried him to the door of a room into which she could throw him when the time came, and while holding him in the air—which is the great secret of the effectiveness of the punishment, since the culprit feels himself, during the infliction, absolutely powerless in the grasp of the dispenser of justice—cuffed him soundly, and then flung him from her into the open door at hand, closing it quickly after him, and so preventing any possibility of a hostile attack from the dog while still writhing and struggling under his penalty. The result was, that the tender-hearted young mistress withdrew sick from giving the painful lesson she had been imperatively called on to teach. But, as in the case of Wallace, and as in that of the mastiff which Emily Brontë cowed by one box in the ear, the lesson had been learned thoroughly; Dick never again, unless in such an instance of wilful protracted teasing as I have referred to, took to biting his friends.

His affection was ardent as his temper was quick, and the convulsions of delight, the ecstatic caresses he lavished on members of the family when they returned from a temporary absence, were demonstrations to see rather than to hear of.

Dick is said to have been the most entertaining companion in a walk, always making amusing discoveries, full of the freshest zest and the most unwearied energy. He had a passion for sport, of which I shall have more to say hereafter; but, sport or no sport, he never failed to find objects of interest on his way, and to impart the interest to his fortunate companion.

Like Wallace, Dick could be easily induced to go through a variety of tricks—which, in my opinion, are slightly disparaging to very sensible or bright dogs, seeing that these tricks are purely artificial, entirely distinct from the dog's natural sagacity and genuine feats, can be imparted, if proper pains be taken, to far inferior dogs—I mean dogs that have merely the faculty of mimicry, apart from intuition, steadfastness, and a power of love which makes wise. One of Dick's many tricks was to go through the form of sitting in his own chair at table with the family when they were at meals (though his food was taken elsewhere), and of speaking when he was told—that is, at a certain word and sign, starting off in his own dog language of yelping and whining, till he was requested to be quiet.

From his introduction to the farm as a puppy, Dick entertained an immense admiration—rapidly progressing, in a dog of his frank, confident character, into a trustful, rather encroaching affection—for the veteran Wallace. The mastiff responded by testifying the most amiable indulgence for his liliputian friend. The indulgence proved its own reward, for there was no question that the eager, joyous little dog brought some of its own eagerness and joy into what was becoming the fading, failing life of his mighty ally.

A ludicrous position which the dogs often assumed has been described to me. Wallace had the usual sterlingly honest dog's aversion to tramps and disreputable characters (in the dog's eyes). Dick shared this repugnance; but in spite of his constitutional audacity, he was apt to mingle discretion with his valour here. When a particularly ill-looking traveller approached the farm gate, where Wallace and Dick were on sentry, Dick had a custom of nimbly insinuating himself between Wallace's forepaws and standing upright beneath the arch of the chest without difficulty; from this vantage-ground he would issue his sharp volley of barks as a rattling accompaniment to the bass cannon-like boom of Wallace's challenge.

When the two dogs lay down to sleep, Dick would take the most manifest advantage of his friend's neck, or shoulder, or side, nestling himself within or against it, for the promotion of his own warmth and ease, without sustaining the least rebuke from the gentle giant.

Sometimes when Dick wished a game of play, for which Wallace felt himself quite too old, Dick would beset his friend like a little pestering, spoiled child, pawing and pulling, and making darts and dabs at Wallace's ears, which would have nearly covered Dick's body, or at the jaw, one shake from which would have dismissed the life from the little dog in a twinkling. But Dick was comfortably persuaded that he was entirely privileged, and he did not argue with his host, though Wallace, after much endurance, could assert himself so far as to send off his tormentor. Yet he was never known to do it, save in the kindest, most friendly fashion. No paralysing stroke from his paw, no crushing snap from his teeth, ever scared the fun and familiarity out of little Dick. He received his congé in the shape of a mild, if firm, refusal, which left him free to come sidling into his crony's presence again within the next five minutes.

I have mentioned Dick's love of sport. Wallace had the same love to a marked extent; indeed, it was the one temptation which proved irresistible, and seduced him once and again from his adherence to his master. It was not that the dog openly resisted or defied orders, but that he showed craft in snatching an opportunity to evade them, in slipping off unperceived, and conducting his hunts in an independent style in the preserves and on the great moor at hand—coming home with a dogged fidelity, and yet with the self-convicted air of a culprit, after his lust for the pursuit of prey was satisfied, to the punishment which he was perfectly aware remained in store for him. Of course, for a dog like Wallace to roam abroad unattended, on such an errand, was to expose both him and his master to certain penalties, and every effort was made, for the dog's own sake as well as for his master's credit, to break him of so dangerous a propensity. The attempt was not altogether successful. The ruling passion was so strong in Wallace that it rivalled even his conception of duty. But the consequences of his escapades always fell short of the condign punishment at the hands of incensed proprietors which his master dreaded for the dog, and repentance, forgiveness, amendment followed till the next outbreak.

These outbreaks would probably have decreased in number and died out as Wallace's spirit of enterprise abated with his advancing age;† but I am sorry to say Dick proved an artful decoy and subtle tempter. The two dogs did not venture on a forbidden expedition under the very eye of their master; but the moment his back was turned to go from home, I have been assured that the certainty and celerity with which the conspirators detected his absence was something marvellous. Wallace and

---

† However, I have heard of an old terrier who had lived many years leading an entirely domestic life in a large town, and who, on being taken by its owners to country quarters—which happened, unfortunately, to be in a game country—ran off the very night of his arrival, hunted the whole summer night through, and turned up the next morning, after his friends had resigned all hope of recovering him. He was dead tired, and in a few hours was crying out under paroxysms of rheumatism, which his unwonted exposure, together with his weight of years, brought upon him.

Dick set off like the wind—or at least as like the wind as the old dog's lagging limbs would allow—to the nefarious indulgence of their appetite. Nothing short of chaining up Wallace before his master left could prevent the catastrophe. No efforts of his young mistress—of whom, at the same time, he was exceedingly fond, and whose escort and protector he was generally proud to be—were of the least avail to detain him; she has told me how she would run out to intercept the dogs on the first hint of their decamping, and try to hold them back by main force, but Wallace would wrest himself from her grasp, and trot after Dick, already scampering away in the distance.

Sometimes these hunts lasted as long as three or four days. Naturally, the dogs were unwilling to come back to the disgrace which awaited them, and they could subsist in the meantime on the spoil which they caught and slew. The neighbourhood of the great wide moor and fragment of forest—a broad brown and dark green tract stretching, with a suggestion of wonder and mystery, along the whole expanse of cultivated country—rendered it specially difficult to discover the direction the dogs had taken, running as the birds flew, and making nothing of hedges, ditches, and "dykes" in their progress, after they were fairly out of sight. It was the solving of a puzzle to pursue and apprehend them. Sometimes a wayfarer passed and recognised them, and brought the tidings of their whereabouts to "the farm town." Sometimes the dogs' master, when he went to the weekly market in the quaint town I have described, received information from a neighbour which enabled him to track the fugitives. Oftenest they returned of their own accord, spent and sated, brought back by some compulsion of law, some tie of dependence and affection, which was in the end too powerful for their desire to rove, so that they could not become wild dogs again, or desert their aggrieved human friends for a permanence.

Knowing the district as I do, I have great sympathy with Wallace and Dick. Had I possessed Wallace's capacity of endurance, or Dick's youthful fleetness of foot and length of wind—had I shared their capacity of thriving on the same—I too should have liked to wander for days among these fresh fields, with their yellowing corn or rich pasture, on which sturdy bullocks or skittish colts were having a pleasant time. I could have dived with good-will into these tree-girdled quarries, and roamed along these high roads, ample enough for two coaches-and-six to drive abreast, and bordered with bands of yellow lady's bedstraw and azure veronica, and later in the season by miniature forests of nodding harebells; or down these rough by-roads, with their patches of yellow broom and trailing garlands of brambles, to the outlying heather on the verge of the moor, about which great humble bees were always humming. My heart would have hankered, like theirs, for that grand, gaunt old moor of Mendrummond—or, as it is called in local parlance,

"Munrummon"—with its pale liverwort and white grass of Parnassus, its bronze stemmed firs and stunted oaks, its lone green glades. One can still feel that here, as among the mountains of old Scotland, there linger vestiges of a virgin world.

As a human being and not a dog, I am not at all clear that I should have returned so faithfully to cutting reproaches and a good beating as Wallace and Dick had the courage to do.

The dogs used to display judiciousness in selecting the cover of night for their reappearance, and they sometimes brought home a mutilated hare or rabbit, as if it were intended for a propitiation. But Wallace at least reported himself, in full view of the result, with manly straightforwardness and resignation. He was accustomed to go beneath his master's window, and by a deep prolonged "bow-f-f" announce that there he was ready to submit to whatever his master imposed upon him.

I regret to own that Dick, on the contrary, stole round the house on tiptoe, and, if he found an open window on the ground floor, crept in and hid himself beneath a convenient sofa or bed, in a short-sighted, childish notion that he might evade the righteous sentence he had provoked.

On the last secret hunt in which the dog-friends engaged, Wallace was so enfeebled by age that the exertion exhausted the little strength left to him, and he was unable to return home. Dick had to face the wrath of his master alone, while he was unable to account for his missing comrade.

Happily the mastiff reached a neighbouring farm-house, where he was recognised—for he was a well-known and valued dog—and where he was hospitably entertained, till word could be sent to his master, who despatched a cart for the disabled sportsman. But fancy the mortification of poor Wallace, once so invulnerable at every point, so renowned a warrior and hunter, to be brought home like a dead donkey, stretched at the bottom of a cart!

Wallace survived his last hunt some time, but the evidence of the decay of his powers became always more unmistakable. He was a mere bony wreck of what he had been. He subsisted principally on great "diets" of milk freely lavished on him to prolong his days. At last he fell into a habit of stealing away and secreting himself in some solitary spot of the garden or grounds, an ominous inclination which superstitious servants called "looking for his grave," and that was in reality prompted by the curious pathetic instinct which causes every stricken animal to draw away from the herd, and hide itself from its kind.

But Wallace was not to die apart from human hands and the friends he had loved. No one saw him die; but a servant, preparing to sweep out the dining room early one morning, found the old dog stretched stark and cold on his master's sofa—"like a Christian," as she protested, half awed, half scandalised. And what gave the last touch to the situation was that little lively Dick—always fond of establishing himself by his friend—was discovered lying trembling, with that consciousness of death of which a dog is supposed to be unconscious, behind Wallace, that he had not dared to disturb—the first time Wallace had frightened Dick.

I think Wallace's master, by his own choice, helped to dig the dog's grave; I know that the spot selected was one which had been long chosen for his last resting place. Care was taken that Dick should not know the place, or be tempted to disturb it, when it was little thought that the terrier would soon lie by his comrade's side. Not that Dick died of his mourning; I never heard of a dog pining to death for a fellow-dog—only for his master. I am not even aware that Dick gave great signs of missing his companion after the first few days, for dogs will be dogs after all; and undoubtedly Dick recovered the full flow of his constitutionally high spirits within a short period.

Merry Dick's death was so much the more tragical that it was not in the course of nature; it was the result of an accident—the product of such carelessness as it is hard to forgive. The offices belonging to Dick's master's farm were infested with rats to such an extent that even a terrier was insufficient to keep the vermin down, and poison was employed for their destruction. A portion of strychnine passed into the keeping of a kitchen maid, who was to sprinkle it on bread and butter, to be exposed, with due precaution, near the rats' holes. The plate of bread and butter, with the fatal powder invisible on it, was left heedlessly on a kitchen table, where it was only by the good providence of God that some man or woman—ignorant of anything unusual in the innocent-looking slices —did not eat what was intended for the rats, and perish by a horrible death.

Only poor Dick was destined to be the victim. Attending on the footsteps of his mistress as usual, he came into the kitchen, and, spying the attractive luncheon, sprang up and seized a half-slice.

"It is the poisoned bread," cried the rash servant, observing what had happened, and thinking she had done enough when she had given the tardy warning.

Dick's mistress snatched the perilous morsel from between his teeth and flung it in the fire. So instantaneous was the whole occurrence, that even she—never doubting that she had rescued the dog from all evil consequences—forgot the circumstances in the occupation she was engaged in.

Dick, in his usual excellent health and enjoyent of life, accompanied his mistress in a walk, with all his ordinary pleasure in the privilege. It was not till some hours later, in the bustle of guests assembling for dinner, that Dick's master suddenly summoned his mistress from her toilet with the grievous news that Dick was dying. The little dog had been discovered rigid in a fit. So entirely was the result of what had taken place in the morning unapprehended, that it was not till various remedies had been tried in vain that Dick's mistress suddenly recalled the episode of the poisoned bread. A clever young veterinary surgeon who was within reach came and administered antidotes, which poor little Dick, in the intervals between his paroxysms, was induced to take from the mistress who was so bitterly distressed by his fate; but all was of no avail, the dog succumbed speedily to the deadly poison, and died before the dinner guests had met.

So Dick and Wallace rest together, like true comrades, in what was once their pleasant playground.

BYRON'S NEWFOUNDLAND

Inscription on the Monument of a Newfoundland Dog

GEORGE GORDON BYRON

The poet Byron, an expert swimmer, used to throw
himself into the lake on his estate and pretend he was
drowning. Always his big Newfoundland plunged in
after him and "saved" him. Their close comradeship
ended when the dog fell ill of rabies and expired in
his master's arms, never having bitten him despite
his madness. On Byron's own death in Greece, while
fighting for that country's independence from Turkey,
the beloved Boatswain's collar was found in his pos-
session. The epitaph and poem that follow, both
written by Byron, are inscribed on the monument to
Boatswain which marks the dog's grave in the garden
of Newstead Abbey.

When some proud son of man returns to earth
Unknown to glory, but upheld by birth,
The sculptor's art exhausts the pomp of woe,
And storied urns record who rests below;
When all is done, upon the tomb is seen,
Not what he was, but what he should have been;
But the poor dog, in life the firmest friend,
The first to welcome, foremost to defend,
Whose honest heart is still his master's own,
Who labors, fights, lives, breathes for him alone,
Unhonored falls, unnoticed all his worth,
Denied in heaven the soul he held on earth;
While man, vain insect! hopes to be forgiven,
And claims himself a sole exclusive heaven.
Oh man! thou feeble tenant of an hour,
Debased by slavery, or corrupt by power,
Who knows thee well must quit thee with disgust,
Degraded mass of animated dust!
Thy love is lust, thy friendship all a cheat,
Thy smiles hypocrisy, thy words deceit!
By nature vile, ennobled but by name,
Each kindred brute might bid thee blush for shame.

Ye! who perchance behold this simple urn,
Pass on—it honors none you wish to mourn:
To mark a friend's remains these stones arise;
I never knew but one,—and here he lies.

Newstead Abbey, November 30, 1808

                    Near this spot
          Are deposited the Remains of one
          Who possessed Beauty without Vanity,
                    Strength without Insolence,
                    Courage without Ferocity,
          And all the Virtues of Man without his Vices.
          This Praise, which would be unmeaning Flattery
                    If inscribed over human ashes,
          Is but a just tribute to the Memory of
                    BOATSWAIN, a Dog,
          Who was born at Newfoundland, May, 1803,
          And died at Newstead Abbey, Nov. 18, 1808.

GUARDIAN OF THE IRON CHANCELLOR

Tyras

FAIRFAX DOWNEY

Dogs come to resemble their masters, some say. Such
may well be claimed for the massive, formidable creature that was the constant companion of Germany's
powerful Iron Chancellor.

Two great Danes sprang to their feet and stationed themselves on either
side of Prince Otto von Bismarck, whenever he rose to greet a visitor.
More menacing than sentries with bayoneted rifles, they watched the
caller's every move. But for them, an enemy might have been tempted
to strike down the powerful minister who had united all Germany under
the King of Prussia and defeated Austria and France in war. It was
known that Bismarck went unarmed, even when he wore uniform. Yet
visitors hesitated even to argue in the presence of the huge, fierce dogs.

Tyras, companion of the Iron Chancellor's later years, was his favorite
in a long succession of iron-gray or black great Danes, known to him as
German mastiffs and, in fact, originally a German breed. Bismarck spent
few moments apart from his pets. A predecessor of Tyras, that bore the
same name, had accompanied young Otto to the University of Göt-
tingen and stalked in with him to the rector's study where the Prussian
youth had been summoned to be punished for breaking a window. The
rector took one look at the formidable dog, dodged behind a chair, and
increased the fine.

The second Tyras, too, always walked with his master or loped beside
his horse. At meals, Bismarck shocked fastidious guests by ordering
chunks of meat served and flinging them to Tyras and his fellows. Tyras
mounted guard in the bedroom by night and in the Chancellery by day.
During a conference, the Russian minister was incautious enough to
wave his arms wildly in the course of a heated argument. Suddenly an
impact bore him to the floor, and Tyras stood over the gasping Mus-
covite, paws on his chest.

"I love dogs," Bismarck wrote in one of his frequent mentions of his
pets in diary and letters. "They never try to get even with you for having
harmed them." The Chancellor would postpone a trip if Tyras happened
to be ill and could not go with him. Trusting the dog's judgment, he

hired people for his household if Tyras approved of them at the interview. The great Dane actually influenced foreign policy. The Czar of Russia, having asked to see him, the big animal put in a dignified appearance. "A fine dog," remarked the Czar condescendingly. "A pity he has cropped ears like all pugs." Bismarck never forgave that.

An end to Bismarck's sway over Germany approached when Wilhelm II came to the throne. Jealous of the old Chancellor and preparing to oust him, the Kaiser still desired to cater to him for a time and, being unfamiliar with dogs, presented him with a thin, ill-bred specimen, obtained from commercial kennels. Although Bismarck could not refuse the gift and risk the Kaiser's displeasure, he fumed with rage, for he had to send Tyras away to be chained up in a lodge lest he slay the interloper. Yet he could not bring himself to dispose of the cur because it had such faithful eyes.

Tyras, deemed by his master the only friend of his old age, was buried with a long series of other great Danes and favorite steeds in Bismarck's park at Varzin. The news of the famous dog's death had been cabled around the world.

"The Germans of old," declared Bismarck, "had a kindly religion. They believed that after death they would meet in the heavenly hunting grounds all the good hounds that had been their companions. I wish I could believe that."

Part Five

DOG WAGS

Hey diddle diddle,
The cat and the fiddle,
The cow jumped over the moon.
The little dog laughed
To see such sport,
And the dish ran away with the spoon.

Mother Goose Rhymes

DOG BITES MAN; STILL NEWS

Elegy on the Death of a Mad Dog

OLIVER GOLDSMITH

Good people all, of every sort,
  Give ear unto my song;
And if you find it wondrous short,—
  It cannot hold you long.

In Islington there was a man,
  Of whom the world might say,
That still a goodly race he ran,—
  Whene'er he went to pray.

A kind and gentle heart he had,
  To comfort friends and foes;
The naked every day he clad,—
  When he put on his clothes.

And in that town a dog was found,
  As many dogs there be,
Both mongrel, puppy, whelp, and hound,
  And curs of low degree.

This dog and man at first were friends;
  But when a pique began,
The dog, to gain some private ends,
  Went mad, and bit the man.

Around from all the neighbouring streets
  The wondering neighbours ran,
And swore the dog had lost his wits,
  To bite so good a man.

The wound it seemed both sore and sad
  To every Christian eye;
And while they swore the dog was mad,
  They swore the man would die.

But soon a wonder came to light,
    That showed the rogues they lied;
The man recovered of the bite,
    The dog it was that died.

ARTILLERYMAN'S STRATEGY

Ambrose, Dog of War

FAIRFAX DOWNEY

At a crucial moment in maneuvers the battery's mascot and his master save the day.

KENNEDY, the hard-boiled adjutant, was inspecting Camp Hannatoby's summer contingent of National Guard, raking the line from right to left for misplaced heels or escaped whiskers. Simultaneously from left to right a second but unofficial inspection was being conducted. Both were converging on Private Hector Chester, rear rank, Battery "B."

The second inspector was employing somewhat unusual methods. Disregarding the angle of a campaign hat, he took more interest in the legs of the regiment. Every now and then he sniffed, although not critically nor in disapproval. And once in a while he expressed pleasure by wagging his tail. It was clear he was not half so self-contained as the adjutant. But, like him, he passed up the infantry and Battery "A" and made no choice. As Inspector Number 2 came within his line of vision, Private Hector Chester recognized him with one horror-stricken glance as Ambrose, Dog of War.

Hector noted Ambrose had changed but little since they had campaigned together in France. Ambrose's complexion was still white with black spots, and he still wore the same fatuous grin. His shaggy coat still looked as if it were a misfit issue by some canine supply sergeant, and he still pranced from the playful crouch which caused it to be said of him in the artillery that his recoil springs were faulty. Yes, he was the same old Ambrose and just as keen on looking up a friend as ever.

Ambrose and the adjutant, the latter sternly disregarding the former, were about to make selection, the one of an orderly, the other of a comrade.

Hector waited, desperately hopeful. The battery tailor had done something helpful to his uniform. He was tonsorially perfect. His shoes were veritable mirrors. As for his automatic, Mr. Colt could not have cleaned it better himself.

For Hector was determined to win the orderly detail, no mean feat.

First appeared in *Boy's Life*, March 1925. Reprinted by permission of *Boy's Life*, published by The Boy Scouts of America.

The boss would be grudgingly impressed when Hector got back from camp on the job and told him about it. The boss having been an old National Guard officer would have to grant Hector's initiative more than he had for some years.

Suddenly Kennedy confronted Hector with critically approving attention.

But then Ambrose arrived. He sniffed once at the legs of Private Chester; he sniffed twice so there could be no mistake. It was true! It was a buddy from the old outfit in France.

Now Ambrose was one of the clumsiest, hulking hounds that ever fumbled a bone on his own one-yard line, but nothing could balk his enthusiasm. He emitted a delighted yelp, rose on his hind legs, placed forepaws on the chest of Private Chester and licked his chin, his neatly shaven chin.

Since Ambrose had chosen a buddy, Kennedy looked elsewhere for an orderly. There were spots on Hector's uniform now. The adjutant chose the next man and gave the dog of war a boot that sent him yipping from the field.

"Retreat" proceeded on its ordered course, but Private Hector Chester went through the motions mechanically. Another chance for distinction had gone by the board, the boss would tell him he was no use on the job until he was more reconstructed. Old Man Hard Luck, through Ambrose, Dog of War, as proxy, had dealt him a deadly blow. His initiative was severely wounded.

Ambrose also was wounded—mostly his feelings. Soldiers never had treated him that way before. With his tail between his legs, where it nevertheless did not interfere with the speedy time he was making, he double-timed it back to an old soldiers' home near Camp Hannatoby, where he had been pensioned on returning from war, pensioned as a reward for distinguished service in the face of the enemy. True, Ambrose had bitten no Germans, but every time an inspector had approached the battery to which Ambrose had been attached, that well-trained hound had barked and given warning.

Disillusioned, Ambrose determined to roam no more. What if he did become unutterably wearied with the old-fashioned Civil War yarns sprung by the inmates of the old soldiers' home? What if his flopping ears lay supine at the notes of the "Battle Hymn of the Republic" when they would have pricked up joyously at the beloved sound of "K-k-k-katy," or "Hinky-Dinky Parlez-vous"? What if he did yearn for World War cusswords and a phrase of two of punk French? After all, there is no place like a home where you don't get booted.

All unsuspected by Ambrose, fame was his in Camp Hannatoby that night. His saga was sung from cot to cot. Basking in popular notice, his bitter chagrin at the missing of the orderly detail forgotten, Private Hector Chester told and retold the war-service record of the Dog of War, surefire inspector-alarm. And the men of Battery "B," who already in their summer encampment had suffered grievously from the unannounced descent of numerous and crabby inspectors, began a strong agitation for inviting Ambrose to join the command.

"You guys may be right," admitted the still-smarting Hector, "even though Ambrose did do me dirt this aft."

"You bet." "Let's swipe him." "He'll save our lives." Thus clamored Battery "B."

"I know we ought to be kind to dumb animals, but"—here Hector sounded a solemn warning—"Ambrose sometimes is an awful dumb, dumb animal."

But the howling mob would not heed him.

So that night Private Chester undertook an embassy of stealth to the old soldiers' home. The forgiving Ambrose was induced to go A.W.O.L. and be attached to a new outfit for rations.

Metaphorically speaking, he folded his pup tent and at the heels of his old buddy stole silently away.

Not many days passed before it became evident that Ambrose would have an opportunity to justify his reputation, to pay his debt of hospitality to Battery "B." For three days there had been no inspection in Camp Hannatoby. This was distinctly ominous. 'Twasn't natural. It was as good as a warning. Without doubt it was the calm before the storm.

Heeding this, due preparation was made. Equipment was seen to be complete in every detail. Private Hector Chester, taking heart once more, set himself and his tent in order as if for the Last Judgment.

As every soldier knows, no matter how strenuously inspections are anticipated, there always remains something to be done at the last moment. And sometimes a really tricky inspector arrives before the last moment. But that emergency was now provided for, with Ambrose, surefire inspector-proof alarm on duty night and day.

The order came suddenly one morning. Prepare for inspection. Battery "B" sprang into instant well-oiled activity. There was not a foolish virgin, so to speak, in the outfit. In fifteen minutes each man stood in readiness at the side of his cot on which was displayed his equipment. "Ready for inspection, sir," the first sergeant reported.

The earnest youths of Battery "B" thereupon visited from tent to tent to be sure that for the honor of the organization nobody had forgotten anything. Nobody had.

"Woof! Woof! Woof!" resounded the warning bark of Ambrose. Good old Ambrose! The men scurried to their posts at the cots.

The inspection, made by a National Guard officer who had not previously appeared at Camp Hannatoby, was a triumphal procession from the point of view of Battery "B." Not a fault, not a flaw could be found even by this lynx-eyed old bird.

Toward the last tent in the line the inspector progressed. There Private Hector Chester and his fellows waited confidently at rigid attention.

Entered the inspector. Hector, staring straight ahead, sensed his presence. The officer moved from cot to cot in silent approval. It was not until he reached the cot of Private Chester, that he paused, stared and emitted a chuckle of long-deferred, sardonic and unholy glee. He had found something wrong.

One of Hector's pup tent pegs was missing. The inspector came and stood in front of the culprit.

It was the boss!

The old chap had felt he needed some outdoor life that summer, so had returned to the National Guard and been assigned to active duty as inspector. Now with an accusing stare of recognition, he confronted his employee in civil life and flayed him in the most approved military manner.

When the smoke had cleared away and the inspection was over, Battery "B" was restrained from laying heavy hands on Private Hector Chester only by the appearance of Ambrose, mouthing the missing tent peg. Tent pegs had no military significance to the Dog of War. The fighting outfit he had served with in France had used them for kindling and toothpicks.

The fact that Ambrose had purloined the peg lifted some blame from Hector in the eyes of the battery, but in that quarter only. By the nature of things, you can not report to an inspector the misdeeds of an inspector-proof hound.

The day of the war games dawned and found Hector listless. He just didn't want to play—not even war games. But when Battery "B" limbered up as the artillery of the Blue Army and swung out on the road behind its cased guidon, the old thrill seized on Hector again. He sat on a caisson crammed with blank ammunition and gloried in the dust and sun of the open road. The horses' legs warmed, the battery took up a trot. The guns rumbled, toggle chains rattled, teams snorted. Scorning to hold on, Hector sat his caisson easily with two other cannoneers and was shaken into the semblance of a bag of bones. The old spirit surged up within him. Bring on your enemy!

Now war games are just so many solemn bluffs. They would be pretty fair sport if generals and colonels and things did not take them so seriously. Since they do, one must humor them and be grimly warlike until the final whistle blows.

Hector was ready to pretend with the best of them. In fact it was his earnest wish that the umpires would saunter over and designate the rest of his gun crew as dead, so that he could serve the smoking piece alone and save the day. But no such luck, he reflected, lapsing into discouragement. He would doubtless be the first to be declared a casualty. The battery insisted he was dead from the ears up already.

The battery broke into a gallop and with shining eyes Private Hector Chester leaned into the wind. Again he was the master of his fate and ranked his soul by any number of files. He felt the most supreme confidence that his battery would blast a theoretical way through the opposing Red Army for the Blues to win their objective. Nothing adverse could happen, with Ambrose securely detailed as kitchen police and even now, no doubt, discontentedly munching potato peelings.

A scattering fusillade of rifle fire opened up ahead. The infantry advances of the two armies were in contact and were blazing away enthusiastically with no thought of the rifle cleaning their blank ammunition was storing up for them. The fire grew heavier, increased to the left. Some crafty officer visioning great benefit to his efficiency card, was attempting to tear off a flanking movement.

It was a Red Army offensive. Back came orders to Battery "B" to go into action at once and check it. The gallop grew faster, but the battery commander and his detail outstripped the carriages. When the battery came up, markers were waiting behind a crest. Very prettily, the outfit executed "Action Front," cannoneers leaping from their seats and unlimbering. The teams wheeled with the limberers and dashed to the rear as all four guns of the battery opened up.

No umpire could question the repulse of the Red attack by the Blue artillery. It was gallant and conclusive; in fact, the Reds evacuated the sector even before being ruled off.

It was not twenty minutes later that a second Red attack was delivered on the extreme right flank. The truly Napoleonic Red commander had pulled the taxicab-at-the-Marne act and shifted his army from flank to flank by motor trucks. With his field glasses, the discomfited Blue commander could see the excitement created among the inspectors and umpires observing from the hilltop.

Not a minute to lose. The Blue artillery must fill the breach again. The right flank was crumbling and being dead by the squad. Battery "B" to the rescue!

Limber! Cannoneers, mount. Trot, gallop! Battery "B" cut across country at a breakneck pace. Drivers whipping, carriages careening crazily, they sped on. Now and then a particularly heavy bump would be struck and a cannoneer would sail from a limber seat, describe a graceful arc in the air, and hit the countryside with a thud. But not Hector. He clung for dear life. This time he was resolved to be in at the finish, even if it were his own as usual.

A slower team delayed Hector's gun. It was a good forty yards behind when the advance of the battery swung into a road which seemed to be made to order for more expeditious progress to the threatened flank.

That road was too much of a good thing. It was a snare and a delusion. The Red commander had counted right along on the Blue counterattack taking that road moving to meet his flank feint. So when Battery "B" emerged on that open road, Battery "A" of the Red artillery, in position on a commanding crest, let fly as fast as blanks could be shoved into breeches.

There is an old true saying in the artillery that a battery seen is a battery lost. It fitted Battery "B" as if it were made for it. Umpires pronounced the Amen for three out of the four guns of the Blue artillery.

The fourth section galloping behind had heard the fire and pulled up in time. It retreated hastily to a wooded knoll, unlimbered and manhandled the gun into a position cleverly concealed not far from the road.

All the squad but Hector left the gun to bring up ammunition from the caisson—and were promptly captured along with the caisson by a platoon of Red infantry which had rolled up in a truck. The infantry then began to scout for the gun.

Hector, growing lonesome, began to reconnoiter and nosed out the sad reverse that had come to his companions in arms. There he was at last, the sole survivor of the gun crew. Fate had put a whole darn referendum up to Hector's initiative!

He slipped down the road until he found the empty truck in which the Red infantry had come. It was his for the capturing. But a truck is not counted an offensive weapon—at least not in time of war.

Then flamed forth the latent fire of true initiative. Why not limber up his gun to the truck? Motorize his artillery?

Hector hopped in and drove the truck close to the cache of the gun by the roadside and sprang out, filled with a sense of wild exultation. In the firing and general confusion, the Red infantry was still unaware of his requisition of their transportation.

Making a towline fast to the rear of the truck, Hector slipped into the underbrush where the gun was hidden. The line would just reach the pintle of the trail. Success was almost within his grasp.

Hector bent down to meet a "Woof!" of welcome. It proceeded from beneath the gun wheels. There, crouched expectantly, whacking the ground to right and left with joyous tail, was Ambrose, Dog of War.

Ambrose gave tongue.

Fierce despairing emotions ran riot within the bosom of Private Chester. Was this comedy Hound of the Baskervilles to haunt his most promising moments forever? To leap up and clumsily dash the cup of success from his lips?

Again Ambrose gave tongue with indications that such was his enthusiasm at meeting his buddy he would soon be in full cry. The firing had slackened and the barks of the kill-joy echoed startingly through the wood.

Attracted by the sound, a gray touring car drew up in the road alongside the truck. By the red arm brassards of its occupants, Hector knew them for the Red commander and his staff. Suspecting the enemy, they drew their automatics. Not a chance to capture them, and one man could not manhandle the three-inch gun into position and bring it to bear on the car.

Any minute the towline would catch the attention of the Red officers and inevitably lead them to the last gun of the Blue artillery.

Ambrose pricked up his ears. The creature cleared his throat.

Desperately, Hector snatched and rummaged in the haversack on his back. The silence of the Dog of War must be bought. Out came a condiment can and the artilleryman, unscrewing the lid, thrust the first article that rolled out into the gaping jaws of his Nemesis.

Now the name of a condiment can implies that it is to contain condiments. It should—if there is anything in a name—have supplied some condiment, some delicacy, some hors d'oeuvre to still the voice of Ambrose.

It was on the long, red, receptive tongue of Ambrose that Hector implanted the condiment bribe. The dosee took one bite and one swallow. Then an expression of pained surprise came into his great brown eyes. He emitted an ear-splitting yelp, expressing betrayed friendship and went away from there.

Out into the road bounced Ambrose, spluttering, howling and frothing copiously at the mouth. The Red officers had left their car and approached the truck. With shouts of "Mad dog!" they scrambled frantically back to the car and sped down the road after their army which was pursuing the Blue forces in full retreat.

Hector, filled with incredulous hope, hooked up. He started up the truck, and the gun was nicely towed out of its position to the road. Fairly bursting with initiative, Hector drove after the Reds and unlimbered on a crest in their rear. The carriage of a gun is equipped with ammunition carriers for four rounds and these Private Chester proceeded to discharge with telling effect at the unprotected backs of the foe. Thus supported, the Blue army rallied, charged, and won the day.

"Good work, my boy!" complimented the chief umpire who was none other than Hector's boss. "I'm afraid I've been misjudging you. You took keen advantage of circumstances. But tell me, was that dog really mad?"

"Yes, sir," Hector answered. "He was mad, all right. As peeved as I've ever seen him. I fed him a cake of soap."

AT THE DOG SHOW

Ballad of a Languid Lady, or, My Dogs Hurt

PEG ROLAND

This gay verse was inspired by that annual event of American dogdom, the Westminster Kennel Club Show in Madison Square Garden, New York City.

(With apologies to C. Moore and Santa Claus)

'Twas the birthday of Lincoln and all thru the Garden
The din was terrific, an uproar we'll pardon.
Two days of dog days, and fast falling snow;
Such weather it was for a Westminster Show!
Of the dogs some were benched, some were penned in their crates,
From the judges above they waited their fates.*
Their owners and handlers rushed madly about
With high hopes of winning some ribbons, no doubt.

There were Scotties and Corgis and stately red Setters,
Retrievers and Mastiffs, all canine go-getters.
Hounds, Boxers, French Bulldogs, Salukis and Cockers,
They all had their boosters, and some had their knockers.
There were Yorkies and Poms and upstanding Schnauzers,
Beau Brummels and kids, and ladies in trousers.
Borzois and Dachsies, and all kinds of Terriers,
Wolfhounds and Afghans and even some Herriers.†

The exercise rings, one for dogs, one for bitches,
Were such fun to watch, we were often in stitches.
The basement was teeming with all kinds of ads
Pushing all kinds of dog food, and fashions, and fads.
Such brushing, such primping, such bright shining coats,
Such yipping, such yapping, such outlandish notes!
The rings above stairs, the parading and posing,
The impassioned pleas and the gentle bulldozing

Appeared in March 1944 issue of *Popular Dogs*. Reprinted by permission of the author.

To make poochie-pet step along—stop and go,
And eventually turn out to be Best in Show.
There were classes for youngsters; some smart little guys
Knew how to put many an old handler wise
To ways in the ring with recalcitrant curs††
That wanted to make with a scrap, rumbling gr-rs.§
All dog folk were there (I don't mean they're freaks,
But people in dogs whom we'd not seen in weeks).

The crowds filled the seats for row upon row,
Not a thing came to pass to louse up the show.
The judging of groups was a sight so inspiring
That people watched hour upon hour without tiring.
Each group had its leader, each dog had its day,
But of the six victors, the best—who could say?
Diversions aplenty, 'twas right thrilling, too,
When those marvelous war dogs marched in for review.

They do sentry duty along with the boys,
Their sharp ears and eyes can detect every noise;
They locate the wounded and bring them relief,
They spy out the Nazis, who soon come to grief.
No foxhole escapes their keen vigilance
And villainous saboteurs don't have a chance.
Then a raffle and auction did much for the Cause,
The money rolled in with scarcely a pause.

The auctioneer's voice rang out clear as a bell
And some who bought War Bonds won puppies as well.
At long last came the time to pick Best in Show,
Which one for that spot? All were eager to know.
For Hound group the Foxhound, red Setter for Sporting,
The Yorkie and Poodle were in there cavorting.
The dignified Boxer was looking his best,
But—the little Welsh Terrier led all the rest!

To all who love dogs the show was a treat,
But somebody—give me a new pair of feet!

* Poetic License.
† More P.L. (I know how to spell it.)
†† For rhyming purposes only.
§ This one makes me a licensed poet.

Part Six
DOGS, FAITHFUL, WISE, AND BRAVE

Whenever man is unhappy, God sends him a dog.
Lamartine

FEUD TO THE DEATH

The Cur and the Coyote

EDWARD PEPLE

Joe was part collie, a stray picked up on the prairie by a cowboy. There were two overwhelming urges in Joe's life. This heart-warming story of the West tells how the dog was compelled to settle his moral enmity to a "hell-warbler" before he answered the call of fidelity to his master.

HE was a dog, and they called him Joe. He had no godfather, but was named after Chip Moseby's one rich relative whom the brute resembled physically—and it wasn't a compliment to either.

Joe's ancestry was a matter to pass over politely and forget. He was a large animal, with the unmistakable build of the wolfhound; yet his blood was mixed with many another hardy breed. His hair, of a dirty yellowish brown, grew in every possible direction, except that designed by a beauty-loving Creator, while his undershot jaw hinted at the possibility of a bull terrier figuring as corespondent in some long forgotten scandal.

Reprinted by permission of Edward C. Peple, for the Estate.

Therefore, Joe had little claim to beauty; but, rather, as Frisco Jim expressed it, "was the dernedes' orn'ries'-lookin' beas' wes' of the Mississip."

Chip Moseby thought of his rich relative, and smiled. The criticism, harsh but just, fitted the dog in all respects, with the one exception of his eyes. There spoke the Scotch collie breed. They were beautiful, pathetic, dreamy; yet marred, from a poetical standpoint, by a dash of impishness found only in that cordially despised, but weirdly intelligent, race of canine outcasts—the cur.

In the beginning Chip Moseby found him on the prairie. How he had ever wandered into the center of this trackless plain was indeed a mystery; but there he was, and commanded pity, even from a cowpuncher. Lost and leg-sore, famished for want of food and water, he waited dumbly for the three black buzzards that wheeled in lazy circles above his head.

Chip dismounted and surveyed his find in wonder, striving to decide whether to take the cur into camp or to put him out of misery for once and all by a merciful shot. Wisdom called aloud for the shot; but something—a half-remembered something deep down in the inside of the man—whispered and made him hesitate.

No, he could not decide; but, being a gambler by birth, taste, and education, he shifted the burden of responsibility to the back of Chance. The process was simple. He reached for the heavy gun which lay upon his hip, and poised a silver dollar between the thumb and finger of his other hand.

"Now, stranger," he observed cheerfully, "you're goin' to be the stakes of a showdown. Heads, you go to camp. Tails, you go to hell. You couldn't ask fer anything fairer'n that, could you?"

He spun the coin and caught it in his open palm. The dog cocked his ears, and the Texan cocked his .44. Tails lay uppermost.

"Yo' luck ain't changed much, puppy," sighed the man, shifting his position for a cleaner shot at the back of the sick dog's head. "You've been elected this time, sure, an'—"

Chip paused suddenly, wondering why, but pausing. His victim whined faintly, raised a pair of gentle, fever-touched collie eyes, and waited. The cowpuncher eased the hammer of his gun and slid the weapon into his holster.

"Dern the dawg!" he muttered beneath his breath. "It's jus' like some po' li'l' helpless, moon-eyed gal what's—what's callin' me a sneak!"

Chip Moseby did not know he was muttering sentiment; but, alone on a wide green prairie with his pony and a dog, where none of his fellow rangers could see and laugh at him—well, it made no difference, anyway.

From his saddle tail he untied his water flask, pouring its contents into his wide felt hat; then he added a bit of liquid from another and more precious flask, and made an offering to a new-found friend. The dog lapped it eagerly, and after a time sat up on his haunches to devour the last crumb and fiber of Chip's last ration of corn bread and bacon, while the cowman looked on and cursed him—horribly—but with a smile.

Slipping, sliding, in the dip of his master's saddle, yet wagging a mangy tail to show that he understood, Joe was christened and rode twenty miles to camp. It was just an ordinary camp of twenty cowmen in charge of eighteen hundred longhorns "on the graze." An idle existence at this season, moving as the big "bunch" listed, and dealing greasy cards at all times save when in the saddle or snoring beneath the cold, white stars.

The cowmen lived, drank bad whisky, gambled, and died—sometimes from delirium tremens or snake bite; at other times from purely natural causes, such as being trampled by a peculiarly active steer. A remnant they were of a long departed hero type, still picturesque, yet lacking in certain vital attributes—mainly morality and a bath.

II

The camp accepted Joe for two reasons: firstly, because they did not care one way or the other; secondly, because Chip Moseby had, on various occasions, thrashed three of the cowmen in brutal, bare-knuckled fights—and the others had seen him do it. Therefore, nineteen more or less valuable criticisms were politely withheld.

For four sweet days Joe ate, drank, and slumbered, recovering both in body and in nerve; then he rose up and began to take notice. The first thing he noticed was a lean-flanked, powerful dog that had dwelt in camp for the space of seven months and felt at home. The "homer's" name was Tonque. He belonged to a gentleman known familiarly as Greaser Sam, a gentleman whose breeds were as badly mixed as Joe's— a fact to which pointed reference was made by jovial friends with frequency and impunity.

Tonque was the only member in camp who openly resented Joe's advent. He first made pantomimic overtures, then displayed a spleenish disappointment at the stranger's gender and disposition. He bullied the new dog shamefully, took away the juiciest bones, nipped him in his tenderest spots, and cursed him in Mexican dog-language, a thing conceded by all linguists to be—with the exception of coyote talk—the vilest of obscene vituperation.

Joe bore in silence for many days. He was a guest of Mr. Moseby, virtually a tenderfoot, and uncertain of the etiquette required in his delicate position. The master gave no orders, and what was a dog to do?

True, a bite or two was nothing much, but an insult sinks far deeper than a tooth, and when the cattle camp lay slumbering through the night, Joe's dog heart ached and troubled him. It is a hopeless sort of thing to stand a bullying for the sake of etiquette, but somewhere through the mongrel's many breeds ran the blood of a gentleman dog; so Joe gave up his bones and took his bites without a growl.

"Him damn coward!" tittered Greaser Sam, pointing at the cur contemptuously with his soupspoon. "Tha's fonny. Big dog—no fight."

"How much d'ye think so?" inquired Chip Moseby, puffing at his corncob leisurely.

"Fi' dollar!" chirped the Mexican cook, his little rat eyes twinkling.

"Make it ten," said Chip, with a careless shrug, "an' Joe'll chase that rabbit's whelp of yo'r'n plumb off'n the range."

Greaser Sam laughed joyfully and produced a month's pay in silver and dirty notes. Yank Collins was made stakeholder, while Chip, stone-deaf to the warnings of certain unbelievers, knocked the dottle from his pipe and whistled to his dog. Joe came over—for protection, it seemed —and laid a trembling chin on the master's knee.

"Joe, ole man," asked Chip, in the tone of a mother's tender solicitude, "is that there Mexican skunk a pesterin' of you?"

The dog, of course, said nothing—that is, verbally—but his two great, glorious eyes spoke volumes. In them the master read this earnest, but respectful plea:

"Mr. Moseby, sir, if you will only say the word and allow me to chew up that bowlegged saw-toothed son of a one-eyed Mexikin half-breed, I'll love you till the crack of doom!"

The master, who was a gentleman fighter himself, smiled grimly, stroked the ugly head, and waved his pipestem in the general direction of the bumptious Tonque.

"All right, son, go eat him up!"

It may here be stated that one of Joe's grandest qualities lay in strict obedience; or, failing in the letter of command, he did his best.

The incident occurred just after dinner, when the cowpunchers, replete with coffee and fried bacon, were enjoying a quiet smoke. They rose to a man, formed a whooping ring about the contestants for camp prestige, and wagered on the outcome. The battle, minus revolting details, was soon over and all bets paid, for—briefly—Joe did his best. Only an angel or a ring-seasoned bull terrier could have done more. Greaser Sam lost twenty dollars. Chip Moseby won ninety. Tonque, the bully, yelping in the dim distance, lost all of his pride, the better portion of one ear, and quite a depressing quantity of hide and hair.

Joe barked once, a hoarse shout of unholy joy—which was only human, after all—then sat down modestly, licked his wounds, and counted up the cost of victory. He had made one enemy and many friends; but

Greaser Sam was only a cook, anyway—so the sting of a dozen ragged bites were peace unutterable.

Later, Sam partially squared the account by pouring a dipperful of boiling grease on Joe's back. Thus, by the time ten inches of hide curled up, peeled off, and healed again, the cur-dog loathed all breeds of Mexicans, and one in particular. Also, Joe suffered somewhat in the matter of scraps and bones; then affairs took a turn for the better. Greaser Sam, while reveling in a noontide siesta, inadvertently rolled on a rattlesnake, and, in spite of a copious supply of antidote on hand, swelled up absurdly, made noises, and passed out in hellish agony.

At the unpretentious funeral Joe controlled his features admirably, with the one exception of his tail, which would wag itself in spite of every gentlemanly instinct. This was wrong, of course, but a dog's ideas on the ethics of retribution are simple and direct.

Joe was glad—very glad. He thrashed poor Tonque again—not from malice, but merely in a spirit of exuberance. One of his ancestors had been an Irish setter, though Joe was unaware of it.

III

And now the waif began to find his own. He learned the profession of cowpunching, together with the arts and observances thereof. He could aid in a roundup nobly, for his wolfhound length of limb gave speed, which made even the tough little broncos envious. At branding time he could dive into the herd and "cut-out" any calf desired, then hold the evil-minded mother en tête-à-tête till the irons did their work. This saved the cowmen much exertion, but was hard on the cattle, and harder still, as it proved, on Joe.

His deeds were praised just a fraction too highly, so the cur-dog lost his head, puffed up with pride, and grew "sassy"—an elusive state to which even humans are subject, once or twice in every little while. It was borne in upon Joe that he owned the camp, the bucking broncos, the grazing longhorns, and, yea, even the prairie itself for a most expansive sweep, and life seemed good to him.

"Say, Chip," remarked Frisco Jim, with befitting solemnity, "that there dawg o' yo'n is gettin' jes' too cocky fer to live a minute. He don't need nothin' but a straw hat, 'n' a toothpick shoved in his face, to put me in min' o' thet li'l' English maverick what herded with us las' Augus'. You reck'lect 'im, Chip—one eye-glass 'n' a hired man fer to tote his shotgun!"

Few cowmen, however, are troubled because of a cur-dog's vanity; therefore, they submitted to his patronizing familiarity and rebuked him not. They loved him for his grit, his speed, his brains. They flattered him and spoiled him, sharing, on common terms, their board and bed—

especially the bed composed of a rolled-up blanket with Joe on the outside. Of course, there were fleas—hundreds of fleas—but a hero of the plains soon learns to overlook the little things of life; besides, it was good to feel a warm dog in the small of a fellow's back when the wind was nippy and from the north. Thus Joe waxed fat and prospered in his pride.

It is strange how a mongrel's breeds will crop out singly, and, for the time being, dominate all other traits; yet this was the case with Joe. In a fight of any kind his bull-Irish came to the fore with a rush, the undershot jaw figuring as a conspicuous racial mark. The wolfhound strain developed solely when he caught a lean, healthy jack rabbit in a straightaway race, brought him into camp, and ate him before the eyes of an admiring crowd. His keen, pathetic sensitiveness was no doubt inherited from the collie stock; but of that there is more to follow.

At present Joe's cur-dog intelligence and sense of humor lay uppermost, leading him to the performance of tricks. These he could do without number, fetching, carrying, or standing on his hind legs to beg for bacon and applause. He could imitate a bucking bronco or a pawing bull. Also, he said his prayers in the manner of certain far-distant Christians—a feat, by the way, which none of his associates had achieved in years. He named the values of poker chips by barks, and, finally, could nuzzle a deck of evil-smelling cards, selecting therefrom any named ace or deuce-spot, an accomplishment which was voiced abroad and thrilled the great Southwest with wonder and delight.

Is it, then, to be marveled at that a carelessly born dog, alone and surfeited with adulation, should weaken and lose his grip on modesty? Joe lost it, but not irrecoverably, for about this time he met his Waterloo, and a mangy Napoleon rested for a space on the isle of mortification.

IV

A light frost fell, and with it came the coyotes. Joe had never seen a coyote, and his interest was aroused—Irish interest, mixed with American superiority. A lazy white moon swung over the horizon, quenching the campfire's glow and flooding the plain with a ghostly glory. From far away in the east came a melancholy yapping, and Joe rose up and listened. Suddenly, from nowhere, appeared the first coyote—a splendid, strapping specimen, with yellow black flanks and a flaunting, feathered tail. He took a clump of sagebrush at a bound, lit on his haunches, pointed his nose toward the sky's high dome, and loosed one quivering, ghoulish wail.

As has been said, the dog was interested. There was something more. He was stricken dumb—paralyzed—by this cool effrontery. Here was an arrogant stranger, sitting—without the courtesy of invitation—upon Joe's own prairie, disturbing the peace in a hateful, alien tongue. The serene cheek of it! A devil-lipped pitch-imp! yapping at Joe's moon!

A pair of pathetic collie eyes swept slowly round the circle of recumbent cowmen, resting at last upon the master, and seeming, in camp vernacular, to inquire, as plain as words: "Fer Gawd's sake, Mr. Moseby, what is it?"

A camp humorist kindly supplied the information.

"That there's a hell-warbler. Sick him, Joe!"

Joe took the suggestion without parley. A noiseless brown streak made out toward the serenader, but Mr. Coyote saw it coming. He ended his song with a crisp crescendo and departed in an easy, shambling lope. The dog was too much occupied to hear the coarse ripple of amusement following his exit, or to see the master stir a sleeper with his foot and remark, with a widening grin:

"Come, git up, Tony, 'n' see the spote. My dawg's a-makin' a tearin' ijjit of hisself."

A more perfect stage could not have been desired; the moon for footlights, Tonque and nineteen cowmen as the audience, a coyote for comedian, and Joe, of course, the star. The chase went south for half a mile, doubled on itself, and passed the camp again, the maneuver being repeated six separate times, apparently for the benefit of those who watched. It was a close race, too, or seemed to be, for seldom was the cur's black muzzle more than a yard or so behind his victim's flaunting tail.

Never before had the wolfhound breed cropped out so strongly. Joe ran low; his muscles ached and burned, his eyes protruded, and he whimpered in desire; yet, strive as he would, he failed to reduce the lead, while the beast in front reeled onward with a shambling lope. Think of it! A lope!

But now Joe gained. He moaned aloud with joy. His blood was up, and he went for his enemy in crazy, heartbreaking leaps. Three times he snapped, and bit nothing but his own dry tongue; then something happened. The coyote, tiring of the game, took his foot in his hand, so to speak, and faded away as a woodcock leaves a weasel.

Joe sat down and thought about it. Nothing short of a pistol-ball could travel like that little black dot on the far horizon. There was something wrong about the whole affair, but just what the cur-dog could not figure out. Possibly the cowmen might enlighten him and offer sympathy; so, with this false hope at heart, he went back slowly, his hot breath coming in labored gasps, his stump tail sagging sadly. His reception, however, was very different from the one so fondly hoped. Instead of pats and a courteous explanation, they greeted him with a roar of vulgar laughter—a taunt which stung him to the very quick.

That dogs are sensitive to ridicule is a fact too patent to admit of argument; but collies, perhaps, are the most humanly sensitive of all. And this is where Joe's collie breed cropped out to stay. He was stunned at first. He couldn't take it in; but when the taunts continued, the dog's already heated blood began to boil. He was fighting for his last torn shred of pride—and pride dies hard.

He crouched beside the campfire, his rough hair bristling down his spine, his ugly nose distorted by an uglier wrinkle still. And when at last Sprig Flannigan—the humorist, by the way, who had sicked Joe on —laughed louder than the rest, and pointed a derisive finger at the hero fallen low, then the cur saw red and forgot to be a gentleman.

At best a rawhide boot is a rather tough proposition, but Joe bit through it, through the trousers beneath, through flesh and sinew, till his strong teeth met. With a bellow of rage and pain, the humorist wrenched away and reached for his big blue gun. He was a quick man, but Chip Moseby was a fraction quicker. His hand flew out and disturbed the pot-shot aim, while the bullet went whining out across the prairie, impairing the market value of an innocent longhorn.

"Drop it!" commanded Chip, then added, by way of pacifying argument: "Ef you had made a screamin' ass of yo'se'f like Joe had, an' we'd 'a' laughed at you, burn me ef you wouldn't want to cut our th'oats!"

This was logic, but Sprig, in his misery, failed to see it. He, too, was Irish. His fingers tingled on his smoking gun, while he urged his death claim with a quivering chin.

"Th' murtherin' divil's whelp! He's chawed a piece outer me laig." The dialect lacked purity; but so did Sprig, for that matter, so let it pass.

Chip Moseby retorted promptly and without any marked degree of sympathy:

"Well, charge the so' place up to profit 'n' loss 'n' run 'n' tell yer mommer. Now shet up, or I'll bloody yer dern nose."

This, also, was logic; besides, Sprig's nose had been bloodied once before, and memory lingered. Therefore, he dropped the discussion in a Christian spirit, tied up his leg with a whisky-soaked rag, and strove to forget the incident.

V

So much for the man's wound. The dog had received a deeper one —larger and more pitiless. A bull's-eye had been made of his vanity, and only death or the coyote's blood could soothe the pain away.

Next morning he tried to persuade himself that it all had been a dream; but Sprig Flannigan limped, and a dog's heart doesn't ache so fiercely because of dreams.

The day dragged on and on, but reached a close at last. A purple twilight came sneaking over the west, deeper, darker, till the lazy moon arose, and again the campfire paled—a lonely, flickering blotch on a vast white sea. And silence fell—God's silence, which a whisper mars like a curse on a woman's lips.

From out the east a whisper leaked—a faint yap! yap! that rose and sank again. Joe heard it, and strove to give no sign; but his hair would rise, and his lips rolled back from his yellow fangs. Silence again, more holy than before; then a ghost-beast leaped the sagebrush, squatted and profaned the night with a shattered, driveling howl.

"Hi, Joe!" said a merry-hearted gentleman, "there's yer frien' a calling of you. Run along, son, 'n' play with him."

This sally was received with a shout of mirth, and the dog arose and went, not toward the cause of his degradation, but deep into the silent cattle herd, where his soul—if dogs have souls—was empty of all save hate and shame alone.

The nights which followed were, to Joe, a living death. With fateful punctuality the hell-warbler jumped the sagebrush and began his haunting serenade. He jeered at Joe, and drove him to the verge of hydrophobia. He called the dog by names unbearable, and dared him to a chase. Joe did try it once, just to prove the paradox to his canine mind. Thereafter he resorted to strategy, and laid for Mr. Coyote, but without avail.

This seemed to amuse the cowmen vastly, and each sad failure was a new delight to them. Somehow, they fancied the two words "humor" and "brutality" to be synonymous, and wrought religiously upon that line. They took to tormenting Joe instead of watching his old-time parlor tricks, which now, alas! were played no more. He had no heart for tricks, and even the ace and deuce-spot seemed to have lost their charm. The dog grew thin and hollow-eyed, moaning and battling in his sleep, when false dreams gave his enemy into his jaws.

Then the hell-warbler took to calling in the daytime, bringing his friends and family with him. He would glide into camp and steal something, then glide away unharmed, pursued by raw profanity and a pistol-ball. Joe loathed him, but was ashamed. No longer he waited for the cowmen's nightly jests, but at the sound of the first yap! yap! he would rise from the campfire and slink away into the outer darkness, to hide his face from the sight of man.

Joe's cup of woe was full—and yet, not quite, for another trouble was to come upon him. His master went away.

Chip Moseby had gone in the night—on a hurry call—while the dog was stalking a certain coyote many miles from camp. Of course there might have been a trail, but a heavy rain was falling, which is bad for trails; and when a man in the west simply goes away—well—none but fools, or sheriffs, follow after.

And now was Joe alone indeed. For a time even the coyote was forgotten in a grief for the one square man who had offered pats, low-spoken words, and a sympathetic eye. Shame and bitterness, for a dog, are hard to bear; but grief for a loved one whisked into the Great Unknown is a pang undreamed by man. It rends him, while his dog heart slowly breaks, and he, too, slips away, to hunt—who knows?—till he licks a master's spirit-hand.

The Mexican dog Tonque was lapsing into arrogance of late. Joe thrashed him soundly, but got no pleasure out of it, thus proving to himself that his case was bad. Then he wandered away on the prairie alone, and made a find. It wasn't much in itself—a calfskin tobacco pouch—but it belonged to Chip Moseby. Joe nosed it once, and hope came trickling back to him. And now the collie stock cropped out again, assisted by that other and much maligned canine strain—the cur. Joe noted the distant camp, drew an imaginary line between it and his find, and he knew that the master's bronco had traveled north.

This was enough. The ugly ears lay back, the long limbs stretched themselves in a swinging stride. Straight as a shaft toward the polestar sped a faithful dog, while his heart beat high with a bounding, hungering joy. Somewhere in the north his master waited, and behind him lay the camp, the jeering cowmen, and a gang of mad coyotes yapping at the stars.

Then, suddenly, Joe stopped—so suddenly that he slid. For a long, long time he sat motionless upon his haunches; but at last he arose, looked northward with one wistful glance, then trotted back to camp.

Now this, in a human, might be called heroic courage, or even majestic pride. In a cur, it has no name; but a brazen hell-warbler was still at large—and the cur remembered it.

VI

The next time Joe gave Tonque a thrashing, he did enjoy it—to the very marrow; also, he ate a square meal and began to study the habits of coyotes from a scientific standpoint.

"Say, Joe," said Frisco Jim, with his greasy smile, "why don't you put some salt on yo' cousin's trail?"

Joe passed the jest and insult without apparent notice, for now he had other fish to fry. To be explicit, he went out and lay down among the longhorns, hoping the fumes of their smoking bodies might disguise his scent. If Mr. Coyote chanced to wander carelessly among the cattle, as he did at times, then—perhaps! But Mr. Coyote laughed, as one derides a tenderfoot, and bored a hole in the wind with his shambling lope.

This was disappointing, at least from the dog's side of it, but the next encounter proved to be of greater interest to all concerned, and these were many. Joe made a wide detour, assaulted the enemy in his rear, and got him pocketed in a bunch of sleeping cattle. This was well. The coyote's only road to hope lay directly across the backs of several hundred steers; a perilous path, at best, for the beasts rose up in unexpected places, thus causing the race track to become lumpy and uncertain. The longhorns are peaceful creatures as a rule; but think, my friend! If you yourself were wakened suddenly from dreams of cuds and luscious grass by a charging coyote and a whimpering, foaming dog, perhaps you would think from a bovine point of view. At any rate, the cattle made progress difficult, and once the race was all but run. A big steer tossed the coyote twenty feet; but another one tossed Joe at the same instant, so honors were even, so to speak.

And now, indeed, was pandemonium loosed upon the night. The terror-stricken cattle, fleeing from they knew not what, surged backward, bellowing; in frenzy rushing round and round in a swiftly converging circle, tightening into a sort of whirlpool knot, known technically upon the plains as a "cattle mill." In daylight a "mill" is dreaded. At night—well, ask the cowmen.

"Wake up, boys!" screamed Denver Ed, seeking his tethered bronco on the run. "Joe's millin' the meat fer to ketch his fool ki-yote!"

Now, whether or not it was really Joe's design, is a matter beyond the ken of man; but this we know, ere sweet tranquillity was restored again, the cowpunchers had expended their uttermost supply of plainsmen's three P's, which is to say—powder, perspiration, and profanity. Yet peace and order did arrive at last, and when it came, a little black dot was yapping on the far horizon, while Joe sneaked, panting, into camp, defeated again, but hopeful. The gods had almost smiled upon him. With the cowmen he wasn't quite so popular.

Twice more the cur-dog failed—failed by a narrow margin, though—and the days slipped one by one away. Each day was a brooding time for the memories of wrongs and ridicule, a yearning time for the loved one waiting in the north. Each night the coyote took the sagebrush at a flying leap and stabbed the stillness with his hideous, ghoulish cry.

One day Joe lay thinking—hard. Suddenly he cocked his ears, took a short stroll on the prairie and came back satisfied; then he waited many days for chance and a cold, propitious wind. It came—an icy whistler—tearing from out the east, till the broncos backed their tails against it; while the men blasphemed and built a bigger fire.

At twilight Joe stole out beside a clump of sagebrush, scratching till he made a hole. In this he squatted, his black nose pointing dead toward the blast, the seven senses of his every breed alert for trouble.

Again came night, but without the lazy moon. Again came silence, save for the moaning of the wind; the wind and one other wail—a faint yap! yap! that dribbled from out the east. A horrid note, a very caricature of sound, yet music now to the ears of the waiting dog! Nearer it came, and nearer still; no longer an echo down the wind, but a full, deep-throated challenge, mingled with the pattering of velvet feet. It came! A rush—a swish—the shadow of a ghost-beast sailing over the sagebrush in a beautiful, unsuspicious leap.

'Twas a perfect leap, high, graceful, grand; but it had its disadvantages. In mid-air the coyote saw his fate beneath him, and tried to turn. He did turn, partially, and lit upon his back. In an instant Joe was all over him.

Of the bliss and sublime brutality of that battle in the dark, none save Joe alone will ever know. But, oh, the glory of it! The feel of a scuffling enemy beneath his paws, when teeth met flesh and bone, to lock with a rasping click! The savage joy of a foeman fighting back at last, frothing, tearing, in a coward's fury of despair! The peace unutterable when the quivering brute lay dead!

Joe closed his eyes and rested. His throat-grip was still upon his prey, a grip which relaxed not once till the coyote's body was dragged across the plain, till it lay beside the campfire, bloody, limp, and still.

"By Gawd, he's got 'im!" roared a wondering sentinel, and the camp woke up and cheered.

They formed a ring about the victor and applauded him; but he backed away and snarled. He hadn't asked applause. He wanted justice —justice for a dog.

The cowmen looked and marveled. A dozen hands reached out to pat the ugly head, for human beasts can honor courage, even in a lesser beast; but the cur remembered many things. The black nose wrinkled wickedly; the coarse hair bristled down his spine; he barked—one curse of anger and contempt—then turned and left the camp.

In vain they whistled after him; in vain they shouted and called his name; but their voices were lost in the rush of icy wind, and the dog was gone.

Not once did Joe look back. He settled down into a tireless, swinging trot—measured, monotonous—but having for its goal a loved one waiting somewhere in the trackless north. His soul was satisfied; his dog heart beat with the peaceful pride of one who has wiped a stain away. There was blood upon his coat—the blood of an enemy—and Joe could look his master in the face.

RAB, THE MASTIFF, AND OTHERS

Our Dogs

DR. JOHN BROWN

Rab and His Friends, published in 1858, is one of the great dog books. Far less known but also appealing are these stories from a chapter in Dr. Brown's three-volume work, *Horae Subsecivae* (*Leisure Hours*). Here more is told of Rab, the brindled mastiff "as big as a little Highland bull," along with tales of Wylie, the shepherd's dog, and others. The author is noted for his tenderness and delicate humor and for his remarkable insight into dog nature.

I was bitten severely by a little dog when with my mother at Moffat Wells, being then three years of age, and I have remained "bitten" ever since in the matter of dogs. I remember that little dog, and can at this moment not only recall my pain and terror—I have no doubt I was to blame—but also her face; and were I allowed to search among the shades in the cynic Elysian fields, I could pick her out still. All my life I have been familiar with these faithful creatures, making friends of them, and speaking to them; and the only time I ever addressed the public, about a year after being bitten, was at the farm of Kirklaw Hill, near Biggar, when the text, given out from an empty cart in which the ploughmen had placed me, was "Jacob's dog," and my entire sermon was as follows:—"Some say that Jacob had a black dog (the *o* very long),

and some say that Jacob had a white dog, but I (imagine the presumption of four years!) say Jacob had a brown dog, and a brown dog it shall be."

I had many intimacies from this time onwards—Bawtie, of the inn; Keeper, the carrier's bull terrier; Tiger, a huge tawny mastiff from Edinburgh, which I think must have been an uncle of Rab's; all the sheep dogs at Callands—Spring, Mavis, Yarrow, Swallow, Cheviot, etc.; but it was not till I was at college, and my brother at the High School, that we possessed a dog.

Toby

Was the most utterly shabby, vulgar, mean-looking cur I ever beheld: in one word, *a tyke*. He had not one good feature except his teeth and eyes, and his bark, if that can be called a feature. He was not ugly enough to be interesting; his color black and white, his shape leggy and clumsy; altogether what Sydney Smith would have called an extraordinarily ordinary dog; and, as I have said, not even greatly ugly, or, as the Aberdonians have it, *bonnie wi' ill-fauredness*. My brother William found him the centre of attraction to a multitude of small blackguards who were drowning him slowly in Lochend Loch, doing their best to lengthen out the process, and secure the greatest amount of fun with the nearest approach to death. Even then Toby showed his great intellect by pretending to be dead, and thus gaining time and an inspiration. William bought him for twopence, and as he had it not, the boys accompanied him to Pilrig Street, when I happened to meet him, and giving the twopence to the biggest boy, had the satisfaction of seeing a general engagement of much severity, during which the twopence disappeared; one penny going off with a very small and swift boy, and the other vanishing hopelessly into the grating of a drain.

Toby was for weeks in the house unbeknown to any one but ourselves two and the cook, and from my grandmother's love of tidiness and hatred of dogs and of dirt, I believe she would have expelled "him whom we saved from drowning," had not he, in his straightforward way, walked into my father's bedroom one night when he was bathing his feet, and introduced himself with a wag of his tail, intimating a general willingness to be happy. My father laughed most heartily, and at last Toby, having got his way to his bare feet, and having begun to lick his soles and between his toes with his small rough tongue, my father gave such an unwonted shout of laughter, that we—grandmother, sisters, and all of us—went in. Grandmother might argue with all her energy and skill, but as surely as the pressure of Tom Jones' infantile fist upon Mr. Allworthy's forefinger undid all the arguments of his sister, so did Toby's tongue and fun prove too many for grandmother's eloquence. I somehow think Toby must have been up to all this, for I think he had a peculiar love for my father ever after, and regarded grandmother from that hour with a careful and cool eye.

Toby, when full grown, was a strong, coarse dog; coarse in shape, in countenance, in hair, and in manner. I used to think that, according to the Pythagorean doctrine, he must have been, or been going to be a Gilmerton carter. He was of the bull terrier variety, coarsened through much mongrelism and a dubious and varied ancestry. His teeth were good, and he had a large skull, and a rich bark as of a dog three times his size, and a tail which I never saw equalled—indeed it was a tail *per se*; it was of immense girth and not short, equal throughout like a policeman's baton; the machinery for working it was of great power, and acted in a way, as far as I have been able to discover, quite original. We called it his ruler.

When he wished to get into the house, he first whined gently, then growled, then gave a sharp bark, and then came a resounding, mighty stroke which shook the house; this, after much study and watching, we found was done by his bringing the entire length of his solid tail flat upon the door, with a sudden and vigorous stroke; it was quite a *tour de force* or a *coup de queue*, and he was perfect in it at once, his first *bang* authoritative, having been as masterly and telling as his last.

With all this inbred vulgar air, he was a dog of great moral excellence —affectionate, faithful, honest up to his light, with an odd humor as peculiar and as strong as his tail. My father, in his reserved way, was very fond of him, and there must have been very funny scenes with them, for we heard bursts of laughter issuing from his study when they two were by themselves; there was something in him that took that grave, beautiful, melancholy face. One can fancy him in the midst of his books, and sacred work and thoughts, pausing and looking at the secular Toby, who was looking out for a smile to begin his rough fun, and about to end by coursing and *gurrin'* round the room, upsetting my father's books, laid out on the floor for consultation, and himself nearly at times, as he stood watching him—and off his guard and shaking with laughter. Toby had always a great desire to accompany my father up to town; this my father's good taste and sense of dignity, besides his fear of losing his friend (a vain fear!), forbade, and as the decision of character of each was great and nearly equal, it was often a drawn game. Toby ultimately, by making it his entire object, triumphed. He usually was nowhere to be seen on my father leaving; he however saw him, and lay in wait at the head of the street, and up Leith Walk he kept him in view from the opposite side like a detective, and then, when he knew it was hopeless to hound him home, he crossed unblushingly over, and joined company, excessively rejoiced of course.

One Sunday he had gone with him to church, and left him at the vestry door. The second psalm was given out, and my father was sitting back in the pulpit, when the door at its back, up which he came from the vestry, was seen to move, and gently open, then, after a long pause, a black shining snout pushed its way steadily into the congregation, and was followed by Toby's entire body. He looked somewhat abashed, but snuffing his friend, he advanced as if on thin ice, and not seeing him, put his forelegs on the pulpit, and behold there he was, his own familiar chum. I watched all this, and anything more beautiful than his look of happiness, of comfort, of entire ease when he beheld his friend,—the smoothing down of the anxious ears, the swing of gladness of that mighty tail,—I don't expect soon to see. My father quietly opened the door, and Toby was at his feet and invisible to all but himself; had he sent old George Peaston, the "minister's man," to put him out, Toby would probably have shown his teeth, and astonished George. He slunk home as soon as he could, and never repeated that exploit.

I never saw in any other dog the sudden transition from discretion, not to say abject cowardice, to blazing and permanent valor. From his earliest years he showed a general meanness of blood, inherited from many generations of starved, bekicked, and down-trodden forefathers and mothers, resulting in a condition of intense abjectness in all matters of personal fear; anybody, even a beggar, by a *gowl* and a threat of eye, could send him off howling by anticipation, with that mighty tail between his legs. But it was not always so to be, and I had the privilege of seeing courage, reasonable, absolute, and for life, spring up in Toby at once, as did Athené from the skull of Jove. It happened thus:—

Toby was in the way of hiding his culinary bones in the small gardens before his own and the neighboring doors. Mr. Scrymgeour, two doors off, a bulky, choleric, red-haired, red-faced man—*torvo vultu*—was, by the law of contrast, a great cultivator of flowers, and he had often scowled Toby into all but non-existence by a stamp of his foot and a glare of his eye. One day his gate being open, in walks Toby with a huge bone, and making a hole where Scrymgeour had two minutes before been planting some precious slip, the name of which on paper and on a stick Toby made very light of, substituted his bone, and was engaged covering it, or thinking he was covering it up with his shovelling nose (a very odd relic of paradise in the dog), when S. spied him through the inner glass door, and was out upon him like the Assyrian, with a terrible *gowl*. I watched them. Instantly Toby made straight at him with a roar too, and an eye more torve than Scrymgeour's, who, retreating without reserve, fell prostrate, there is reason to believe, in his own lobby. Toby contented himself with proclaiming his victory at the door, and returning finished his bone-planting at his leisure; the enemy, who had scuttled behind the glass door, glaring at him.

From this moment Toby was an altered dog. Pluck at first sight was lord of all; from that time dated his first tremendous deliverance of tail against the door, which we called "come listen to my tail." That very evening he paid a visit to Leo, next door's dog, a big, tyrannical bully and coward, which its master thought a Newfoundland, but whose pedigree we knew better; this brute continued the same system of chronic extermination which was interrupted at Lochend,—having Toby down among his feet, and threatening him with instant death two or three times a day. To him Toby paid a visit that very evening, down into his den, and walked about, as much as to say "Come on, Macduff!" but Macduff did not come on, and henceforward there was an armed neutrality, and they merely stiffened up and made their backs rigid, pretended each not to see the other, walking solemnly round, as is the manner of dogs. Toby worked his new-found faculty thoroughly, but with discretion. He killed cats, astonished beggars, kept his own in his own garden against all comers, and came off victorious in several well-fought battles; but he was not quarrelsome or foolhardy. It was very odd how his carriage changed, holding his head up, and how much pleasanter he was at home. To my father, next to William, who was his Humane Society man, he remained stanch. And what of his end? for the misery of dogs is that they die so soon, or as Sir Walter says, it is well they do; for if they lived as long as a Christian, and we liked them in proportion, and they then died, he said that was a thing he could not stand.

His exit was miserable, and had a strange poetic or tragic relation to his entrance. My father was out of town; I was away in England. Whether it was that the absence of my father had relaxed his power of moral restraint, or whether through neglect of the servant he had been desperately hungry, or most likely both being true, Toby was discovered with the remains of a cold leg of mutton, on which he had made an ample meal; this he was in vain endeavoring to plant as of old, in the hope of its remaining undiscovered till to-morrow's hunger returned, the whole shank bone sticking up unmistakably. This was seen by our excellent and Radamanthine grandmother, who pronounced sentence on the instant; and next day, as William was leaving for the High School, did he in the sour morning, through an easterly *haur*, behold him "whom he saved from drowning," and whom, with better results than in the case of Launce and Crab, he had taught, as if one should say, "thus would I teach a dog," dangling by his own chain from his own lamppost, one of his hind feet just touching the pavement, and his body preternaturally elongated.

William found him dead and warm, and falling in with the milk-boy at the head of the street, questioned him, and discovered that he was the executioner, and had got twopence, he—Toby's every morning crony, who met him and accompanied him up the street, and licked the outside of his can—had, with an eye to speed and convenience, and a want of taste, not to say principle and affection, horrible still to think of, suspended Toby's animation beyond all hope. William instantly fell upon him, upsetting his milk and cream, and gave him a thorough licking, to his own intense relief; and, being late, he got from Pyper, who was a martinet, the customary palmies, which he bore with something approaching to pleasure. So died Toby; my father said little, but he missed and mourned his friend.

There is reason to believe that by one of those curious intertwistings of existence, the milk-boy was that one of the drowning party who got the penny of the twopence.

Wylie

Our next friend was an exquisite shepherd's dog; fleet, thin-flanked, dainty, and handsome as a small greyhound, with all the grace of silky waving black and tan hair. We got him thus. Being then young and keen botanists, and full of the knowledge and love of Tweedside, having been on every hill-top from Muckle Mendic to Hundleshope and the Lee Pen, and having fished every water from Tarth to the Leithen, we discovered early in spring that young Stewart, author of an excellent book on natural history, a young man of great promise and early death, had found the *Buxbaumia aphylla*, a beautiful and odd-looking moss, west of Newbie heights, in the very month we were that moment in. We resolved to start next day. We walked to Peebles, and then up Haystoun Glen to the cottage of Adam Cairns, the aged shepherd of the Newbie hirsel, of whom we knew, and who knew of us from his daughter, Nancy Cairns, a servant with Uncle Aitken of Callands. We found our way up the burn with difficulty, as the evening was getting dark; and on getting near the cottage heard them at worship. We got in, and made ourselves known, and got a famous tea, and such cream and oat cake!— old Adam looking on us as "clean dementit" to come out for "a bit moss," which, however, he knew, and with some pride said he would take us in the morning to the place. As we were going into a box bed for the night, two young men came in, and said they were "gaun to burn the water." Off we set. It was a clear, dark, starlight, frosty night. They had their leisters and tar torches, and it was something worth seeing— the wild flame, the young fellows striking the fish coming to the light— how splendid they looked with the light on their scales, coming out of the darkness—the stumblings and quenchings suddenly of the lights, as the torch-bearer fell into a deep pool. We got home past midnight, and slept as we seldom sleep now. In the morning Adam, who had been long up, and had been up the "*Hope*" with his dog, when he saw we had wakened, told us there was four inches of snow, and we soon saw it was too true. So we had to go home without our cryptogamic prize.

It turned out that Adam, who was an old man and frail, and had made some money, was going at Whitsunday to leave, and live with his son in Glasgow. We had been admiring the beauty and gentleness and perfect shape of Wylie, the finest colley I ever saw, and said, "What are you going to do with Wylie?" " 'Deed," says he, "I hardly ken. I canna think o' sellin' her, though she's worth four pound, and she'll no like the toun." I said, "Would you let me have her?" and Adam, looking at her fondly—she came up instantly to him, and made of him—said, "Ay, I wull, if ye'll be gude to her"; and it was settled that when Adam left for Glasgow she should be sent into Albany Street by the carrier.

She came, and was at once taken to all our hearts, even grandmother liked her; and though she was often pensive, as if thinking of her master and her work on the hills, she made herself at home, and behaved in all respects like a lady. When out with me, if she saw sheep in the streets or road, she got quite excited, and helped the work, and was curiously useful, the being so making her wonderfully happy. And so her little life went on, never doing wrong, always blithe and kind and beautiful. But some months after she came, there was a mystery about her: every Tuesday evening she disappeared; we tried to watch her, but in vain, she was always off by nine P.M., and was away all night, coming back next day wearied and all over mud, as if she had travelled far. She slept all next day. This went on for some months and we could make nothing of it. Poor dear creature, she looked at us wistfully when she came in, as if she would have told us if she could, and was especially fond, though tired.

Well, one day I was walking across the Grassmarket, with Wylie at my heels, when two shepherds started, and looking at her, one said, "That's her; that's the wonderfu' wee bitch that naebody kens." I asked him what he meant, and he told me that for months past she had made her appearance by the first daylight at the "buchts" or sheep-pens in the cattle market, and worked incessantly, and to excellent purpose, in helping the shepherds to get their sheep and lambs in. The man said with a sort of transport, "She's a perfect meeracle; flees about like a speerit, and never gangs wrang; wears but never grups, and beats a' oor dowgs. She's a perfect meeracle, and as soople as a maukin." Then he related how they all knew her, and said, "There's that wee fell yin; we'll get them in noo." They tried to coax her to stop and be caught, but no, she was gentle, but off; and for many a day that "wee fell yin" was spoken of by these rough fellows. She continued this amateur work till she died, which she did in peace.

It is very touching the regard the south-country shepherds have to their dogs. Professor Syme one day, many years ago, when living in Forres Street, was looking out of his window, and he saw a young shepherd striding down North Charlotte Street, as if making for his house; it was midsummer. The man had his dog with him, and Mr. Syme noticed that he followed the dog, and not it him, though he contrived to steer for the house. He came, and was ushered into his room; he wished advice about some ailment, and Mr. Syme saw that he had a bit of twine round the dog's neck, which he let drop out of his hand when he entered the room. He asked him the meaning of this, and he explained that the magistrates had issued a mad-dog proclamation, commanding all dogs to be muzzled or led on pain of death. "And why do you go about as I saw you did before you came in to me?" "Oh," said he, looking awkward, "I didna want Birkie to ken he was tied." Where will you find truer courtesy and finer feeling? He didn't want to hurt Birkie's feelings.

Mr. Carruthers of Inverness told me a new story of these wise sheep dogs. A butcher from Inverness had purchased some sheep at Dingwall, and giving them in charge to his dog, left the road. The dog drove them on, till coming to a toll, the toll-wife stood before the drove, demanding her dues. The dog looked at her, and, jumping on her back, crossed his forelegs over her arms. The sheep passed through, and the dog took his place behind them, and went on his way.

Rab

Of Rab I have little to say, indeed have little right to speak of him as one of "our dogs"; but nobody will be sorry to hear anything of that noble fellow. Ailie, the day or two after the operation, when she was well and cheery, spoke about him, and said she would tell me fine stories when I came out, as I promised to do, to see her at Howgate. I asked her how James came to get him. She told me that one day she saw James coming down from Leadburn with the cart; he had been away west, getting eggs and butter, cheese and hens for Edinburgh. She saw he was in some trouble, and on looking, there was what she thought a young calf being dragged, or, as she called it, "haurled," at the back of the cart. James was in front, and when he came up, very warm and very angry, she saw that there was a huge young dog tied to the cart, struggling and pulling back with all his might, and as she said "lookin' fearsom." James, who was out of breath and temper, being past his time, explained to Ailie, that this "muckle brute o' a whalp" had been worrying sheep, and terrifying everybody up at Sir George Montgomery's at Macbie Hill, and that Sir George had ordered him to be hanged, which, however, was sooner said than done, as "the thief" showed his intentions of dying hard. James came up just as Sir George had sent for his gun; and as the dog had more than once shown a liking for him, he said he "wad gie him a chance"; and so he tied him to his cart. Young Rab, fearing some mischief, had been entering a series of protests all the way, and nearly strangling himself to spite James and Jess, besides giving Jess more than usual to do. "I wish I had let Sir George pit that charge into him, the thrawn brute," said James. But Ailie had seen that in his foreleg there was a splinter of wood, which he had likely got when objecting to be hanged, and that he was miserably lame. So she got James to leave him with her, and go straight into Edinburgh. She gave him water, and by her woman's wit got his lame paw under a door, so that he couldn't suddenly get at her, then with a quick firm hand she plucked out the splinter, and put in an ample meal. She went in some time after, taking no notice of him, and he came limping up, and laid his great jaws in her lap; from that moment they were "chief," as she said, James finding him mansuete and civil when he returned.

She said it was Rab's habit to make his appearance exactly half an hour before his master, trotting in full of importance, as if to say, "He's all right, he'll be here." One morning James came without him. He had left Edinburgh very early, and in coming near Auchindinny, at a lonely part of the road, a man sprang out on him, and demanded his money. James, who was a cool hand, said, "Weel a weel, let me get it," and stepping back, he said to Rab, "Speak till him, my man." In an instant Rab was standing over him, threatening strangulation if he stirred. James pushed on, leaving Rab in charge; he looked back, and saw that every attempt to rise was summarily put down. As he was telling Ailie the story, up came Rab with that great swing of his. It turned out that the robber was a Howgate lad, the worthless son of a neighbor, and Rab knowing him had let him cheaply off; the only thing, which was seen by a man from a field, was, that before letting him rise, he quenched (*pro tempore*) the fire of the eyes of the ruffian, by a familiar Gulliverian application of Hydraulics, which I need not further particularize. James, who did not know the way to tell an untruth, or embellish anything, told me this as what he called "a fact *positeevely*."

Wasp

Was a dark brindled bull terrier, as pure in blood as Cruiser or Wild Dayrell. She was brought by my brother from Otley, in the West Riding. She was very handsome, fierce, and gentle, with a small, compact, finely-shaped head, and a pair of wonderful eyes,—as full of fire and of softness as Grisi's; indeed she had to my eye a curious look of that wonderful genius—at once wild and fond. It was a fine sight to see her on the prowl across Bowden Moor, now cantering with her nose down, now gathered up on the top of a dyke, and with erect ears, looking across the wild like a moss-trooper out on business, keen and fell. She could do everything it became a dog to do, from killing an otter or a polecat, to watching and playing with a baby, and was as docile to her master as she was surly to all else. She was not quarrelsome, but "being in," she would have pleased Polonius as much, as in being "ware of entrance." She was never beaten, and she killed on the spot several of the country bullies who came out upon her when following her master in his rounds. She generally sent them off howling with one snap, but if this was not enough, she made an end of it.

But it was as a mother that she shone; and to see the gypsy, Hagar-like creature nursing her occasional Ishmael—playing with him, and fondling him all over, teaching his teeth to war, and with her eye and the curl of her lip daring any one but her master to touch him, was like seeing Grisi watching her darling "*Gennaro*," who so little knew why and how much she loved him.

Once when she had three pups, one of them died. For two days and nights she gave herself up to trying to bring it to life—licking it and turning it over and over, growling over it, and all but worrying it to awake it. She paid no attention to the living two, gave them no milk, flung them away with her teeth, and would have killed them, had they been allowed to remain with her. She was as one possessed, and neither ate, nor drank, nor slept, was heavy and miserable with her milk, and in such a state of excitement that no one could remove the dead pup.

Early on the third day she was seen to take the pup in her mouth, and start across the fields towards the Tweed, striding like a race-horse—she plunged in, holding up her burden, and at the middle of the stream dropped it and swam swiftly ashore; then she stood and watched the little dark lump floating away, bobbing up and down with the current, and losing it at last far down, she made her way home, sought out the living two, devoured them with her love, carried them one by one to her lair, and gave herself up wholly to nurse them; you can fancy her mental and bodily happiness and relief when they were pulling away— and theirs.

On one occasion my brother had lent her to a woman who lived in a lonely house, and whose husband was away for a time. She was a capital watch. One day an Italian with his organ came—first begging, then demanding money—showing that he knew she was alone, and that he meant to help himself, if she didn't. She threatened to "lowse the dowg"; but as this was Greek to him, he pushed on. She had just time to set Wasp at him. It was very short work. She had him by the throat, pulled him and his organ down with a heavy crash, the organ giving a ludicrous sort of cry of musical pain. Wasp thinking this was from some creature within, possibly a *whittret*, left the ruffian, and set to work tooth and nail on the box. Its master slunk off, and with mingled fury and thankfulness watched her disembowelling his only means of an honest living. The woman good-naturedly took her off, and signed to the miscreant to make himself and his remains scarce. This he did with a scowl; and was found in the evening in the village, telling a series of lies to the watchmaker, and bribing him with a shilling to mend his pipes—"his kist o' whussels."

THE KING'S GREYHOUND

The Master of Game

GASTON DE FOIX AND EDWARD, DUKE OF YORK

Here is praise of hounds and the story of a faithful one
from a volume acclaimed as the most famous hunting book of all time: De Foix's *Livre de Chasse*. It
was translated into English and added to by Edward,
second Duke of York, who is a character in Shakespeare's *Richard II*.

AFTER that I have spoken of the nature of beasts of venery and of chase
which men should hunt, now I will tell you of the nature of the hounds
which hunt and take them. And first of their noble conditions that be
so great and marvellous in some hounds that there is no man can believe
it, unless he were a good skilful hunter, and well knowing, and that he
haunted them long, for a hound is a most reasonable beast, and best
knowing of any beast that ever God made. And yet in some case I neither except man nor other thing, for men find it in so many stories and
(see) so much nobleness in hounds, always from day to day, that as I
have said there is no man that liveth, but must think it. Nevertheless
natures of men and all beasts go ever more descending and decreasing
both of life and of goodness and of strength and of all other things so
wonderfully, *as the Earl of Foix Phebus sayeth in his book*, that when
he seeth the hounds that be now hunting and thinketh of the hounds
that he hath seen in the time that is passed, and also of the goodness
and the truth, which was sometimes in the lords of this world, and
other common men, and seeth what now is in them at this time, truly
he saith that there is no comparison, and this knoweth well every man
that hath any good reason. But now let God ordain thereof whatever
His good will is. But to draw again to my matter, and tell the nobleness
of the hounds, the which have been, some good tales I shall tell you
the which I find in true writing. First of King Claudoneus of France,
the which sent once after his great court whereof were other kings which
held of him land, among the which was the King Appollo of Lyonnys
that brought with him to the court his wife and a greyhound that he
had, that was both good and fair. The King Claudoneus of France had
a seemly young man for his son, of twenty years of age, and as soon
as he saw the Queen of Lyonnys he loved her and prayed her of (for

her) love. The Queen was a good lady and loved well her lord, forsook
him and would him not, and said (to) him that if he spake to her any
more thereof that she would tell it to the King of France, and to her
Lord. And after that the feast was passed, King Appollo of Lyonnys
turned again, he and his wife to their country. And when they were so
turned again, he and his wife, the King Claudoneus son of France was
before him with a great fellowship of men of arms for to ravish his wife
from him. The King Appollo of Lyonnys that was a wonderful good
knight of his hounds (hands?) notwithstanding that he was unarmed,
defended himself and his wife in the best wise that he could unto the
time that he was wounded to the death, then he withdrew himself and
his wife into a tower. And the King Claudoneus son, the which would
not leave the lady, went in and took the lady, and would have defiled
her, and then she said to him "Ye have slain my lord, and (now) ye
would dishonour me, certes I would sooner be dead," then she drew
herself to (from) a window and leapt into the river of Loire that ran
under the tower and anon she was drowned. And after that within a
little while, the King Appollo of Lyonnys died of his wounds that he
had received, and on the same day he was cast into the river. The greyhound that I have spoke of, the which was always with the king his
master, when his lord was cast in the river leapt after him into the
river, insomuch that with his teeth he drew his lord out of the river,
and made a great pit with his claws in the best wise that he could, and
with his muzzle. And so the greyhound always kept his lord about half
a year in the pit, and kept his lord from all manner of beasts and fowls.
And if any man ask whereof he lived I say that he lived on carrion
and of other feeding such as he might come to. So it befell that the
King Claudoneus of France rode to see the estate of his realm, and (it)

befell that the king passed there where the greyhound was that kept his lord and master, and the greyhound arose against him, and began to yelp at him. The King Claudoneus of France the which was a good man and of good perception, anon when he saw the greyhound, knew that it was the greyhound that King Appollo of Lyonnys had brought to his court, whereof he had great wonder, and he went himself there where the greyhound was and saw the pit, and then he made some of his men alight from their horses for to look what was therein, and therein they found the King Appollo's body all whole. And anon as the King Claudoneus of France saw him, he knew it was the King Appollo of Lyonnys, whereof he was right sorry and sore aggrieved, and ordained a cry throughout all his realm, that whoso would tell him the truth of the deed he would give him whatsoever that he would ask. Then came a damsel that was in the tower when the King Appollo of Lyonnys was dead, and thus she said to the King Claudoneus of France, "Sir," quoth she, "if you will grant me a boon that I shall ask and assure me to have it, before all your men, I shall show you him that hath done the deed," and the King swore to her before his men, and it so befell that the King Claudoneus son of France was beside his father. "Sir," she said, "here is your son the which hath done this deed. Now require I you as ye have sworn to me that ye give him to me, I will no other gift of you." The King Claudoneus of France turned him then towards his son and said thus: "Thou cursed harlot, thou hast shamed and shent (disgraced) me and truly I shall shend (disgrace) you. And though I have no more children yet shall I not spare." Then he commanded to his men to make a great fire, and cast his son therein, and he turned him toward the damsel when the fire was great alight, and thus to her he said: "Damsel, now take ye him for I deliver him to you, as I promised and assured you." The damsel durst not come nigh, for by that time he was all burnt. This ensample have I brought forth for the nobleness of hounds and also of lords that have been in olden times. But I trow that few lords be now that would do so even and so open justice. A hound is true to his lord and his master, and of good love and true.

A hound is of great understanding and of great knowledge, a hound hath great strength and great goodness, a hound is a wise beast and a kind (one). A hound has a great memory and great smelling, a hound has great diligence and great might, a hound is of great lightness and of great perseverance, a hound is of good obedience, for he will learn as a man all that a man will teach him. A hound is full of good sport; hounds are so good that there is scarcely a man that would not have of them, some for one craft, and some for another. Hounds are hardy, for a hound dare well keep his master's house, and his beasts, and also will keep all his master's good, and he would sooner die than anything be lost in his keeping.

BOYS' DOG

All-American Mutt

S. OMAR BARKER

King was only a mongrel. But he and the other dogs
of the ranch proved that pedigree was not essential to
all the loyal service a dog can give.

THE freshet of 1904 had played havoc with the creek-bottom acres of
the Barker homestead in the Sapello Canyon, New Mexico; but to a
couple of barefooted, hillbilly young'uns and our curly black and brown
dog, its aftermath was wonderful. When the torrent subsided it left in
every meadow a dozen seepy pools with no running outlets—and in
every pool were dozens of cutthroat trout, trapped there to die as fast
as the pools dried up.

Armed with waterbuckets, our Levi's rolled to the knees, my brother
Marion and I set out to the rescue. For once, wading in cold water
was both virtuous and useful. With due parental permission, we were
to catch these trout with our hands, save out the larger ones for the frying pan, and transfer the rest alive to their proper home in Sapello Creek.

Of course—as always—King, the curly black dog, went along. He
cocked his head sidewise and watched us corner the first few trout under an overhang of sod and pull them out, wiggly and gleaming. Then,
with no suggestion from us, King joined the game himself. Wading
water over his back, his curly-plumed tail wigwagging delightedly, he
plunged his broad muzzle first here, then there under the water at the
flitting shadows that were frightened, darting trout.

For a while he caught nothing, but within five minutes, when we
moved on to an unmuddied pool, he had learned to stand on three
legs, ears at alert, and watch until he saw a fish dart to hiding under a
rock or overhanging bank. Then he approached cautiously until he
could make a swift, one-motion grab under the water. The third try
of this kind netted him a ten-inch, red-bellied beauty.

From that moment on, King was a fisherman. He caught as many
trout as either of us kids. As his were usually the larger ones, we saved
his catch for the frying pan, transplanting our own uninjured fish alive
to the creek. King liked raw fish, so we let him eat a few. But plainly

Reprinted by permission of the author.

he had not turned fisherman for the sake of food. His tail wagged constant delight in the sport. Before long he was leaving the pools as soon as they became too muddied and leading us importantly to the next.

Do dogs think? Whether they do or not, is pedigree so essential to canine intelligence as we are often led to believe? From childhood I have never been without a dog, and I have never owned one with a pedigree. Yet. . . .

Well, to begin with, there was old King. A somewhat conjectural estimate of his breeding gave him about one half water spaniel, one quarter black shepherd of some sort, and one eighth some kind of square-jawed bull. The last paternal eighth could have been nothing but "jest dawg"—and for all we knew, yellow at that. We acquired him as the average rural American family of some years ago usually acquired its dogs. A good many still do. He was a cute puppy, so a neighbor gave him to Pa Barker—"for the kids."

Let me hasten to grant that King's ready knack for trout fishing was undoubtedly the gift of his water-spaniel ancestry. But it was King, the mutt, who figured out the most effective method so quickly. Thanks to that quarter of shepherd blood, he also readily became a good stock dog. He learned to help drive cattle by heel nipping instead of frontal attack; he could chase hogs out of the corn without doing them serious injury, and bring in the milk cows on command. He could catch a chicken and hold it with his paws, indulging his "canine ferocity" only to the extent of a mouthful of feathers.

Just dog. A plain mutt. Yet he attained a career wholly unpredictable from any known elements of his ancestry, getting "his picture in the paper," and everything. For King became, in his day, one of the best bobcat and mountain lion hunters that ever trailed and treed the big cats in our section of the Rockies. Sure, I know that cat hunting is the proper business of hounds, bred and trained for that purpose. But old King didn't know it; he never had a chance to run with a pack of trained cougar hounds or learn by imitation. Like a good many Americans of the two-legged variety who attain success in unexpected fields, unhampered by traditions of family and blue-blooded ancestry, King "just taken him a notion to tree lions—and done so."

He trailed and treed his first bobcat and first mountain lion without canine assistance, alone except for the encouragement of my farmer-ranchman-hunter dad. On his third lion hunt he jumped four longtails feasting on a fresh deer kill, took after them, and treed them all, one at a time, going on after the next as soon as each had been shot.

Yet the very next day after his record lion hunt, King went out with me, a ten-year-old kid, and treed chickaree squirrels for me to throw rocks at; and he did it with as much barking enthusiasm as if he had not, just the day before, sunk his teeth bravely into the haunch of a big, wounded tom-cougar. And the next summer he and I had just as much sport as ever rousting chipmunks out of rock piles for him to catch—and eat. He would eat anything—from raspberries to turnips to fish guts to bear meat.

At haying time in late summer he went around bulging like an over-fed shoat. Mice. Under the last forkful of fragrant timothy hay shocks there usually were field mice—and King got most of them, some seemingly gobbled alive.

There were only two ways to get him out of a hayfield while loading was going on. One was to start some place with a gun; that indicated more important business. The other way was to insult him. This was done with a pitchfork handle. Maybe it wasn't very kind, but it was funny, and we did it disgracefully often.

We would wait until King had taken his stance at the alert, ready to pounce on the first gray wiggle under the hay that might be a mouse. Then we would quietly poke the rounded end of a pitchfork handle through the stubble between his legs—from behind. Invariably, when he saw it, some instinct in him cried "Snake!" and made him high jump like a startled deer. Then, when he saw what it was and we laughed, his big brown eyes looked foolish and reproachful.

If it was our first offense of the day he might merely reproach us by staying away from the next shock or two. But about the third or fourth time we pulled the joke on him, it was good-by old King! Away he would stalk to the house. Neither wheedling nor scolding could bring him back for several hours. He was afraid of snakes (though he often killed them), and it hurt his dignity to be laughed at.

If there was any possible sport of woods or mountain farm that King didn't like, from chipmunk chousing to helping horseback men work cattle, we never discovered it. That is one thing I have liked about the plain, run-of-the-mill, unpedigreed pooches I have known: they weren't overspecialized in their interests. Had they been people, one might well call them broadminded, courageous, tolerant good scouts. I have no doubt that many blue-bloods of dogdom may be like that too. But I speak for the kindly treated, family-owned, much beloved all-American mutt, because I know him better.

For all their versatility, most of my mongrels have shown a remarkable sense of relative values. Old King, to instance him again, seemed to figure out such things for himself.

It is illegal and is considered unsportsmanlike—not to say futile—to run mule deer with dogs in New Mexico. Yet despite many whippings we were never able to cure King of it entirely. Their musky scent seemed to tantalize him beyond all control.

One day, on the steep pine slopes of Vaur Canyon, old King broke away pell-mell at the heels of a big buck. Out of sight some four hundred yards down the hill, his sharp "deer yelp" suddenly changed to a loud, ferocious baying. Sometimes, especially in rutting season, an old buck deer will stop to fight almost anything that jumps him. Old King, it seemed, must have run into such a one. As he ran down toward him, my brother Elliott broke off a good, sharp switch of buckbrush. King would have to be whipped again for chasing deer.

But it didn't turn out that way. Elliott came over a small ridge at the scene of action to find, not a bayed buck, but a huge, snarling mountain lion that had stubbornly refused to tree from a single dog. King had quit the deer chase instantly when he crossed the lion's track. Now, with Elliott to encourage him—even before there was time to shoot— this curly, squatty, unpedigreed black pooch leaped smack into the middle of one of the most deadly fighters of the woods. The big cat was at least four times the dog's weight and well equipped with both claw and fang. But it was a battle royal while it lasted—which was only until Elliott could get in a close-range shot. Believe it or not, the dead lion's claws were full of black, curly dog hair, but King was practically unscathed. He was also plainly proud of himself.

The point I make, however, is that in King's category of things worthwhile, cougar scent was No. 1. He would leave any track or chase, no matter how hot, to take the trail of a mountain lion, even if the track were twenty-four hours old.

Bobcats were No. 2 on his list. Then, beginning at the other end, mice and chipmunks rated about the same. But he would quit a chipmunk to tree a squirrel. If a rabbit hopped by, he would abandon the squirrel. Grouse scent threw him into a frenzy of delight and far outranked rabbits. Without any training, he would point them briefly, then cavort all over the mountain side when they flew. It was the same on his rare encounters with wild turkeys.

Skunks, badgers, and raccoons graded upward in importance to coyotes. These slim wolves he hated and feared, yet he would chase and sometimes even fight them if they turned on him. But on his canine rating chart, the smell of mountain lion was always No. 1, with deer just a weakness on the side.

Bear he was frankly afraid of. Yet once when two of us kids in our excitable early teens had wounded a big she-bear with cubs and were having trouble getting our old black-powder .40-60 reloaded as she charged us, King faced her as vigorously as he would have run from her if only his own hide had been at stake. He got pretty badly hurt, but he stopped the enraged lady-bruin's charge long enough for Marion's shaking hands to get the gun loaded and fired—a killing shot. Probably he saved our fool young lives. Certainly he gave us an example of true canine courage.

Unquestionably, certain breeds of dogs are natural hunters, others natural watchdogs, others retrievers, others lap pets, others guardians of the flocks, just as, for instance, the Irish seem to be natural politicians, policemen, and poets. But in the mongrel mutt there's no telling what talents may turn up.

Ted, approximately half collie and half bull terrier, teamed up with Nig, about three quarters black shepherd, to make a first-rate pair of cat hunters, even though only "snow-trailers." And the sole guardian and herder of a small flock of sheep near our ranch, day and night, summer and winter, was a self-trained mongrel, half Airedale and half what his Spanish-American owner called "*quién sabe?*" This dog never had a bit of training except that his master had taught him, while still a little pup, to suckle a ewe. Thereafter he lived with the sheep. He grew up with them. I am even inclined to believe that he thought he *was* a sheep, albeit a superior one and therefore responsible for the safety and welfare of his less fortunate companions.

He almost never left his charges for anything except his meals, and then only when they were safely bedded in their shed. If his woollies were in the road and he saw a car coming, he would begin driving them out of danger while the car was still a hundred yards away. The anxiety with which he would labor to keep his sheep from getting run over was both amusing and almost pitiful. Not until they were exactly where he considered them safe would he indulge his natural canine weakness for barking at speeding wheels. Don't ask me where and how he learned all this. I only testify that he was one more mutt who knew his stuff.

Puse (short for the misnomer of his gangling puppyhood: Pusillanimous) was an Airedale—mostly. His sire may or may not have had a pedigree. His dam had some smidgen of hound in her blood and a reputation as a huntress. Puse was raised and trained by my brother Elliott. Outright mutt or not, he was no blue-blood. When Elliott moved to Santa Fe as New Mexico's State Game Warden and left Puse with me, he had already been in at the kill of dozens of mountain lions and hundreds of bobcats. He loved to hunt wild cats, yet was friendly and tolerant with our house cats.

If I happened to have enough silver in my pocket to jingle, and jingled it in Puse's hearing, he paid me no mind whatsoever. But let me jingle a handful of .30–30 cartridges in the same manner and his ears pricked up at once. Immediately he was up and whining to go, his stub tail wigwagging eagerly. Similar as the sounds are, money-jingle meant nothing to him. Cartridge-jingle meant much: guns, gunfire, hunting!

Saddling a horse would boil him over with joyous anticipation, for all horseback trips into the woods were hunting trips to him. Yet a quiet word was all it ever took to make him stay back if the ride was to be a deer hunt. He would look mournfully and pleadingly out of his doghouse at us as we rode away, but with no move to follow unless invited. His companion, an aging veteran called "Pup," being practically stone-deaf, would keep a weather eye on Puse to make sure what the orders were. If Puse followed, Pup followed. If Puse stayed back, he stayed back.

Elliott's education of both of these Airedale mutts required a considerable amount of judicious whipping while they were still quite young, mostly for chasing deer. But once trained, they stayed trained. Nor did the whippings ever lessen their adoration of their master.

The smartest, most astonishingly reasonable thing Puse ever did was on a mountain-lion hunt in the Vermejo Park country. Elliott was trailing five mountain lions with Puse, Pup, and a hound. One of the cougars treed. The others ran on. The instant that Elliott came in sight of the treed longtail, Puse came running to him. He jumped up, forefeet on Elliott's leg, whined, looked up at the treed cat, back at his master, let out a little yelp, whirled, and sped away on the trail of the other four lions.

As plainly as if he had spoken words, Puse had said:

"See that lion? You take care of this one! I've got to go on after those others before they get away!"

This performance he repeated as each lion was treed, and not one of the long-tailed deer-slayers escaped.

If my experience with unpedigreed specimens of the breed means anything, Airedales and part-Airedales fear nothing that lives. Old Pup, at the ripe age of fifteen, without a tooth in his head sharper than the end of your finger, went straight to the throat of a huge mountain lion that a poor shot of mine had tumbled from a tree wounded instead of killed. Deadly claws caught his head and pulled it, literally, into the lion's mouth. If Pup had tried to pull away, the rip of those great claws would have torn him to death. But Pup wasn't pulling away. He was attacking. Only a hasty shot at ten-foot range saved him. Though his age-gray head was a mass of blood, it took me a full minute to pry his jaws loose from the dead cougar's throat.

As the old cowboy song says, "there was blood on the saddle" as I carried the wounded dog home in the growing darkness. Without stopping for even so much as a cup of coffee, Elsa and I piled old Pup into the car and drove twenty-seven snow-banked miles to town, where a veterinarian who also loved dogs doctored and sewed up his hurts. A lion fang had scratched his jugular vein, but he recovered and lived to hunt lions again.

Courage! Linked with the story of humankind, always there will be true tales of the courage of dogs, whether blue-blooded or mutts!

Unfortunately, this fearlessness sometimes extends too far. Take porcupines, for instance. A dog hasn't a Chinaman's chance against them. His first attack nets him a muzzleful of cruelly painful quills. Yet I have never known a mutt that wouldn't tackle a porky just the same—at least until taught to let them alone. And getting "quilled" is rarely sufficient to teach them. Too brave—or just a little dumb?

Once Puse killed a half-grown porcupine and carried it home. But at what cost! It took my wife and me four hours to pull out the many hundred quills, mostly with pliers. How much do dogs understand? Attacking a porky in the first place was idiotic. But lying still through the long ordeal of "dequilling" without being tied or held, without anesthetic, without a single effort to escape or resist, somehow hints at an intelligence that approaches reason. Porky quills do not come out easily. We pulled them from as far back in Puse's throat as long pliers would reach, with only my fingers to hold his mouth open. Puse whimpered a little to ask for brief rests, but that was all; and he showed his appreciation by wagging his tail when we got through.

This was only one of many similar sessions, for getting hurt by porcupines never taught this otherwise smart dog to let them alone. Yet when he was all of nine years old, I broke him of it. Oddly enough, we had never come across a porky on the ground when I was out in the woods with him. Then one day it happened. The instant Puse started after the porcupine I ordered him back. He stopped, looked at me inquiringly, then started on. With a second stern command, I stepped quickly off my horse and grabbed him. I made him sit on his haunches with his front feet in my hand and listen to a stern and prolonged lecture consisting mostly of the word "Back!" The porky had climbed a nearby tree, and every time Puse turned his head in that direction, I cuffed his ears. Finally Elsa, my wife, shot the porcupine while I held the dog. I led him within a couple of yards of the dead porky, turned him loose and ordered him not to touch it. For ten minutes or so I stood there with a switch, giving him a little whack every time he came closer than six feet to the porky, then we rode on home. Incredible as it may seem, you *can* teach an old dog new tricks. Never again did Puse get a dose of porcupine quills. In his old age he even learned to tree porkies by circling them and barking ferociously, but he never tackled one again.

That dogs hate cats is axiomatic. But on any sunny day during the years when Puse and Pup lived with us on a New Mexico mountain side, you might see house cats rubbing unafraid against the legs of a couple of somewhat bored but tolerant Airedales. I have even seen a kitten lying across Puse's front paws, both animals peacefully asleep. And these were dogs whose principal occupation in life was hunting cats—wild ones, that is!

Of all animals—except man—the dogs I have known have always liked horses best. Cats, calves, and cows they might tolerate, but horses they loved.

Riding homeward from high cattle range one day, Marion and I had the misfortune to cripple Nellie, one of our saddle mares, in the tangle of a snaggy logfall. No bones were broken and it was not a terribly serious hurt, but the skin of one hind leg was badly ripped by a sharp snag, causing the little mare to limp quite painfully. Some three miles from home we unsaddled Nellie, dressed her leg as best we could, and turned her loose. Without more immediate travel the wound should heal all right. In a few days we would come back to check on it.

We were nearly home when we noticed that old King was no longer with us. He did not come home that night, nor the next day, nor the next night. A rush job of haying under a threat of rain kept us from going back at once to look for him. There were no traps out in the woods that we knew of. Besides, King was trapwise. We could think of nothing serious that might have happened to him. Pa thought it likely that he might have encountered female company, and loitered to enjoy it. Surely he would come on home soon. But the third day passed, and still no King.

Marion and I saddled and rode up the trail to Beaver Creek where we had left the injured mare. We meant, after tending to her, to spend the rest of the day, and more days, too, if need be, searching for our dog.

We didn't have to. When we found Nellie, old King was with her, gaunt, hungry, but still on guard. He was overjoyed to see us, but when we started home again without the mare (her wound was healing nicely), King went back and sat down near her, watching us go, stubbornly disobedient to our calling. We might have made him come along without the mare, but we didn't have the heart. We caught Nellie again and led her home, with old King trotting happily—and faithfully—at her heels.

Here in the cow country, when we say "old," we don't necessarily refer to age. More often "old" is a term of endearment. That's why it always seems natural for me to speak of that curly black mongrel as "old King." Similarly it is always old Towser, old Rock, old Jack, old Ted, old Nig, old Snip, old Bob, old Queenie, old Puse, and old Pup, as a somewhat wistful memory reviews the procession of good, smart dogs without a pedigree that I have been privileged to know and handle over the years. Some of them lived to a ripe old age, and I am not ashamed that their passing was not without tears on my part.

Not all were such personalities as old King, old Puse, and old Pup, and all, no doubt had their faults, even as you and I. But remembering them, I am moved to rise and offer tribute to the mutt, the "jest plain dawg," the kind of canine that, in America as nowhere else, has won a place for himself in both the homes and hearts of ordinary folks without benefit of certified ancestry.

I have nothing against the blue-bloods, whether they be field, show, or lap dogs. But as a plain, ordinary citizen, myself undistinguished by any record of aristocratic family tree, my heart warms most, somehow, to the kind of dog I have always known the best. Whether, after all, he is sometimes a thinker in his own right, or just a dog, I hereby nominate him to a most honorable title: The All-American Mutt!

BOAR HUNTER

"A Dog's Life"

GEORGE SURDEZ

An aged hound of an old French breed, the Bastard of
High Poitou, relives his triumphs in the hunting field.
In this vivid sketch the author speaks for the dog, a
device often employed but rarely so expertly done.

I KNOW very well why they didn't leave me at the kennel, why I am here
on the terrace with these old people—people too old to walk far or to
even ride a horse. I am here because I am an old dog.

"Watch Zephyr," the Monkey said when I arrived and stretched out.
"You can follow the hunt that way. He knows all about it, don't you,
my good old Zephyr?"

The Monkey is seventy-eight years old. His real name is Monsieur le
Baron; but at the kennel, at the stable, in the kitchen, everybody calls
him the Monkey. I think he is a nice old boy, and not more of a pest
to have around than an old dog. He likes me, and he likes to think
I am crazy about him. He gives me a bit of biscuit, and he explains
to the old ladies and gentlemen that it is all right, that my work is done
for the day, and that at my age it doesn't matter much.

"Another season," he says, "and I'll retire him completely. But what
a marvelous dog he was in his day—well, we can say the same about
most of us, eh-eh-eh! Watch those ears, that tail—listen—see, he heard
before we did."

What a feat, what an exploit! Half of them are deaf as pots, and the
others don't know they're hearing when they do hear. Sure, I heard that
horn, and I know that call: a boar. They're after a boar! Of course, that's
thrilling news, after all that scouting for a scent yesterday and early
this morning! There were three of us old dogs spotting, with three
grooms—old grooms, too. I am the oldest by a year, and yet it was me
spotted the right scent. No trick to it; the grooms know where to take
you.

Anyway, a lot of this boar hunting is fake stuff. There are so few
boars nowadays that they're all known to the guards and the grooms.
That's why they hunt boar on this estate only once a season—one boar.

I used to go along with the pack, and I was head dog for three seasons, because I had what it takes: a good nose, a good voice, good sense, speed, endurance, and plenty of guts. I was just as good at anything else —deer, hare—but I was supposed to be "it" for boar.

"That's what he liked," the Monkey says: "—boar. Because there's more danger, I guess; he is a fighter."

Just because I got raked a couple of times! When the boar comes to bay, sometimes you just can't stop yourself, and you go for his ear or his throat, before you remember it's sap's business, and all you're supposed to do is hold him there until a man pops up. You're drunk as a gamekeeper on an off-night by the time a boar stops, drunk with excitement and with his smell—you have kept getting steady sniffs for so long—see?

"He's all French, that hound," the Monkey explains: "What is known as a Bastard of High Poitou. The breed dates back centuries, some claim as far as Louis XI. Best hunting dog on earth—look at those solid legs and heavy paws, that chest . . . You can trace this one back more generations than the Bourbons can trace themselves! And what a magnificent voice! You'll hear him when he gets excited—he can't help howling when the going gets hot. He can tell by the barks and by the horn, follows everything from here! You'll see—a magnificent voice! You saw some English foxhounds in the pack: they're very good hounds, yes, but no voice, no voice."

That is not so bright of him. The head groom knows better, I have heard him talk. He says a hound is a hound, and it depends on the hound as to his speed, endurance, and voice. He is right; we had an English hound here for stud at one time and he had as good a voice as any French dog. The head groom says you can't go by averages; you've got to pick and select—just as he picked and selected the boar for today.

The rich people get on horses and follow the dogs. They don't know what goes into a successful hunt at all, what goes before. The head groom does what he can to pick an old boar, not because they're wiser, fiercer, and more sport, but because they have settled habits, and you know where they'll go, so you can spot the relays right. You get a very young boar, and you don't know what to expect; he may go crazy and start for the dogs right away and cut matters short, while a middle-aged boar may run in a straight line and refuse to circle, strew the hunters for fifty-odd kilometers, and get away safely to the next county.

An old boar with big tusks looks formidable, but he is more settled. Usually, he's been living in the neighborhood for years, and he hates to leave it. That's where he met his females, where he had his fights. It looks good to him; he feels safer there; moreover, he thinks nobody should push him out. Also, he's heard the hounds often before, has usually been chased by them by mistake a couple of times, so he thinks it will all come out all right.

"See that tail, those ears?" the Monkey asks. "He hears the horn; he knows what's happening, and we don't."

What's happening? The boar has circled the first time, and the first relay is after him. The head groom knows his business. That boar is an old, smart fellow, too smart to be daring. He doesn't want to start galloping over country he doesn't know. Ah, you get too smart, too smart . . .

And too damn' old to be much damn' good. I am still useful, really the most important dog around. It takes experience and wisdom to spot a scent and follow it enough to make the man sure you've picked up a good trail, without butting in too soon and flushing the boar out of the bushes with a rush and a yell. I spotted the scent last night, and we checked up this morning, after I had my breakfast of bread soaked in oil, and—that makes me laugh—had my nose rinsed in vinegar and water. It's supposed to clear your nostrils! No sense in it, but it's always been done, so they always do it. As the Monkey says, boar hunting has its traditions!

So, after getting my nose washed out, we checked up. The grooms washed their mouths out too, but not with vinegar! I was taken to the scent I'd picked up and followed it, checking. Yes, he was around; once or twice I got a straight scent, and we found droppings. I knew my job was done and turned around; and on the way back, we met the grooms with part of the pack on leash. I grunted around, kidding the dogs, and the grooms said: "Look at old Zephyr, he wants to run, doesn't know he is too old."

I know damn' well I am too old. I know it better than anyone else, because it's my legs that are stiff after a few miles, and it's my back that aches. Run all day? No, they can have it.

But even the young dogs looked as if they pitied me, felt sorry for me. I know all about that—when you're young, you look at an old chap and you imagine he feels the way you would feel—forgetting that if your body doesn't feel so good, it's automatic; your mind doesn't want it to do anything that hurts it. Like the Monkey: he used to get on his horse and gallop with the best of them, but when it started to hurt him, he stopped. He only rode two seasons while I was on the pack. And I was nothing but a pup at the time.

I used to watch Cupidon, when he had my job—he was about the age I am now, but he looked older. Same breed, though—big and strong, black and white, with liver patches on the jowls and the two spots over the eyes. I used to hope that I'd never live to be the wisest, oldest dog around and be used for spotting.

Here is what I used to think: When I get sort of oldish, when I realize that I can't keep up with the pack much longer, I'm going to die game. I'll lunge in on a boar deliberately, and get myself ripped open good. So that I won't have to hear how the whole pack got fed on the entrails and won't be given a little slice of the liver by the head groom, after it has been *boiled*. I always picked a boar to end with, never a stag —although I was good with stag, too. Why? Because a stag seldom really fights dogs; and when he does, you get a broken spine if he stabs down, or a broken jaw if he kicks back, and the second groom who has the gun has to finish you, and it's a mess and an embarrassment all around. Losing a dog mars the hunt, they say, makes the ladies sad.

"Look at him," the Monkey says.

Why not? They're getting hot after him out there. He has circled and twisted back. I can hear Lurette yelling like a crazy dog, but that doesn't mean much. He is dumb, even if he yells louder than any other. He doesn't know what's going on; he's what you'd call a tenor, a show-off —he's seventh or eighth; he's not even smelling, just running, but he yells louder than the leaders.

Yes, as I was saying, I used to think I'd rush the boar and get it over with. If you get a good rip, they can't try to sew you up, but how many dogs do you know who survived that for long? So what happened, why didn't I do it? It's simple enough: by the time I got old enough to try it, I was tired when the boar made his stand; I'd be yards back, and the pack would be circling—and the boar'd look awfully big and nasty; and rushing him seemed silly, something for the young dogs to do.

So the men noticed that I was getting slow and winded easily. And they put me on this job. Grooms and dogs think I am sorry for myself, humiliated. They're crazy. I like a little exercise; the head groom lets me run a hare now and then, on my own, when there's no big hunt meeting on. I feel fine; the sun feels good; and I enjoy eating my food and I can digest as well now as I could four years ago!

They think I feel humiliated when they come back, with their jaws bloody, and sucking bits of raw meat out of their fangs. They think I am jealous. They amuse me. I like to see them come back, all alike and all different. The tired-out dogs who should never have been hunters. The leaders, muddy and bursting with conceit; the so-sos, who liked it all right but are glad it's done with, and the best part for them was the eating.

Then there are those who feel that they didn't do so well, and act as if they just hadn't got well started, you know, the bristling ones who sniff and grumble around, saying over and over again: "Where is he? Let me at him!" And the nervous ones, who drop off to sleep from fatigue, and go over the whole business again in their dreams, yapping and jerking their paws.

Yes, it sure is fun to watch them come in. And tonight I'll get a good hunk of the liver, boiled specially for me. I would not want to be out there running my head off, thirsty, my lungs aching, I have the best role. Just like the Monkey . . . It's fun to be old, and to let others do the work.

That wild stuff is all over for me, all over—me for the kennel, me for the terrace. And if the old Monkey thinks I'm going to give those old people a show, he—

The horn! . . . They've spotted him . . . They've seen him . . .

Go to it, go to it, go to it!

Ahoo-ahow-whooo, ahoo, ahoo, wowooo!

BOOK RETRIEVER

Peter Chapin

P. HAMILTON GOODSELL

Instead of a bird dog, the black cocker spaniel became a book dog. In his memory was founded what is probably the most notable library of books on dogs in the world. It is located at the College of William and Mary, Williamsburg, Virginia.

The article following describes some of the library's treasures.

IN many parts of the world are to be found memorials to dogs, dedicated, erected, or written by people who desired to pay a lasting tribute to some devoted canine pal who had preceded them into the great unknown, but who had left them an indelible memory of all those lovable qualities of which a dog is capable. Some of these memorials are in the form of monuments erected over the last resting place of the departed friend, such as the one set up over the grave of Lord Byron's Boatswain at Newstead Abbey, or a public monument, such as stands in the Cowgate in Edinburgh to the memory of Greyfriars Bobby, a little dog who had endeared himself to all the citizens of that old town. And countless books have been written extolling the virtues of some well-loved dog.

But perhaps the most unique, and in a way perchance the most worthwhile to those humans within whose heart beats the love of a dog is the Peter Chapin Collection of Books on Dogs, which is housed in the fine Library of William and Mary College in Williamsburg, Virginia. Peter Chapin was a black cocker spaniel, who for years had been the devoted companion and trusted friend of Mr. and Mrs. Howard M. Chapin of Providence.

After his death, Mr. and Mrs. Chapin undertook to establish as a unique memorial to their beloved pal a comprehensive collection of books on dogs. Before starting the work, they made an exhaustive search as to the number of books on the subject of dogs in the more prominent libraries throughout the country. Much to their surprise, they discovered in one of the largest libraries only eighty titles, and in a second a mere

First appeared in The New Haven Register, November 10, 1940.
Reprinted by permission.

ninety, while many libraries, embracing even some important ones, could boast of only a meager few titles.

A long and painstaking attempt, which extended over many years, was made to locate titles in various languages, English, French, Dutch, German, Swedish, Spanish, Italian, Latin, and Greek. The results of this patient search, carried on as a labor of love, was the collection now

known as the Peter Chapin Collection. It contains 1,993 titles and 2,300 volumes, many of them exceedingly rare and not as a rule found outside the great museums of England and Europe. The collection was presented to the Library of the College of William and Mary by Mr. and Mrs. Chapin in the spring of 1938, and Mr. Chapin himself prepared a short-title list of its contents, which has been printed by the Library in a bulletin with an introductory note by the librarian, Dr. E. G. Swem, and which is dedicated to Mrs. Anne Caroline Brown Chapin, who had died after the donation of the collection was made.

While recently visiting the fascinating town of Williamsburg, it was my great pleasure and privilege to examine the collection, which was made all the more interesting by the courteous and helpful assistance of Dr. Swem and his assistant, Mr. Jennings. I had heard of the collection of course, but as I had never seen the Title List, I was quite unprepared for the size, scope, and value of it. It runs from the sub-lime to the ridiculous, so to speak, from works of priceless value in old and tattered bindings, to paper-covered, illustrated little books of poetry about dogs for little children and pamphlets issued by various dog-food and dog-remedy companies, for the donors were entirely catholic in their selection, and assembled all they could find—history, prose, verse, and purely academical works on the subject of dogs.

Among the most valuable and highly prized volumes is a perfect copy of *De Canibus* by John Caius, printed in London in 1570, the first book about dogs to be printed in England. There are of course other copies of this book in existence, but I only know of the one in the British Museum. Then there are a first and second edition of a short satire by Jonathan Swift, printed in London in 1736, entitled *Bounce to Fop, an Heroick Epistle from a Dog at Twickenham to a Dog at Court*. The satire is delightful, and is all the more appreciated by one who can realize and understand the difference between the life of a dog leading a normal, healthy existence and one of the pampered, spoiled, neurotic lap dog.

Then too one finds a superb example of the printer's art in a volume of *The Master of Game* by a Plantagenet, Edward, Duke of York, re-printed in London in 1904 with an introduction by Theodore Roosevelt, and illustrated with hand-illuminated title page and illustrations of the text in a manner that is a joy to behold. There is also a second edition of the same work printed in 1909. Here too is to be found Sydenham Edwards' Cynographia Britannica, printed in London in 1800, and to which I have often referred in this column. Quite amusing is *Another Ministerial Defeat, The Trial of the Dog for Biting the Noble Lord*, printed in London in 1817 and with a cut of a dog on the title page, and bound with "official account of the noble Lord's Bite!" And the books on all breeds of dogs by Comte Henri de Bylandt, whose *Dogs of All Nations*, printed in 1905 was for many years the book on different breeds used by the American Kennel Club as authority.

So well known is the collection that many letters are received from all over the world by Dr. Swem requesting information on subjects connected with dogs. As for instance one received not long ago from England asking for information on the use of dogs in churning, which oddly enough could not be furnished for lack of data on this subject, although in the Low Countries, and in certain sections of this country dogs have been so used in the past, if not today.

Apart from the technical and historical works, a person interested in dogs could spend weeks in perusing the many famous volumes of stories about dogs, both fiction and fact. But as to these, I was surprised to find that Mr. and Mrs. Chapin in their collection had not included two great dog stories, one fiction, the other historically true. Namely, Ouida's

Pierot, Dog of Flanders, which no one should essay to read without a bountiful supply of handkerchiefs at hand, and *Greyfriars Bobby*, the life story of the gallant little dog of the Edinburgh Cowgate. But all the others are here, by the writers whose names are familiar to all who love a dog.

The Library welcomes additions to the collection, and undoubtedly it will receive from time to time gifts which will increase and add to its value and scope. Anyone who loves a dog and goes to Williamsburg should not fail to spend an hour or two browsing among these books and pamphlets. To do so will but serve to increase his wonder that a dog can so achieve the affection of man that he can spend time, money, patience, and effort to erect such a unique and lasting memorial to a loved one gone before.

Peter Chapin did not live in vain, and to this fact the collection named for him in the famous old College of William and Mary bears witness. William and Mary in the arcade of the old Wrenn building has a marble tablet, setting forth several "first" things and achievements of which it is justly proud. Engraved upon it might be added another "first"; the first college to boast of what is probably the finest dog library in the world!

LION-HUNTING PACK

"Leading a Dog's Life"

ELLIOTT S. BARKER

Treed several times, the lion leaped down and ran.
Then the hunter, riding to the hounds, dismounted
to stalk him on his next perch. His strategy was: to
think like a dog and act like one.

IN June, 1930, I was in charge of game-management and predator control work at Vermejo Park, a 360,000-acre cattle ranch and game park in the mountains of northern New Mexico. A Government hunter and trapper, I. T. Ritchie, who was camped at the McChristal place just south of the park boundary, had lost a big old tom lion several times when his dogs failed to keep it treed until he could get through the rough country to it. The half-trained dogs, which he had acquired, would trail and tree the big lion, but leave the tree and come back to him before he could get there. As soon as the dogs left, the lion would come down, and get away. When that happens a time or two, a lion learns that he can get away and becomes very hard to keep up a tree, even when the dogs stay.

Mr. Ritchie had asked me to go out with him, which I was glad to do, for I had yet to see the lion that my dogs couldn't keep up a tree, and was anxious to try them out on this one. Besides, he had done me several big favors, and I welcomed the chance to return one, especially if a lion hunt was involved.

On my saddle horse I left Castle Rock at sun-up and started across the hills to Mr. Ritchie's camp with my three good Airedales and big red hound. I took my old reliable .45 six-shooter, which I often carried, instead of my rifle, on lion and bobcat hunts because it is handier to carry when riding through thick brush and timber, and in almost every case one can ride right up under a tree and shoot a lion or cat out without difficulty at close range. While I realized we were going after a difficult lion, I knew Mr. Ritchie would have his rifle and, since it was his lion, he would do the shooting anyway.

Soon after we topped out into the aspen country at the head of Rock

Reprinted by permission of the University of New Mexico Press and *Field and Stream*.

Creek, only half-way to the camp, the dogs hit a very hot trail headed the same way we were going. Queenie, Puse, Pup and Kate opened up on the trail and made the woods ring with their baying and yelping.

Of the three Airedales, only little Queenie would give tongue on a cold trail, while Pup and Puse trailed silently until the trail became hot or their quarry was jumped. Old Kate, my big red hound, talked freely in her heavy, deep voice on any kind of trail. The way they were talking now, I knew the trail was smoking hot.

I also felt sure they were on a lion track, but it was at least a half mile before I saw any sign to prove it, if, indeed, any proof other than the testimony being given by my four reliable dogs were needed. Then I glimpsed the scrape of a big tom lion under a pine tree as I galloped after the dogs. Striking a fresh lion track here was entirely unexpected. There was no mistaking it from their incessant barking and the ring of their excited, high-pitched voices. I knew the trail was so hot fresh that Mr. Lion would have to take a tree very soon, and that is just what he did.

When the dogs barked treed, the sound of their sharp-cut, eager voices made my pulse beat faster. Tingling with satisfaction at our rare good luck, I slowed my sweating horse down to a walk, for there was now no need to hurry, and rode straight toward the dogs.

When within about a hundred and twenty-five yards, I could see, through an opening in the timber, the dogs frantically barking up a big white fir tree. From their actions and unusual excitement it was evident that the lion was either perched on a very low branch in plain sight of the dogs, or coming down the tree.

Then I saw a big, yellowish-red, long-tailed lion, not twenty feet from the ground, slowly backing down the tree. It was too far for a safe shot with my .45. So I touched spurs to my horse and yelled a couple of times, thinking I might scare Mr. Longtail back up the tree. But no such luck. When he was about fifteen feet from the ground, he jumped and took out over the ridge at a tremendously fast pace. The dogs were right after him as he went out of sight.

By the time he jumped I had gotten pretty close to him, but did not have time to shoot. He was a beauty—very sleek and fat-looking, with well-colored reddish sides, a white belly, and sharply contrasting markings about the head. He was as handsome a lion as I ever saw, and the picture of him bounding away, tail high in the air and the dogs right after him, is still clear in my mind.

At first I thought nothing much of the incident. I had several times seen lions do that, and occasionally had had a lion jump out two or three times before I got a shot. Then it occurred to me that this might be Mr. Ritchie's lion; and if so, it might be a bit difficult to get close enough for a pistol shot.

When I topped the ridge, the dogs were again eagerly barking treed in the bottom of a sharp canyon, about a quarter of a mile away. I rode on slowly and as quietly as I could, keeping out of sight behind timber, with the intention of leaving my horse when I got within a couple of hundred yards to sneak up on him afoot from behind cover.

When I got off my horse, out he came again, this time leaping from a height of thirty feet or more onto the slope on the other side of the draw. In this way he gained a few yards' head start on the dogs, but the fast Airedales caught up with him just over the top of the first ridge and forced him up another tree.

This time I rode only half-way up the slope, left my horse, took off my chaps and spurs, in order to go quietly, and made a circle to come in from an angle. I got within about a hundred yards and was trying to locate the exact tree he was in. Suddenly he either saw, smelled or heard me, for out he jumped again and bounded off down the slope into Mc-Christal Canyon. This time he ran over a half mile, and when he took to a tree it was not a hundred yards from a long strip of slide rock which extends down from the Wall and Ash Mountain above.

So that was it. He was making a desperate effort to get into the rock slides; and if he made it, perhaps we would have difficulties sure enough. The location of the tree could be determined only by the baying of the dogs. I made up my mind that I must find some way to get close enough for a shot with my .45 without his seeing me and jumping again. He had seemed content to stay in the trees so long as the dogs were there, and I stayed a long way off, but each time as I had approached the lion had jumped. So it was evident he jumped out because he was afraid of me.

If I had had my .32 Special rifle, I could have shot him at the first tree, but I did not want to risk a pistol shot at more than fifty yards, and would much prefer twenty-five for a sure, clean kill. A wounded lion dropped out of a tree in the midst of a pack of dogs might do great harm. I couldn't risk getting a dog killed or badly crippled even if I had to let the lion get away.

After a few moments' cogitation I hit upon a plan which I hoped would work. It seemed worth a trial, anyway, and I could think of nothing better to try to get me out of the predicament.

The lion had gone off the ridge down into the canyon, angling just a little upstream toward the rock slide. As nearly as I could determine the location of the tree he was in was about a hundred yards from the end of the slide. Between the slide and the canyon bottom there was a strip of thick aspen and young spruce, perhaps fifty to seventy yards wide, with an occasional larger fir and spruce. At the end of the slide the cover was not so dense, only a scattering of aspen with a few large fir and spruce. The last hundred yards was too open to hope to stalk the treed lion, for he had too much the advantage from his lookout tower.

I rode up the ridge for over three hundred yards; then, being sure that I was out of sight, I dismounted, took off my spurs and my hat and left them with my horse. Then I went quietly down into the canyon at a point about three hundred yards upstream from where the lion was perched in his tree. While I felt that I could walk quietly up to within a hundred yards of the tree without being seen or heard, I dared not risk it. I went only within twice that distance.

There I got down on my hands and knees and began to bark to make Mr. Lion think I was another dog coming up to join the pack. The ground was rocky, and I was glad I had left on my leather chaps and gloves to protect my knees and hands. I needed more than that before I had crawled that two hundred yards.

Although in twenty years of married life I had been in the doghouse many times, this was the first time I had ever pretended to be a dog! When I first started to pretend I was a dog, I debated whether to be an Airedale or a hound. If you are going to make your pretense realistic, you can't be just a dog; you have to be some special kind of dog. I decided I would be a hound because it would be easier on the tonsils to imitate the bellowing of a hound than the shrill yelping of an Airedale.

As I crawled along I kept barking as nearly like old Kate as I could. One can't go very fast through a rocky thicket on all fours with chaps on, but at last I reached the end of the rock slide and the edge of the thicket. I could now locate the tree the lion was in, about where I had figured it was. When I had approached a little closer, the lion could be seen, about thirty-five feet up in a Douglas fir, lying quietly, with one front leg thrown over a limb and his hind feet braced against another. I was still too far to shoot.

I started on across the intervening space with confidence that the ruse would be a complete success. By now, however, I was getting a bit hoarse from barking. Did you ever have your dogs call you a damfool? Well, mine did. They came to me several times and said it with their actions just as plainly as if they could have spoken. They would come to me as if to say, "Quit your foolin'! Get your gun and shoot that lion!" Then they would rush back to the tree, barking more vigorously than ever. But their coming and going back and forth from the tree to me was good strategy, and kept the lion's attention on their movements more than on me. I might be fooling the lion, but certainly not the dogs; they just looked on me as their master. I didn't care what their temporary opinion of me was, for I knew they would forget all about it at the crack of the pistol.

When within thirty feet of the tree, which put me within about forty-five or fifty feet of the lion, I cautiously drew my old reliable .45 six-shooter from its holster. Then I crouched on my haunches like a dog and drew a bead on the lion's big, round head, aiming right between the eyes.

He slid backward off the limb and fell to the ground, stone-dead, with a heavy lead slug through the brain. The dogs wooled him good. I was so delighted that my strategy had worked, and by now so accustomed to being a dog that I was tempted to join them!

He was a beautifully marked lion, with vivid, contrasting coloring, fat, fully mature and fairly large, but not old. He was well worth a pair of sore knees, a hoarse voice and the humiliating criticism of my dogs.

I went back for my horse and rode down near where the lion lay. As I needed the meat for dog food, I really wanted to take the whole lion in. I tried to pack the lion on him, but this pony's name was Cyclone, and he lived up to it by positively refusing. My dogs were all very fond of lion meat, and in my opinion it is one of the best meats for hunting dogs.

It was only a couple of miles down to Mr. Ritchie's camp. He was very much pleased at what had been accomplished, but sorry he had not been in on the fun, and was sure that this was the lion that had been getting away from him and his dogs. I borrowed a pack-horse, went back and packed the lion on into Castle Rock, literally dog-tired from my day's work.

GHOST DOG

Quiquern

RUDYARD KIPLING

Quiquern, in a legend of the Far North, is the phantom of a gigantic dog, hairless and toothless. The Eskimo boy and girl were sure they saw the dreaded
creature in the last stage of their desperate hunt for
seals to save their starving tribe. This story from *The
Second Jungle Book* is told with the Kipling mastery.

The People of the Eastern Ice, they are melting like the snow—
They beg for coffee and sugar; they go where the white men go.
The People of the Western Ice, they learn to steal and fight:
They sell their furs to the trading-post: they sell their soul to the white.

The People of the Southern Ice, they trade with the whaler's crew;
Their women have many ribbons, but their tents are torn and few.
But the People of the Elder Ice, beyond the white man's ken—
Their spears are made of the narwhal horn, and they are the last of
    the Men.

Translation.

"HE has opened his eyes. Look!"

"Put him in the skin again. He will be a strong dog. On the fourth
month we will name him."

"For whom?" said Amoraq.

Kadlu's eye rolled round the skin-lined snow-house till it came to fourteen year old Kotuko sitting on the sleeping-bench, making a button out
of walrus ivory. "Name him for me," said Kotuko, with a grin. "I shall
need him some one day."

Kadlu grinned back till his eyes were almost buried in the fat of his
flat cheeks, and nodded to Amoraq, while the puppy's fierce mother
whined to see her baby wriggling far from reach in the little sealskin
pouch hung above the warmth of the blubber-lamp. Kotuko went on

From *The Second Jungle Book* by Rudyard Kipling. Reprinted by
permission of Mrs. George Bambridge, The Macmillan Company of
Canada and Doubleday and Company, Inc.

with his carving, and Kadlu threw a rolled bundle of leather dog-har-
nesses into a tiny little room that opened from one side of the house,
slipped off his heavy deerskin hunting-suit, put it into a whalebone net
that hung above another lamp, and dropped down on the sleeping-
bench to whittle at a piece of frozen seal-meat till Amoraq, his wife,
should bring the regular dinner of boiled meat and blood-soup. He had
been out since early dawn at the seal-holes eight miles away, and had
come home with three big seal. Half way down the long low snow passage or tunnel that led to the inner door of the house you could hear
snappings and yelpings, as the dogs of his sleigh-team, released from the
day's work, scuffled for warm places.

When the yelpings grew too loud Kotuko lazily rolled off the sleeping-
bench and picked up a whip with an eighteen-inch handle of springy
whalebone, and twenty-five feet of heavy plaited thong. He dived into
the passage, where it sounded as though all the dogs were eating him
alive; but that was no more than their regular grace before meals. When
he crawled out at the far end, half a dozen furry heads followed him
with their eyes as he went to a sort of gallows of whale jawbones, from
which the dogs' meat was hung; split off the frozen stuff in big lumps
with a broad-headed spear; and waited, his whip in one hand and the
meat in the other. Each beast was called by name—the weakest first,
and woe betide any dog that moved out of his turn, for the tapering lash
would shoot out like thonged lightning and flick away an inch or so of
hair and hide. Each beast simply growled, snapped once, choked over
his portion, and hurried back to the passage, while the boy stood up on
the snow under the blazing Northern Lights and dealt out justice. The
last to be served was the big black leader of the team, who kept order
when the dogs were harnessed, and to him Kotuko gave a double al-
lowance of meat as well as an extra crack of the whip.

"Ah!" said Kotuko, coiling up the lash, "I have a little one over the
lamp that will make a great many howlings. Sarpok! Get in!"

He crawled back over the huddled dogs, dusted the dry snow from his
furs with the whalebone beater that Amoraq kept by the door, tapped
the skin-lined roof of the house to shake off any icicles that might have
fallen from the dome of snow above, and curled up on the bench. The
dogs in the passage snored and whined in their sleep, the boy-baby in
Amoraq's deep fur hood kicked and choked and gurgled, and the mother
of the newly-named puppy lay at Kotuko's side, her eyes fixed on the
bundle of sealskin, warm and safe above the broad yellow flame of the
lamp.

And all this happened far away to the north, beyond Labrador; beyond Hudson's Strait where the great tides throw the ice about—north
of Melville Peninsula—north even of the narrow Fury and Hecla Straits
—on the north shore of Baffin Land where Bylot's Island stands above

the ice of Lancaster Sound like a pudding-bowl wrong side up. North of Lancaster Sound there is little we know anything about, except North Devon and Ellesmere Land; but even there live a few scattered people, next door, as it were, to the very Pole.

Kadlu was an Inuit—what you call an Esquimau—and his tribe, some thirty persons, all told, belonged to the Tununirmiut—"the country lying at the back of something." On the maps that desolate coast is written Navy Board Inlet, but the Inuit name is best because that country lies at the very back of everything in the world. For nine months of the year there is only ice and snow and gale after gale; with a cold no one can realise who has never seen the thermometer go down even to zero. For six months of those nine it is dark, and that is what makes it so horrible. In the three months of summer it only freezes every other day and every night, and then the snow begins to weep away from the southerly slopes, and a few ground-willows put out their wooly buds, a tiny stone-crop or so makes believe to blossom; beaches of fine gravel and rounded stones run down to the open sea, and polished boulders and streaked rocks lift up above the granulated snow. But all that goes in a few weeks, and the wild winter locks down again on the land; while at sea the ice tears up and down the offing, jamming and ramming, and splitting and hitting, and pounding and grounding till it all freezes together, ten feet thick, from the shore outward to deep water.

In the winter Kadlu would follow the seal to the edge of this land-ice and spear them as they came up to breathe at their blow holes. The seal must have open sea-water to live and catch fish in, and the ice would sometimes run eighty miles without a break from the nearest land. In the spring he and his people retreated from the thawing ice to the rocky mainland, where they put up tents of skins and snared the sea-birds, or speared the young seal basking on the beaches. Later, they would go south into Baffin Land after the reindeer and to get their year's store of salmon from the hundreds of streams and lakes of the interior; coming back north in September or October for the musk-ox hunting and the regular winter sealery. This travelling was done with dog-sleighs, twenty and thirty miles a day, or sometimes down the coast in big skin "woman-boats," when the dogs and the babies lay among the feet of the rowers, and the women sang songs as they glided from cape to cape over the glassy, cold waters. All the luxuries that the Tununirmiut knew came from the south—drift-wood for sleigh-runners, rod-iron for harpoon-tips, steel knives, tin kettles that cooked food much better than the old soapstone affairs, flint and steel, and even matches, coloured ribbons for the women's hair, little cheap mirrors and red cloth for the edging of deerskin dress-jackets. Kadlu traded the rich creamy-twisted narwhal horn and musk-ox teeth (these are just as valuable as pearls) to the Southern Inuit, and they in turn traded with the whalers

and the missionary posts of Exeter and Cumberland Sounds; and so the
chain went on till a kettle picked up by a ship's cook in the Bhendy
Bazar might end its days over a blubber lamp somewhere on the cool
side of the Arctic Circle.

Kadlu being a good hunter was rich in iron harpoons, snow-knives,
bird-darts and all the other things that make life easy up there in the
great cold, and he was the head of his tribe, or, as they say, "the man
who knows all about it by practice." This did not give him any authority,
except now and then he could advise his friends to change their hunting-
grounds; but Kotuko used it to domineer a little, in the lazy fat Inuit
fashion, over the other boys when they came out at night to play ball
in the moonlight, or to sing The Child's Song to the Aurora Borealis.

But at fourteen an Inuit feels himself a man, and Kotuko was tired
of making snares for wild-fowl and kit-foxes, and very tired of helping
the women to chew seal and deer-skins (that supple them as nothing
else can) the long day through while the men were out hunting. He
wanted to go into the *quaggi*, the Singing-House, when the hunters
gathered there for their mysteries, and the *angekok*, the sorcerer, frightened them into the most delightful fits after the lamps were put out,
and you could hear the Spirit of the Reindeer stamping on the roof, and
when a spear was thrust out into the open black night it came back
covered with hot blood. He wanted to throw his big boots into the net
with the tired air of the head of a family, and to gamble with the hunters
when they dropped in of an evening and played a sort of home-made
roulette with a tin pot and a nail. There were hundreds of things that
he wanted to do, but the grown men laughed at him and said, "Wait
till you have been in the buckle, Kotuko. Hunting is not *all* catching."

Now that his father had named a puppy for him things looked
brighter. An Inuit does not waste a good dog on his son till the boy
knows something of dog-driving; and Kotuko was more than sure that
he knew more than everything.

If the puppy had not had an iron constitution he would have died
from over-stuffing and over-handling. Kotuko made him a tiny harness
with a trace to it, and hauled him all over the house-floor shouting:
"Aua! Ja aua!" (Go to the right). "Choiachoi, Ja choiachoi!" (Go to
the left). "Ohaha!" (Stop). The puppy did not like it at all, but being
fished for in this way was pure happiness beside being put to the sleigh
for the first time. He just sat down on the snow and played with the
seal-hide trace that ran from his harness to the *pitu*, the big thong in
the bows of the sleigh. Then the team started and the puppy found the
heavy ten-foot sleigh running up his back and dragging him along the
snow, while Kotuko laughed till the tears ran down his face. There followed days and days of the cruel whip that hisses like the wind over
ice, and his companions all bit him because he did not know his work,

and the harness chafed him, and he was not allowed to sleep with Kotuko any more, but had to take the coldest place in the passage. It was a sad time for the puppy.

The boy learned, too, as fast as the dog; though a dog-sleigh is a heartbreaking thing to manage. Each beast is harnessed—the weakest nearest to the driver—by his own separate trace, which runs under his left foreleg to the main thong, where it is fastened by a sort of button and loop which can be slipped by a turn of the wrist, thus freeing one dog at a time. This is very necessary, because young dogs often get the trace between their hind legs, where it cuts to the bone. And, they one and all *will* go visiting their friends as they run; jumping in and out among the traces. Then they fight, and the result is more mixed than a wet fishing-line next morning. A great deal of trouble can be avoided by scientific use of the whip. Every Inuit boy prides himself as being a master of the long lash; but it is easy to flick at a mark on the ground and difficult to lean forward and catch a shirking dog just behind the shoulders when the sleigh is going at full speed. If you call one dog's name for "visiting" and accidentally lash another the two will fight it out at once, and stop all the others. Again, if you travel with a companion and begin to talk, or by yourself and sing, the dogs will halt, turn round, and sit down and hear what you have to say. Kotuko was run away from once or twice through forgetting to block the sleigh when he stopped; and he broke many lashings and ruined a few thongs ere he could be trusted with a full team of eight and the light sleigh. Then he felt himself a person of consequence, and on smooth black ice, with a bold heart and a quick elbow, he smoked along over the levels as fast as a pack in full cry. He would go ten miles to the seal-holes, and when he was on the hunting-grounds he would twitch a trace loose from the *pitu* and free the big black leader, who was then the cleverest dog in the team. As soon as the dog had scented a breathing-hole Kotuko would reverse the sleigh, driving a couple of sawed-off antlers that stuck up like perambulator handles deep into the snow, so that the team could not get away. Then he would crawl forward inch by inch and wait till the seal came up to breathe. Then he would stab down swiftly with his spear and running line, and presently would haul his seal on to the lip of the ice while the black leader came up and helped to pull the carcass across the ice to the sleigh. That was the time when the harnessed dogs yelled and foamed with excitement, and Kotuko laid the long lash like a red-hot bar across all their faces till the carcass froze stiff. Going home was the heavy work. The loaded sleigh had to be humoured among the rough ice, and the dogs sat down and looked hungrily at the seal instead of pulling. At last they would strike the well-worn sleigh-road to the village, and toodle-ki-yi along the ringing ice, heads down and tails up, while Kotuko struck up the "Angutivun tai-na tau-na-ne taina" (The

Song of the Returning Hunter), and voices hailed him from house to house under all that dim, star-litten sky.

When Kotuko, the dog, came to his full growth, he enjoyed himself too. He fought his way up the team steadily, fight after fight, till one fine evening over their food he tackled the big black leader (Kotuko, the boy, saw fair play) and made second dog of him, as they say. So he was promoted to the long thong of the leading dog, running five feet in advance of all the others: it was his bounden duty to stop all fighting, in harness or out of it, and he wore a collar of copper wire, very thick and heavy. On special occasions he was fed with cooked food inside the house, and sometimes was allowed to sleep on the bench with Kotuko. He was a good seal-dog, and would keep a musk-ox at bay by running round him and snapping at his heels. He would even—and this for a sleigh-dog is the last proof of bravery—he would even stand up to the gaunt Arctic wolf, whom all dogs of the north, as a rule, fear beyond anything that walks the snow. He and his master—they did not count the team of ordinary dogs as company—hunted together, day after day and night after night—fur-wrapped boy and savage, long-haired, narrow-eyed, white-fanged, yellow brute. All an Inuit has to do is to get food and skins for himself and his family. The women-folk make the skins into clothing, and occasionally help in trapping small game; but the bulk of the food—and they eat enormously—must be found by the men. If the supply fails there is no one up there to buy or beg or borrow from. The people must die.

An Inuit does not think of these chances till he is forced to. Kadlu, Kotuko, Amoraq, and the boy baby who kicked about the fur hood and chewed pieces of blubber all day, were as happy together as any family in the world. They came of a very gentle race—an Inuit seldom loses his temper, and almost never strikes a child—who did not know exactly what telling a real lie meant; still less how to steal. They were content to spear their living out of the heart of the bitter, hopeless cold; to smile oily smiles, and tell queer ghost and fairy-tales of evenings; and eat till they could eat no more, and sing the endless woman's song: "Amna aya, aya amna, ah! ah!" through the long lamp-lighted days as they mended their clothes and hunting gear.

But one terrible winter everything betrayed them. The Tununirmiut returned from the yearly salmon fishing and made their houses on the fresh ice to the north of Bellot's Island ready to go after the seal as soon as the sea froze. But it was an early and savage autumn. All through September there were continuous gales that broke up the smooth seal ice where it was only four or five feet thick and forced it inland, and piled a great barrier some twenty miles broad of lumped and ragged and needlely ice, over which it was impossible to draw the sleighs. The edge of the floe off which the seal were used to fish in winter lay perhaps twenty miles beyond this barrier and out of reach of the Tununirmiut. Even so, they might have managed to scrape through the winter on their stock of frozen salmon and stored blubber and what the traps gave them, but in December one of their hunters came across a *tupik*, a skin-tent, of three women and a girl nearly dead, whose men had come down from the far north and been crushed in their little skin hunting-boats while they were out after the long-horned narwhal. Kadlu, of course, could only distribute the women among the huts of the winter village, for no Inuit dare refuse a meal to a stranger. He never knows when his own turn may come to beg. Amoraq took the girl, who was about four-teen, into her own house as a sort of servant. From the cut of her sharp-pointed hoop, and the long diamond pattern of her white deer-skin leggings, they supposed she came from Ellesmere Land. She had never seen tin cooking-pots or wooden-shod sleighs before; but Kotuko the boy and Kotuko the dog were rather fond of her.

Then all the foxes went south, and even the wolverine, that growling, blunt-headed little thief of the snow, did not take the trouble to follow the line of empty traps that Kotuko set. The tribe lost a couple of their best hunters, who were badly crippled in a fight with a musk-ox, and this threw more work on the others. Kotuko went out, day after day, with a light hunting-sleigh and six or seven of the strongest dogs, looking till his eyes ached for some patch of clear ice where a seal might, perhaps, have scratched a breathing-hole. Kotuko, the dog, ranged far and wide, and in the dead stillness of the ice-fields Kotuko, the boy, could hear his half-choked whine of excitement, above a seal-hole three miles away, as plainly as though he were at his elbow. When the dog found a hole the boy would build himself a little low snow wall to keep off the worst of the bitter wind, and there he would wait ten, twelve, twenty hours for the seal to come up to breathe, his eyes glued to the tiny mark he had made above the hole to guide the downward thrust of his harpoon, a little sealskin mat under his feet, and his legs tied together in the *tutareang*—the buckle that the old hunters had talked about. This helps to keep a man's legs from twitching as he waits and waits and waits for the quick-eared seal to rise. Though there is no excitement in it, you can easily believe that the sitting still in the buckle with the thermometer perhaps forty degrees below zero, is the hardest work an Inuit knows. When a seal was caught, Kotuko, the dog, would bound forward, his trace trailing behind him, and help to pull the body to the sleigh where the tired and hungry dogs lay sullenly under the lee of the broken ice.

A seal did not go very far, for each mouth in the little village had a right to be filled, and neither bone, hide, nor sinew was wasted. The dogs' meat was taken for human use, and Amoraq fed the team with pieces of old summer skin-tents raked out from under the sleeping-bench, and they howled and howled again; and waked to howl hungrily.

One could tell by the lamps in the huts that famine was near. In good seasons, when blubber was plentiful, the light in the boat-shaped bowls would be two feet high—cheerful, oily, and yellow. Now it was a bare six inches: Amoraq carefully pricked down the moss wick when an unwatched flame brightened for a moment, and the eyes of all the family followed her hand. The horror of famine up there in the great cold is not so much dying as dying in the dark. All the Inuit dread the dark that presses on them without a break for six months in each year; and when the lamps are low in the houses the minds of people begin to be shaken and confused.

But worse was to come.

The underfed dogs snapped and growled in the passages, glaring at the cold stars and snuffing into the bitter wind night after night. When they stopped howling the silence fell down again as solid and as heavy as a snowdrift against a door, and men could hear the beating of their blood in the thin passages of the ear and the thumping of their own hearts that sounded as loud as the noise of sorcerers' drums beaten across the snow. One night Kotuko the dog, who had been unusually sullen in harness, leaped up and pushed his head against Kotuko's knee. Kotuko patted him, but the dog still pushed blindly forward, fawning. Then Kadlu waked and gripped the heavy wolf-like head and stared into the glassy eyes. The dog whimpered as though he were afraid, and shivered between Kadlu's knees. The hair rose about his neck and he growled as though a stranger were at the door; then he barked joyously and rolled on the ground and bit at Kotuko's boot like a puppy.

"What is it?" said Kotuko, for he was beginning to be afraid.

"The sickness," Kadlu answered. "It is the dog-sickness." Kotuko the dog lifted his nose and howled and howled again.

"I have not seen this before. What will he do?" said Kotuko.

Kadlu shrugged one shoulder a little and crossed the hut for his short stabbing-harpoon. The big dog looked at him, howled again, and slunk away down the passage, while the other dogs drew aside right and left to give him ample room. When he was out on the snow he barked furiously, as though on the trail of a musk-ox, and, barking and leaping and frisking, passed out of sight. His trouble was not hydrophobia but simple plain madness. The cold and the hunger, and above all the dark, had turned his head: and when the terrible dog-sickness once shows itself in a team it spreads like wild-fire. Next hunting day another dog sickened, and was killed then and there by Kotuko as he bit and struggled among the traces. Then the black second-dog who had been the leader in the old days suddenly gave tongue on an imaginary reindeer track, and when they slipped him from the *pitu* he flew at the throat of an ice-cliff, and ran away as his leader had done, his harness on his back. After that no one would take the dogs out again. They needed them for something else, and the dogs knew it; and though they were tied down and fed by hand their eyes were full of despair and fear. To make things worse the old women began to tell ghost-tales, and to say that they had met the spirits of the dead hunters lost that autumn who prophesied all sorts of horrible things.

Kotuko grieved more for the loss of his dog than anything else, for though an Inuit eats enormously he also knows how to starve. But the hunger, the darkness, the cold, and the exposure told on his strength, and he began to hear voices inside his head, and to see people, who were not there, out of the tail of his eye. One night—he had unbuckled himself after ten hours waiting above a "blind" seal-hole, and was staggering back to the village faint and dizzy—he halted to lean his back against a boulder, which happened to be supported like a rocking-stone on a single jutting point of ice. His weight disturbed the balance of the thing, it rolled over ponderously, and as Kotuko sprang aside to avoid it, slid after him squeaking and hissing on the ice-slope.

That was enough for Kotuko. He had been brought up to believe that every rock and boulder had its owner (its *inua*), who was generally a one-eyed kind of a Woman-Thing called a *tornaq*, and that when a *tornaq* meant to help a man she rolled after him inside her stone house, and asked him whether he would take her for a guardian spirit. (In summer thaws the ice-propped rocks and boulders roll and slip all over the face of the land, so you can easily see how the idea of live stones arose.) Kotuko heard the blood beating in his ears as he had heard it all day, and he thought that was the *tornaq* of the stone speaking to him. Before he reached home he was quite certain that he had held a long conversation with her, and as all his people believed that this was quite possible no one contradicted him.

"She said to me: 'I jump down, I jump down from my place on the snow,'" cried Kotuko with hollow eyes, leaning forward in the half-lighted hut. "She said, 'I will be a guide.' She said, 'I will guide you to the good seal-holes.' To-morrow I go out and the *tornaq* will guide me."

Then the *angekok*, the village sorcerer, came in and Kotuko told him the tale a second time. It lost nothing in the telling.

"Follow the *tornait* (the spirits of the stones) and they will bring us food again," said the *angekok*.

Now the girl from the north had been lying near the lamp, eating very little and saying less for days past, but when Amoraq and Kadlu next morning packed and lashed a little hand-sleigh for Kotuko, and loaded it with his hunting gear and as much blubber and frozen seal-meat as they could spare, she took the pulling-rope, and stepped out boldly at the boy's side.

"Your house is my house," she said, as the little bone-shod sleigh squeaked and bumped behind them in the awful Arctic night.

"My house is your house," said Kotuko, "but I think that we shall both go to Sedna together."

Now Sedna is the Mistress of the Underworld, and the Inuit believe that every one who dies must spend a year in her horrible country before going to Quadliparmiut, the Happy Place, where it never freezes and fat reindeer trot up when you call.

Through the village people were shouting:—"The *tornait* have spoken to Kotuko. They will show him open ice. He will bring us the seal again." Their voices were soon swallowed up by the cold empty dark, and Kotuko and the girl shouldered close together as they strained on the pulling-rope or humoured the sleigh through the ice, in the direction of the Polar Sea. Kotuko insisted that the *tornaq* of the stone had told him to go north, and so north they went under Tuktuqdjung the Reindeer—those stars that we call the Great Bear.

No European could have made five miles a day over the ice-rubbish and the sharp-edged drifts; but those two knew exactly the turn of the wrist that coaxes a sleigh round a hummock, the jerk that neatly lifts it out of an ice-crack, and the exact strength that goes to the few quiet strokes of the spear-head that make a path possible when everything looks hopeless.

The girl said nothing, but bowed her head, and the long wolverine-fur fringe of her ermine hood blew across her broad, dark face. The sky above them was an intense velvety black, changing to bands of Indian red on the horizon, where the great stars burned like street-lamps. From time to time a greenish wave of the Northern Lights would roll across the hollow of the high heavens, flick like a flag and disappear; or a meteor would crackle from darkness to darkness trailing a shower of sparks behind. Then they could see the ridged and furrowed surface of the floe all tipped and laced with strange colours—red, copper, and bluish; but in the ordinary starlight everything turned to one frost-bitten gray. The floe, as you will remember, had been battered and tormented by the autumn gales till it was one frozen earthquake. There were gullies and ravines; and holes like gravel-pits cut in ice, lumps and scattered pieces frozen down to the original floor of the floe; blotches of old black ice that had been thrust under the floe in some gale, and heaved up again; roundish boulders of ice; sawlike edges of ice carved by the snow that flies before the wind and sunk pits where thirty or forty acres lay five or six feet below the level of the rest of the field. From a little distance you might have taken the lumps for seal, or walrus, overturned sleighs or men on a hunting expedition, or even the great Ten-legged White Spirit-Bear himself, but in spite of these fantastic shapes, all on the very edge of starting into life, there was neither sound nor the least faint echo of sound. And through this silence and through this waste where the sudden lights flapped and went out again, the sleigh and the two that pulled it crawled like things in a nightmare —a nightmare of the end of the world at the end of the world.

When they were tired Kotuko would make what the hunters call a "half-house," a very small snow hut, into which they would huddle with the travelling lamp, and try to thaw out the frozen seal-meat. When they had slept, the march began again—thirty miles a day to get five miles northward. The girl was always very silent, but Kotuko muttered to himself and broke out into songs he had learned in the Singing-House—summer songs, and reindeer and salmon songs—all horribly out of place at that season. He would declare that he heard the *tornaq* growling to him, and would run wildly up a hummock tossing his arms and speaking in loud threatening tones. To tell the truth, Kotuko was very nearly crazy for the time being; but the girl was sure that he was being guided by his guardian spirit, and that everything would come right. She was not surprised, therefore, when at the end of the fourth march, Kotuko, whose eyes were burning like fire-balls in his head, told her that his *tornaq* was following them across the snow in the shape of a two-headed dog. The girl looked where Kotuko pointed, and some Thing seemed to slip into a ravine. It was certainly not human, but everybody knew that the *tornait* preferred to appear in the shape of bear and seal and such like.

It might have been the Ten-legged White Spirit-Bear himself, or it might have been anything, for Kotuko and the girl were so starved that their eyes were untrustworthy. They had trapped nothing and seen no trace of game since they had left the village; their food would not hold out for another week, and there was a gale coming. A Polar storm will blow for ten days without a break, and all that while it is certain death to be abroad. Kotuko laid up a snow-house large enough to take in the hand-sleigh (it is never wise to be separated from your meat), and while he was shaping the last irregular block of ice that makes the keystone of the roof he saw a Thing looking at him from a little cliff of ice half a mile away. The air was hazy, and the Thing seemed to be forty feet long and ten feet high, with twenty feet of tail and a shape that quivered all along the outlines. The girl saw it too, but instead of crying aloud with terror, said quietly: "That is Quiquern. What comes after?"

"He will speak to me," said Kotuko, but the snow-knife trembled in his hand as he spoke, because however much a man may believe that he is a friend of strange and ugly spirits he seldom likes to be taken quite at his word. Quiquern, too, is the phantom of a gigantic toothless dog without any hair, who is supposed to live in the far north, and to wander about the country just before things are going to happen. They may be pleasant or unpleasant things, but not even the sorcerers care to speak about Quiquern. He makes the dogs go mad. Like the Spirit Bear he has several extra pairs of legs—six or eight—and this Thing jumping up and down in the haze had more legs than any real dog needed.

Kotuko and the girl huddled into their hut quickly. Of course if Quiquern had wanted them he could have torn it to pieces above their heads, but the sense of a foot-thick snow wall between themselves and the wicked dark was great comfort. The gale broke with a shriek of wind like the shriek of a train, and for three days and three nights it held, never varying one point and never lulling even for a minute. They fed the stone lamp between their knees and nibbled at the half-warm seal meat, and watched the black soot gather on the roof for seventy-two long hours. The girl counted up the food in the sleigh; there was not more than two days' supply, and Kotuko looked over the iron heads and the deer-sinew fastenings of his harpoon and his seal-lance and his bird-dart. There was nothing else to do.

"We shall go to Sedna soon—very soon," the girl whispered. "In three days we shall lie down and go. Will your *tornaq* do nothing? Sing her an *angekok's* song to make her come here."

He began to sing in the high-pitched howl of the magic songs, and the gale went down slowly. In the middle of his song the girl started, laid her mittened hand and then her head to the ice floor of the hut. Kotuko followed her example, and the two kneeled staring into each other's eyes, and listening with every nerve. He ripped a thin sliver of whalebone from the rim of a bird snare that lay on the sleigh, and after straightening set it up upright in a little hole in the ice, firming it down with his mitten. It was almost as delicately adjusted as a compass needle, and now, instead of listening, they watched. The thin rod quivered a little—the least little jar in the world—then vibrated steadily for a few seconds, came to rest and vibrated again, this time nodding to another point of the compass.

"Too soon!" said Kotuko. "Some big floe has broken far away outside."

The girl pointed at the rod and shook her head. "It is the big breaking," she said. "Listen to the ground-ice. It knocks."

When they kneeled this time they heard the most curious muffled grunts, and knockings apparently under their feet. Sometimes it sounded as though a blind puppy were squeaking above the lamp; then as if a stone were being ground on hard ice; and again, like muffled blows on a drum; but all dragged out and made small, as though they had travelled through a little horn a weary distance away.

"We shall not go to Sedna lying down," said Kotuko. "It is the breaking. The *tornaq* has cheated us. We shall die."

All this may sound absurd enough, but the two were face to face with a very real danger. The three days' gale had driven the deep water of Baffin's Bay southerly, and piled it on to the edge of the far reaching land-ice that stretches from Bylot's Island to the west. Also, the strong current which sets east out of Lancaster Sound carried with it mile upon mile of what they call pack-ice—rough ice that has not frozen into fields; and this pack was bombarding the floe at the same time that the swell and heave of the storm-worked sea was weakening and undermining it. What Kotuko and the girl had been listening to were the faint echoes of that fight thirty or forty miles away, and the tell-tale little rod quivered to the shock of it.

Now, as the Inuit say, when the ice once wakes after its long winter sleep there is no knowing what may happen, for solid floe-ice changes shape almost as quickly as a cloud. The gale was evidently a spring gale sent out of time and anything was possible.

Yet the two were happier in their minds than before. If the floe broke up there would be no more waiting and suffering. Spirits, goblins, and witch-people were moving about on the racking ice, and they might find themselves stepping into Sedna's country side by side with all sorts of wild Things, the flush of excitement still on them. When they left the hut after the gale, the noise on the horizon was steadily growing, and the tough ice moaned and buzzed all round them.

"It is still waiting," said Kotuko.

On the top of a hummock sat or crouched the eight-legged Thing that they had seen three days before—and it howled horribly.

"Let us follow," said the girl. "It may know some way that does not lead to Sedna," but she reeled from weakness as she took the pulling-rope. The Thing moved off slowly and clumsily across the ridges, heading always toward the westward and the land, and they followed while the growling thunder at the edge of the floe rolled nearer and nearer. The floe's lip was split and cracked in every direction for three or four miles inland, and great pans of ten-foot-thick ice, from a few yards to twenty acres square, were jolting and ducking and surging into one another and into the yet unbroken floe as the heavy swell took and shook and spouted between them. This battering-ram-ice was, so to speak, the first army that the sea was flinging against the floe. The incessant crash and jar of these cakes almost drowned the ripping sound of sheets of pack-ice driven bodily under the floe as cards are hastily pushed under a tablecloth. Where the water was shallow these sheets would be piled one atop of the other till the bottommost touched mud fifty feet down and the discoloured sea banked behind the muddy ice till the increasing pressure drove all forward again. In addition to the floe and the pack-ice, the gale and the currents were bringing down true bergs, sailing mountains of ice, snapped off from the Greenland side of things or the north shore of Melville Bay. They pounded in solemnly, the waves breaking white round them, and advanced on the floe like an old-time fleet under full sail. But a berg that seemed ready to carry the world before it would ground helplessly, reel over, and wallow in a lather of foam and mud, and flying frozen spray, while a much smaller and lower one would rip and ride into the flat floe, flinging tons of rubbish on either side, and cutting a track a mile long before it was stopped. Some fell like swords, shearing a raw-edged canal, and others splintered into a shower of blocks, weighing scores of tons apiece, that whirled and skirled among the hummocks. Others, again, rose up bodily out the water when they shoaled, twisted as though in pain, and fell solidly on their sides, while the sea threshed over their shoulders. This trampling and crowding and bending and buckling and arching of the ice into every possible shape was going on as far as the eye could reach all along the north line of the floe. From where Kotuko and the girl were, the confusion looked no more than an uneasy rippling crawling movement under the horizon, but it came towards them each moment, and they could hear far away to landward a heavy booming, as if it might have been the boom of artillery through a fog. That showed that the floe was being jammed home against the iron cliffs of Bylot's Island, the land to the southward, behind them.

"This has never been before," said Kotuko, staring stupidly. "This is not the time. How can the floe break *now?*"

"Follow *that!*" the girl cried, pointing to the Thing half-limping, half-running distractedly before them. They followed, tugging the hand-sleigh, while nearer and nearer came the roaring march of the ice. At last the fields round them cracked and starred in every direction, and the cracks opened and snapped like the teeth of wolves. But where the Thing rested, on a mound of old and scattered ice-blocks some fifty feet high, there was no motion. Kotuko leaped forward wildly, dragged the girl after him, and crawled to the bottom of the mound. The talking of the ice grew louder and louder round them, but the mound stayed fast, and as the girl looked at him he threw his right elbow upwards and outwards; making the Inuit sign for land in the shape of an island. And land it was that the eight-legged limping Thing had led them to—some granite-tipped, sand-beached islet off the coast, shod and sheathed and masked with ice so that no man could have told it from the floe, but at the bottom solid earth, and no shifting ice. The smashing and rebound of the floes as they grounded and splintered, marked the borders of it, and a friendly shoal ran out to the northward, turning aside the rush of the heaviest ice exactly as a ploughshare turns over loam. There was a danger, of course, that some heavily-squeezed ice-field might shoot up the beach and plane off the top of the islet bodily, but that did not trouble Kotuko and the girl, when they made their snow-house and began to eat, and heard the ice hammer and skid along the beach. The Thing had disappeared, and Kotuko was talking excitedly about his power over spirits as he crouched round the lamp. In the middle of his wild sayings the girl began to laugh and rock herself backwards and forwards.

Behind her shoulder, crawling into the hut crawl by crawl, there were two heads, one yellow and one black, that belonged to two of the most sorrowful and ashamed dogs that ever you saw. Kotuko the dog was one and the black leader was the other. Both were now fat, well-looking, and quite restored to their proper minds; but coupled to each other in an extraordinary fashion. When the black leader ran off, you remember, his harness was still on him. He must have met Kotuko the dog and played or fought with him, for his shoulder-loop had caught in the plaited copper wire of Kotuko's collar, and had drawn tight, so that neither dog could get at the trace to gnaw it apart, but each was fastened sidelong to his neighbour's neck. That, with the freedom of hunting on their own account, must have helped to cure their madness. They were very sober.

The girl pushed the two shame-faced creatures towards Kotuko, and, sobbing with laughter, cried, "That is Quiquern, who led us to safe ground. Look at his eight legs and double head!"

Kotuko cut them free, and they fell into his arms, yellow and black together, trying to explain how they had got their senses back again. Kotuko ran a hand down their ribs, which were round and well clothed. "They have found food," he said, with a grin. "I do not think we shall go to Sedna so soon. My *tornaq* sent these. The sickness has left them."

As soon as they had greeted Kotuko these two, who had been forced to sleep and eat and hunt together for the past few weeks, flew at each other's throat, and there was a beautiful battle in the snow-house. "Empty dogs do not fight," Kotuko said. "They have found the seal. Let us sleep. We shall find food."

When they waked there was open water on the north beach of the island, and all the loosened ice had been driven landward. The first sound of the surf is one of the most delightful that the Inuit can hear, for it means that Spring is on the road. Kotuko and the girl took hold of hands and smiled: the clear full roar of the surge among the ice reminded them of salmon and reindeer time and the smell of blossoming ground-willows. Even as they looked the sea began to skim over between the floating cakes of ice, so intense was the cold, but on the horizon there was a vast red glare, and that was the light of the sunken sun. It was more like hearing him yawn in his sleep than seeing him rise, and the glare lasted for only a few minutes, but it marked the turn of the year. Nothing, they felt, could alter that.

Kotuko found the dogs fighting outside over a fresh-killed seal who was following the fish that a gale always disturbs. He was the first of some twenty or thirty seal that landed on the island in the course of the day, and, till the sea froze hard, there were hundreds of keen black heads rejoicing in the shallow free water and floating about with the floating ice.

It was good to eat seal-liver again; to fill the lamps recklessly with blubber and watch the flame blaze three feet in the air; but as soon as the new sea-ice bore, Kotuko and the girl loaded the hand-sleigh and made the two dogs pull as they had never pulled in their lives, for they feared what might have happened in their village. The weather was as pitiless as ever; but it is easier to draw a sleigh loaded with good food than to hunt starving. They left five-and-twenty seal carcasses buried in the ice of the beach all ready for use and hurried back to their people. The dogs showed them the way as soon as Kotuko told them what was expected, and though there was no sign of a landmark, in two days they were giving tongue outside Kadlu's village. Only three dogs answered them; the others had been eaten, and the houses were nearly dark. But when Kotuko shouted, "Ojo!" (boiled meat) weak voices answered, and when he called the roll-call of the village name by name, very distinctly, there were no gaps in it.

An hour later the lamps blazed in Kadlu's house, snow-water was heating, the pots were beginning to simmer, and the snow was dripping from the roof as Amoraq made ready a meal for all the village, and the boy-baby chewed at a strip of rich nutty blubber, and the hunters slowly and methodically filled themselves to the very brim with seal-meat. Kotuko and the girl told their tale. The two dogs sat between them, and whenever their names came in they cocked an ear apiece and looked most thoroughly ashamed of themselves. A dog who has once gone mad and recovered, the Inuit say, is safe against all further attacks.

"So the *tornaq* did not forget us," said Kotuko. "The storm blew; the ice broke, and the seal swam in behind the fish that were frightened by the storm. Now the new seal-holes are not two days' distant. Let the good hunters go to-morrow and bring back the seal I have speared—twenty-five seal buried in the ice. When we have eaten those we will all follow the seal on the floe."

"What do *you* do?" said the village sorcerer, in the same sort of voice as he used to Kadlu, richest of the Tununirmiut.

Kotuko looked at the girl from the North and said quietly: "*We* build a house." He pointed to the north-west side of Kadlu's house, for that is the side on which the married son or daughter always lives.

The girl turned her hands, palm upward, with a little despairing shake of her head. She was a foreigner, picked up starving, and she could bring nothing to house-keeping.

Amoraq jumped from the bench where she sat and began to sweep things into the girl's lap—stone-lamps, iron skin-scrapers, tin kettles, deer-skins embroidered with musk-ox teeth, and real canvas-needles such as sailors use—the finest dowry ever given on the far edge of the Arctic circle, and the girl from the North bowed her head down to the very floor.

"Also these!" said Kotuko laughing and signing to the dogs, who thrust their cold muzzles into the girl's face.

"Ah," said the *angekok*, with an important cough, as though he had been thinking it all over. "As soon as Kotuko left the village I went to the Singing-House and sang magic. I sang all the long nights and called upon the Spirit of the Reindeer. *My* singing made the gale blow that broke the ice and drew the two dogs towards Kotuko when the ice would have crushed his bones. *My* song drew the seal in behind the broken ice. My body lay still in the *quaggi*, but my spirit ran about on the ice and guided Kotuko and the dogs in all the things they did. *I* did it."

Everybody was full and sleepy, so no one contradicted; and the *angekok* helped himself to yet another lump of boiled meat and lay down to sleep with the others, in the warm, well-lighted, oil-smelling home.

Now Kotuko, who drew very well in the Inuit style, scratched pictures of all these adventures on a long flat piece of ivory with a hole at one end. When he and the girl went north to Ellesmere Land in the year of the Wonderful Open winter, he left the picture-story with Kadlu, who lost it in the shingle when his dog-sleigh broke down one summer on the beach of Lake Netilling at Nikosiring, and there a Lake Inuit found it next spring and sold it to a man at Imigen who was interpreter on a Cumberland Sound whaler, and he sold it to Hans Olsen, who was afterwards a quartermaster on board a big steamer that took tourists to the North Cape in Norway. When the tourist season was over the steamer ran between London and Australia, stopping at Ceylon, and there Olsen sold the ivory to a Cingalese jeweller for two imitation sapphires. I found it under some rubbish in a house at Colombo, and have translated it from one end to the other.